TOYS SAMPLER

A History & Price Guide

Michelle L. Smith

Marx Toys Promotional Catalog
Weirton Steel Employees Bulletin

Above logos and references: Authorized by the Marx Toy Corporation.

Marx, Marx Toys, Louis Marx & Co., Magic Marxie, and the Marx circle logotype are all registered trademarks and are used here by permission of Marx Toys, Inc. of Miami.

Published by

700 E. State Street • Iola, WI 54990-0001
Telephone: 715/445-2214

Please call or write for our free catalog.
Our toll-free number to place an order or obtain a free catalog is 800-258-0929
or please use our regular business telephone 715-445-2214
for editorial comment and further information.

Library of Congress Catalog Card Number: 00-104628
ISBN: 0-87341-894-8

Printed in the United States of America

Dedication

This book is dedicated to the memory of my wonderful parents,
William David and Mary Evelyn (Fluharty) Ingold
It is also dedicated to Gaylord Andrew Whipkey,
Floyd "Joe" Chamberlain and to all former Marx Toy
Company Employees

Acknowledgments

I would like to thank Marx Toys, Inc. President, Jay Horowitz for his enormous generosity and time assisting with this book's accuracy. Thanks, too, to Louis and David Marx for making all of this "Marx Mania" possible.

Without the enormous support and assistance of Gaylord Andrew Whipkey and Eric Chamberlain, son of the late Floyd "Joe" Chamberlain, this book would not be possible. Gaylord gave me a wealth of photographs and research materials from his own collection for use in this book. Eric provided a wealth of information about his artist father's working days at the Marx Toys plant and on some of the toys his father created. Both Gaylord and Joe are now deceased. These men were two of the many talented people who contributed much to the success of the Marx Toys Company in Glen Dale, West Virginia.

Thanks to Weirton Steel Corporation for permission to use photographs from the Weirton Steel Employees Bulletin, dated December, 1970.

To my husband, Jack, thanks for his countless hours in assisting me with the photographs and text, and for his never-ending encouragement.

Contents

Introduction

The true magic of Marx Toys lives on, not only for many former Baby Boomers, who enjoyed these toys as children, but also for today's avid toy collectors. A number of Louis Marx's Toy Company creations can still be found today. The Louis Marx Toy company built toys that were meant to be "played with" and last for a long time. The toys' durability has truly withstood the test of time.

The information presented in this book pertains to a significant sampling of the type of toys produced at the Marx Toy Company's Glen Dale, West Virginia, plant site. The Marx Toys Listing in this book was compiled by Gaylord A. Whipkey in the early 1970s, and covers about thirty years of production. The Marx Toy Company produced thousands of high quality toy items at a number of locations over many years, and this research material documents an important segment of items made at the Glen Dale site.

Louis Marx purchased the former Fokker Aircraft Corporation plant in Glen Dale, West Virginia, in the early 1930s, and had additions "built on" over the years as the company's toy line expanded. The first major addition was made in the late 1930s, which allowed for plastics production. The Glen Dale plant was one of several located in North America, and was believed by many who worked there to be the biggest and busiest of the Marx Toy Company plants. Glen Dale proved to be an ideal location for Louis Marx since it offered easy access to a nearby river and rail lines, and also was accessible to a major highway. Even though the plant has been closed for some years now, many former employees have vivid recollections of what it was like to work at this toy plant. Overall, most employees seemed to enjoy working at the toy plant, and they were saddened by its demise. More information on this subject can be found in The Toy Trader magazine's issue of November 1993, (Volume 1, Number 3, previously published by Antique Trader Publications), in an article titled "Memories From The Marx Toy Box," by Michelle L. Smith.

Keep in mind that the information on Marx toys presented in this book covers only a portion of the extensive line of toy items produced at the Glen Dale plant site. This undertaking is the result of several years of research, including interviews with several former employees. A great deal of important first-hand information was provided by one former Marx Toy Company modeler, Gaylord Whipkey, who also provided supporting material in the form of toys, catalogs, and photographs. We worked together on the book's research materials for about three years. Although Gaylord died in November, 1996, his wife very graciously permitted me to finish my research on the toys. Gaylord worked a large part of his life in the toy plant at Glen Dale, and was very disappointed when it closed. He stated that, over the years, he had received a great deal of self-satisfaction from his endeavors in helping to create toys for countless thousands of children.

The former toy plant in Glen Dale had quite a significant impact on the local Ohio Valley's economy during its years of operation—not only in a business sense, but also in terms of its impact on the lives of employees who worked there. Numerous stories could be written from former employees' accounts of both good and bad times at the plant. Many of the former employees, after the plant closed, were able to find work in nearby steel mills, industries, and local businesses, and some even in local public office. Rather than do many different interviews, I chose instead to focus on two individuals' contributions in making these fine toys, and to meet with one other individual who still had his favorite Marx toy. One of the two former employees' stories was told to me personally, while the employee's son related the other. Many area residents can still remember that the toy plant "was just there" (in Glen Dale), and that it provided employment for some of the people they knew, including family and friends. Over the years, a large number of hard working and talented individuals spent a good portion of their lifetimes working at this plant site.

In the pages that follow, I will share the photographs and information that I've collected over the past few years, as well as some of the photographs available in old Marx Toys Promotional Catalogs. It is with the kind cooperation and courtesy of the current president of The Marx Toy Corporation, Jay Horowitz, that I've been able to present some of these catalog images in the book. I'm sure that fellow "Baby Boomer" collectors, as well as toy dealers, will find this information both informative and enjoyable. It's amazing, even in today's highly researched and much studied marketplace, that many Marx collectors and enthusiasts are not very well informed about many of the Marx toys produced at the Glen Dale plant site.

Initially, I was intrigued by the many "blanks" in available information relating to the production of toys at the Glen Dale plant site. This prompted me to establish contact with a few former employees. One individual in particular, Gaylord Whipkey of Cameron, West Virginia, helped me immensely. His knowledge was extensive, especially when it came to identifying one of my favorite line of toys: dollhouses. He not only provided me with detailed research materials and photographs from his private collection, but he also helped to identify many of the Marx toys I have in my collection. The information I am providing in this book has been made possible through the wonderful generosity of Mr. Whipkey. He compiled and maintained, over the many years since his tenure at the former Glen Dale plant, detailed information on many of the Marx toys that were produced at this plant site. This partial toy listing—The Marx Toy Listing dated 10/73—was compiled by Gaylord while he worked in the Model Department. Gaylord, with the help of a few colleagues, literally "combed through" numerous old model files and retrieved information for this listing. He did this at a time when no one else attached any importance to saving the old model information. Gaylord believed that it was very important to save and preserve this toy history in Glen Dale. It is because of his long hours and hard work that a segment of Marx's toy history in the Ohio Valley remains. Even though this toys listing may not be complete, it has been made as comprehensive as possible, and it certainly should assist Marx toy collectors and dealers in properly identifying the majority of toys made at Glen Dale during this thirty-year time period.

I have provided herein a great deal of information on the extensive line of lithographed dollhouses made by the Marx Toy Company at the Glen Dale plant. I have seen collector books that offer limited information about Marx Toy Company dollhouses, and the effort has been made here to fill in some of the blanks.

Gaylord often spoke of the fine craftsmanship of the Model Room artists and modelers in depicting detail and realism. This is quite apparent as you look at any of the lithographed items, action figures and accessories made at Glen Dale. He was, along with most of the people who worked at the toy plant, quite proud of all the toy items produced.

Chapter One

Life at the Marx Toy Plant

Two of the following men worked for the Marx Toy plant as did the father of the third. They have many interesting insights into the making of the Marx legacy. Two of the men agreed to be interviewed, the third decided to speak strictly for himself.

In My Words. . . by Gaylord Whipkey

Conversation with Gaylord Whipkey, Saturday, May 21, 1994, at his home in Cameron, West Virginia. Gaylord was employed at the Glen Dale plant for more than thirty years.

My years at the Marx Toy Company! I'm not sure just where to start, there's so much one could talk about. I found working at the plant very interesting, but it would take quite some time to cover all of the events and memories. I'll reflect on, and talk about, a few key things.

I spent a large part of my working days in the former Glen Dale Marx Toy Company plant. In fact, in mid-August of 1949, I quit a steady job I was working at a local conduit company just to get an opportunity to work at the Marx Toy plant. My last working day was

Gaylord "Andrew" Whipkey, Marx Modeler, 1974. Photograph taken on July 8, 1974, last day of the Glen Dale R&D department. (G. A. Whipkey collection)

December 30, 1979, and the company even paid me for the New Year's day holiday. Sometimes, when I was not working during the off-season, it was difficult to make ends meet, but I managed. I remember that I always looked forward to getting back to work at the toy factory.

When I first starting working at the plant, it was only for a brief time. During that time of the year things were slowing down, and those with low seniority were laid off until the startup of the spring season. In the early spring of the following year, I was fortunate to be called back to work, and I started in the Oven Spray Room/ Paint Shop areas of the plant.. Over the next few years I periodically "bid out" on different positions which, when awarded to me, offered the opportunity to work and learn a variety of work tasks and positions. I eventually was offered the chance to bid on a position in the Model Department—it was always my dream to work there—initially starting out as a Model Department stock boy and model apprentice in 1957.

I loved working this position because it helped to open the door to the job I always longed for: one in the Model Department at the plant. I wanted to learn how to create and design prototype toys for children. As a stock boy and apprentice, I ran daily errands and did any odd jobs for the modelers. This learning environment among the artists and models provided me the opportunity of a lifetime: a chance to learn the modeler's trade work from beginning to end. I started my apprenticeship with artists and modelers, learning the trade literally from the floor up. I assisted in the creation of Powerhouse Trucks and lithographed buildings and dollhouses. I advanced quickly, and within a few years was working alongside the other artists and modelers. My creativity and responsibility expanded while working with these talented, creative artists and modelers. Everyone in this department worked well together and we became a team, sharing ideas and suggestions for new toys.

Later in my years in the Model Department, I helped come up with ideas for creation of the "Lift Off" roof modern dollhouse (large dollhouse) in the 1950s. I enjoyed working with the talented artist, Joe Chamberlain, on his ideas in the creation of the "Imagination Dollhouse," which was produced from 1968 through 1971. I liked the "see-through" dollhouse concept and the ultra-modern furniture and accessories. This dollhouse did not live up to the expectations of the Company, and its production was phased out after 1971. I believe it was just too futuristic for its time.

I can still recall one trip that I took with fellow Model Department employees. We traveled to New York City to meet with Louis Marx. His corporate office complex in New York City was immense. I enjoyed the trip, and found Louis Marx to be a very interesting and likable man. He was not pretentious or overbearing, but a man with a genuine interest in the production and marketing of his toys. I was amazed by the fact that his office was not as luxurious as some others were, but, instead, was quite plain, with just a simple desk and several straight-back chairs.

During the years I worked at the Glen Dale plant site, I remember Louis Marx making a few visits to the plant, but not many. With several company plant locations in the U.S. and a few around the world, he probably visited them all on occasion, as needed. The employees knew that Louis Marx believed in "mass production and saturation in the toy market" of any Marx toys. Marx believed that toys should be produced cheaply, maintain good quality and durability, and be affordable to the consumers. Marx really knew how to market the toys and make money from them. He utilized his plant in Hong Kong to do a lot of the detailed hand-painted figures. These figures were made in Glen Dale, and then shipped to the Hong Kong plant where they were painted and subsequently returned to the West Virginia plant for packaging in various play sets. The Hong Kong plant site also had their own set of molds, which were used to produce many items in the Marx plastic toy line. Labor was cheaper in Hong Kong, and many small items were sent over there to be painted and returned to other plant locations.

Most individuals who I knew well enjoyed their years working at the Glen Dale plant site. I know I enjoyed all my years working at the plant. As my seniority built over the years, I was not laid off very often. Of course, I did not work during the time when I served my tour of duty in the Korean War.

My son always seemed delighted with his dad's profession, and he regularly and thoroughly played with any new toy samples that I would bring home. I believe he still may have a few Marx toys. Even my grandchildren today have played with some of my original Marx toys, such as the Johnny West series and the Flintstones Play Set.

I truly believe that the Marx Toy Company produced the finest in lithographed dollhouses and other structures. Over the years, some artists and/or modelers went to work for competitors such as Wolverine and Ohio Art, and if you look closely enough, you will see some very similar detailing in the competitors' dollhouses. Some of the other notable manufacturers of tin lithograph dollhouses were T. Cohn, Inc., Playsteel, Jayline, and Meritoy during the late 1940s, 1950s, and so forth.

Sadly, as the years went on, I think most employees in all of the plant locations realized that the Marx Toy Company was declining in popularity. Too much competition, and ever-increasing production and labor costs, probably were the main reasons. The Marx Toy Company's main competitors were Ideal, Kenner, and Mattel. Marx Toy Company eventually lost the crown it wore as the once-reigning "king" in the marketplace to other big toy makers.

May 10, 1972—a very sad day! A memorandum was issued to all Marx plant employees at all locations. The memorandum announced a planned merger between Louis Marx & Co., Inc. and the Quaker Oats Company. This takeover by Quaker Oats was regarded by many of my fellow workers as the beginning of the end for the Marx Toy Company. Things never would be the same for Marx employees over the remaining years before the final closure of the plant. They endured many changes in plant procedures and the like following this sale to Quaker Oats. The Model Department where I worked was eventually phased out, and reorganized into an engineering-type department. I left the Model Department shortly after the sale to Quaker Oats, and went to work in other areas of the plant until its closure.

As to what my favorite toy was...it's very hard to say. I enjoyed most of the toys made at our Marx Toy Company plant. I enjoyed working on the lithographed dollhouses and other buildings in the numerous play sets made over the years, and stated that the Marx-a-Mansion and the Imagination (see-through) Dollhouses were some of the finest ones created by the Marx artists. Even though the Imagination Dollhouse (1968-1971) did not sell as well as the company thought it would, its futuristic concept was unequaled by any toy competitor. Joe Chamberlain's artistic and creative talents flourished on his initial drawings for the Imagination Dollhouse plans, and his drawings and ideas were sent to New York and approved for production. Another favorite in the dollhouse series was the modern dollhouse with the "lift off" roof. The Marx-a-Mansion (early 1960s) was the grand dame in dollhouses, and it stood above all the other dollhouses in terms of realistic detail and accessories.

I firmly believe, and I've mentioned it before, that the Marx Toy Company made the finest lithographed dollhouses in the market place. Our lithographs displayed more realistic imagery than similar products made by our competitors. Many competitors could not replicate the same process. If you were to compare several different dollhouses made by different companies in the same time period, you would see how Marx's lithography stood out from the rest. I can recall when several former employees left to go to work at a competitor's company, and how their creations in lithography resembled the artwork on some of our company's dollhouses.

I have kept many records, along with many photographs, of the activities that went on in the plant: the production lines, the Model Department "gang," retirements, birthdays and office parties, union meetings, supervisors, etc. I still maintain and update my collection of photographs and albums whenever I come across news of any former Marx Toys' employee or of any get-together of former employees.

Interview with Marx Toy Company artist Joe Chamberlain's son, Eric

MS: Tell me about your dad, "Joe" Chamberlain.

EC: Well, my dad started working at the Marx Toy plant in 1941, in the Model Room as an Artist Apprentice. He worked there for a short time, and then went into the service when World War II started. He was in the service several years, returning to work at the Marx plant in 1946. I believe that his starting wages in 1941 were $36.66 for a 40-hour workweek. When I graduated from high school in 1963, he was making $99.66 a week. It's horrible and a shame that the guys in the Model Room didn't make better wages. They were all so talented! But, my dad liked the work he did, so he stayed there. The others that stayed on felt the same way, too.

MS: Gaylord Whipkey told me, on more than one occasion, how much he enjoyed his work. He said that

Floyd "Joe" Chamberlain, Marx Artist, at work. (E. Chamberlain collection)

Dianna Chamberlain, niece of Floyd "Joe" Chamberlain. Ms. Chamberlain posed as a model for the creation of Princess Wildflower in the Johnny West Series.

from the time he started working out on the floor area of the plant, his goal was to work in the Model Room. Within a few years his goal became reality, and he stayed there until the plant closed. Did your dad really enjoy his job, as well?

EC: Yeah, my dad felt about the same as what Gaylord must have felt. Even though the wages weren't very good, he really enjoyed creating new toys.

MS: How did your dad come by the name of "Joe," since his real name was Floyd?

EC: Dad was named "Joe" because many people thought he looked like his uncle Joe. Most people that he worked with called him Joe, though some called him by his given name, Floyd Chamberlain. He generally initialed his artwork with an "FC" or a "C," and a few times with "JC."

MS: What are some of the things you remember that your dad created or help create for Marx Toys?

EC: He did so many designs for new toys, dollhouses and furnishings, various play sets, service stations, airports, etc. He came up with the design for Princess Wildflower from the Johnny West series figures. In fact, my cousin, Dianna Chamberlain, modeled for him when he was creating the face of Princess Wildflower. If you look at an earlier photo of her when she was in high school, you can see a definite resemblance in the face of that figure. Other toys I remember include figures from the Jungle Book and Prince Valiant, for which I still have the original hand-carved prototype figures.

MS: Did each of the original artists receive recognition for their new toy design creations? How can you tell your dad's artwork from that of other artists who worked for the Marx Toy Company?

EC: No, the artists and modelers where not really given the credit due them. That generally went to the supervisor or department head. It's a shame that each person in the Model Room didn't receive recognition for his own designs, or even for the combined team efforts. My dad, as well as Gaylord and many of the others, didn't like this, but that was the way things were done back then. An artist was not supposed to leave his name on any of the artwork. My dad had a rather unique way though, of leaving his mark on his designs. Although on some of the artboards I have from his portfolio his name was not spelled out, he sometimes worked his initials, or another family member's initials, into the finished artwork. On the popular Moon Base final artboard (box top layout) you can find Joe Chamberlain's signature "C"—a rocket that is outlining a "C" around the earth—as well as different family members' initials on the part listing in the corner of the box.

He applied similar "initialing" to different artboards that I have in my collection, and sometimes only a trained eye such as mine can detect his initials or markings. My dad was very proud of his artwork and the toy designs that he did for the Marx Toy company. He was always pleased to see the final toy that would make kids happy.

MS: Did you know the Model Room guys? How did your dad get along with them?

EC: Yes, I knew them. Sometimes dad would bring a few of the guys home for lunch. They seemed to get along very well. They were a close-knit team responsible for creating many great toys. They were very creative guys who enjoyed working on new toy ideas.

I remember the Model Room as not being very big for the number of guys who worked in it. There was no air conditioning in hot weather. I used to go there sometimes during the summers that I worked at the plant while I was in college. The guys had a good sense of humor, and could be quite creative when it came to playing an ornery, practical joke on someone.

MS: What did your dad say about work conditions after the plant was sold to the Quaker Oats Company in 1972?

EC: He and many of the others didn't like it, but there really wasn't anything the workers could do. Things changed in the Model Room. Morale in general was down a lot. Despite the new company's many work changes, the guys kept on creating new toy ideas, although many times they

Princess Wildflower, with accessories.
(G. A. Whipkey collection, photo by J. S. Smith)

Joe Chamberlain's Signature "C".
(E. Chamberlain collection, photo by J. S. Smith)

Joe Chamberlain's artboard for Operation Moon Base box. (E. Chamberlain collection, photo by J. S. Smith)

were changed or turned down by the new owners. The company just wasn't the same as it was when Louis Marx was in charge.

MS: Do you remember your dad working on a futuristic dollhouse in the late 1960s and early 1970s called the Imagination Dollhouse? Gaylord Whipkey said that he and your dad had worked together on that project.

EC: I'm not sure if I remember just that specific dollhouse since dad worked on so many different ones, but I wouldn't be surprised since the term "futuristic" fit right into his way of thinking about some things. Some of his sketches show designs for a rocket launcher. Quite impressive, even for those days.

MS: The artwork in his portfolio is quite extensive, and covers so many of the popular play sets, trucks, figures, etc. The artboards for the various play sets are very detailed and colorful. Gaylord said that the studios in Hollywood would send promotional pictures of stars and various film scenes to the Model Room, and these were used as guidelines in creating new toys. Have you ever seen any of these? I know Gaylord had several from the Daniel Boone and Davy Crocket series, as well as others.

EC: No, I can't say that I remember seeing those, although I know my dad's work showed a lot of realism and detail. He dealt a lot with the detail of a figure or toy, whether it was for a play set piece or a dollhouse wall or whatever. He was very talented, and seemed able to draw anything. My grandmother once said that when my dad was about four or five years old, he enjoyed getting the comics from the newspapers. He would set the comics aside, and proceed to draw similar comics that were as good as, if not better than, the ones in the newspapers. His artistic talent seemed to be natural from a very early age. I have his certification of apprentice artist that he completed when he went to work for the Marx Toy plant. My dad had no formal training, but he was very talented and good at his job. I was always in awe of his great artistic talent. He was able to do anything he set his mind to.

MS: Did your dad design the covers on any of the Marx Promotional Catalogs? A lot of work went into the design of these covers didn't it? Did you say he did instructional sheets, too?

EC: Yes, he did many of them, and I have several of the catalogs that he designed. Besides doing that, he designed many of the instructional sheets (White House, Capitol Building, etc.) that went into the various play sets and accompanied some toys. He also designed the layout artwork for the Alamo Play Set.

Joe Chamberlain's Signature "C" on an artboard for Operation Moon Base. Rocket trail makes outline of a "C" as it goes around the earth. (E. Chamberlain collection, photo by J. S. Smith)

MS: Did your dad ever bring home any of the new toys that had been made?

EC: No, he didn't believe in doing that. On occasion he might bring home a toy that had a slight defect, or possibly one of his prototype models, but he didn't bring home finished toys.

MS: Did your dad ever do any oil paintings or artwork outside his job?

EC: Yes, but he'd only do it free for something special like for a church, a high school minstrel, or something along that line. He didn't paint anything for sale for himself.

MS: Do you have a favorite thing that your dad did?

EC: Yes, he did an oil still life painting for me. In it, he shows some of my collectible bottles next to some fruit. It's my favorite thing, since he did it just for me.

MS: When did you work at the plant and did you like working in the toy plant?

EC: First, no, I didn't really enjoy working there. . . it was just a job. I needed the money when I was going to college. I worked at the plant during the summers of 1963 and 1964. My job was helping the women on the assembly lines. It was a hard and busy job being a ware guy, stocking the various parts for the toys. I had to make sure that I kept up with whatever the women needed on the line. I would see that boxes of ware were kept stacked by each woman's workstation. These women did piece work, and they were paid according to volume, or the number of items that they produced. They really got after me in no uncertain terms if they thought I was slacking or not working fast enough. The language that went back and forth with these ladies was sometimes pretty bad. I was raised to respect ladies, but these women really shocked me sometimes. They worked hard and long hours at that plant, in not the best or safest working conditions.

I remember one summer I worked in the gluing sections, where the workers would "glue" together plastic horses. They would dip the horses in buckets of glue (methylethylketone) chemical that dissolved the plastic somewhat. When cooled, this process "set up" a hard seal. Sometimes the fumes from this glue would be pretty strong, and would affect the workers that had been working with it. You have to remember that, back then, there weren't a lot of preventative safety measures in place for working with any chemicals. The women were hard workers. Again, I didn't like the work there, but it helped me with college expenses.

Vintage photograph of Marx Employees in 1935. (G. A. Whipkey collection)

Former Model Room employees for Louis Marx Inc., of New York, Glen Dale, West Virginia plant (prior to the plant's sale to the Quaker Oats Company)

* Anderson, Edgar
Bigelow, Walter
Bishop, James
Bonar, Bill
* Burkett, Roy
Calhoun, John
Cetorelli, Libero
Chamberlain, Bill
Chamberlain, "Joe" Floyd
Clark, Robert
Cornwell, Harold
Curtis, L. D.
Davis, Larry
Duffy, Tom
* Ericison, George
Emblem, Robert
Fisher, Clarence
* Genensky, Stanley
Gower, Bert
Grosso, Floyd
Harler, Robert
Hicks, Robert
Joseph, Bill
* Klem, John
* Koch, Bill
Koloskus, Vic
Kvinta, Vince
Landers, John
* Larson, Al
* Lilgenberg, Harry
* Lindsey, Bill (D)
Long, Thomas
* Lovrak, Pete
Loy, Harold
* Mack, Andy (D)
Marshall, James
McDowell, Norman
Mercer, Carl
* Merle, Carl
Metz, Charles
Mickey, Robert
* McGill, Don
Miller, Robert
Minkemyer, John
Mobley, Frank
Morris, Stanley
Moris, James
Nadolski, Stanley
* Nisperly, Walter
* Norman, Walker
* Olex, Thomas
Palmer, Larry
Peabody, P. R.
Peabody, Carl
* Pennybacker, Bill
Polen Carroll
Pruit, John
Ray, James
Reister, James
Rhome, Jesse
Rhome, Danny
Rich, Alex
Robinson, Robert
Roxby, Richard
Sharp, Robert
* Siburt, Kenneth
Siglar, Dale
Siglar, Junior
* Simms, Robert
Sintonavich, Tony
Steadman, John
Strope, Carroll
Tusina, Edward
Whipkey, Gaylord
Williams, Thomas
Witsberger, William

** Deceased prior to 1978 sale to Quaker Oats*

Vintage photograph of Marx Employees in 1934. (G. A. Whipkey collection)

Model Room Employees in the 1950s. (E. Chamberlain collection)

Model Room Employees in the 1960s. (E. Chamberlain collection)

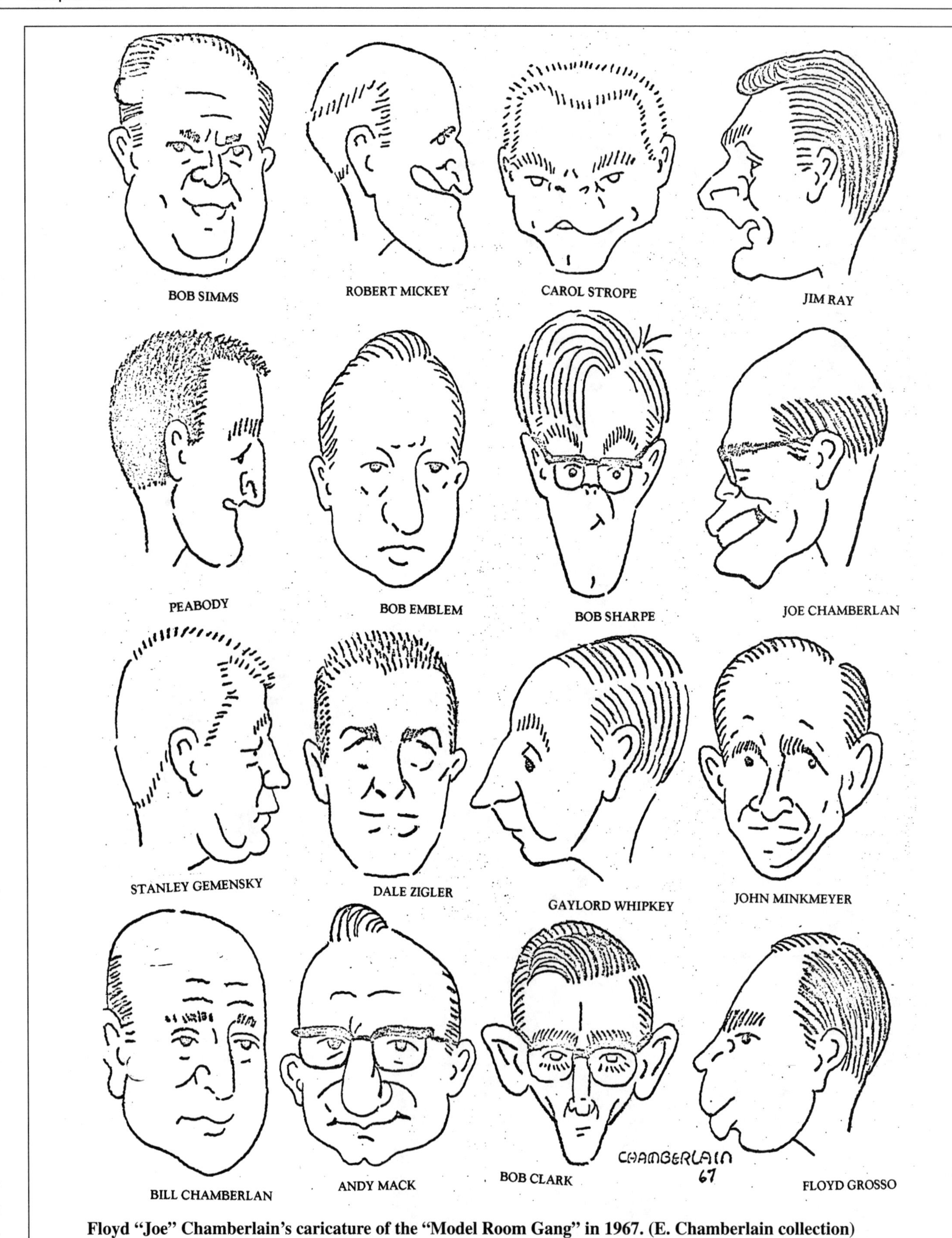

Floyd "Joe" Chamberlain's caricature of the "Model Room Gang" in 1967. (E. Chamberlain collection)

LeRoy Leach, with his favorite childhood toy: the Marx Army & Navy Shooting Gallery from the 1940s. (L. Leach collection, photo by B. Harter)

Interview with LeRoy Leach

MS: Tell me about your Marx shooting gallery [the metal Marx Army-Navy Shooting Gallery].

LL: I figure it's from the early Forties; around about the time of World War II. I don't think the gun came with it, but that was all right 'cause I had a lot of guns that worked with it. I think even the guns were metal back then, too. And the dart with the suction cup on the end was just like a lollipop stick. I used to save all of my lollipop sticks cause (the dart) is usually what got broken. What's amazing to me is that it still works. Look how old this toy is, and it still works good. I played with it many years growing up, and it has held up. I was probably seven when I got this toy for Christmas. I loved to shoot those suction cup guns. I got to be pretty good with them, and dad was so brave as to smoke a cigarette and cover his eye and then I would shoot it out of his mouth.

I had 75 to 100 Marx metal soldiers at one point. My friend and I would set 'em up and (using the suction-cup gun) shoot 'em down. We also had some of the first plastic cars that Marx made. I also had two or three of the Marx metal cap guns, too.

Most of the stuff that I had held onto I've since given to my son. This shooting gallery was just a unique piece that I've kept for myself.

I was born and raised in Moundsville, West Virginia, and it was nothing to go up behind the old Marx plant and go through discarded cardboard packing and find toys. If only we'd kept some of that old stuff! We knew (the factory) was there, but we didn't give much thought to it. When you have something in your backyard, you very often don't pay that much attention to it.

I just loved this old shooting gallery. It's a great toy! That's the trouble with the toys today—the kids don't need as much imagination to play with them. That was part of the fun, coming up with how to play with your toys.

Marx Jungle Book character prototypes by Joe Chamberlain. (E. Chamberlain collection, photo by J. S. Smith)

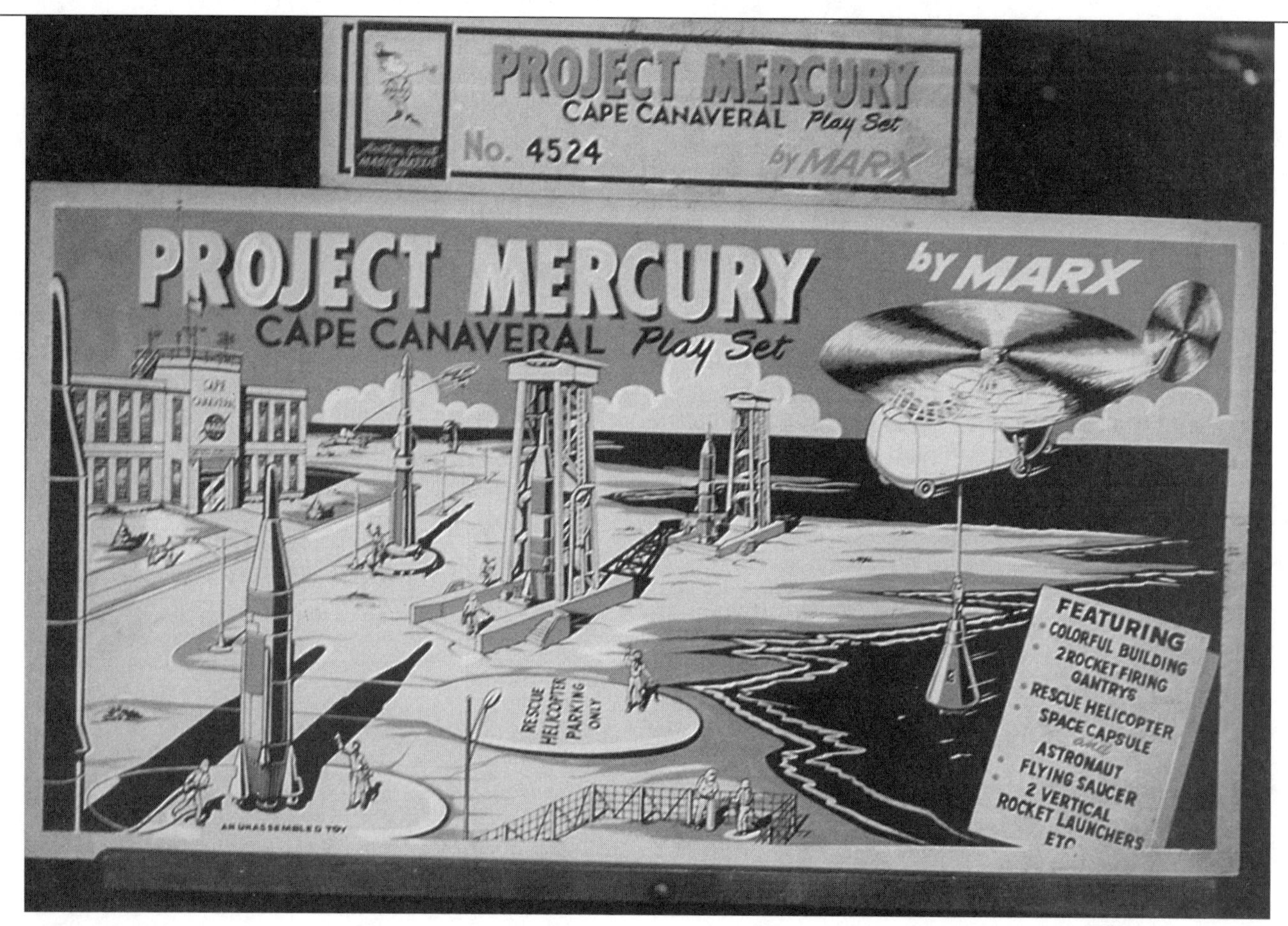

Project Mercury Cape Canaveral Play Set artboard by Joe Chamberlain. (E. Chamberlain collection, photo by J. S. Smith)

Prehistoric Monsters and Cavemen artboard by Joe Chamberlain. (E. Chamberlain collection, photo by J. S. Smith)

Marx "Old Jalopy" artwork by Joe Chamberlain. Initials on car represented different family members. (E. Chamberlain collection, photo by J. S. Smith)

Chapter Two

Play Sets

Many "Baby Boomers" can surely recall at least one or more of the famous Marx Toy Company play sets, such as Johnny West, Fort Apache, Battleground, Battle of the Blue and Gray, the farm sets, castles, service stations, space base sets, Flintstones, and so forth. Marx play sets were not only colorful, but some even included lithographed accessories. The artists' and modelers' detail excelled over rival toy competitors. All their play sets featured very detailed and authentic-looking replicas. The many plastic accessories also helped to compliment each set or play set.

Production of Marx Toy Company play sets at the Glen Dale plant site started in the 1950s with item number 3930 Barn Set, items number 3955-6 and 3965-6 Wild West Ranch Sets, items number 3959-60 and 3962-3 Western Ranch Sets, and item number 3964 Western Frontier Set. Over the years, a select number of play sets were produced in a miniature series, a standard series, and a giant (large) series. Listed below, from available research information, are play sets and/or sets that were issued during the 1950s. Many of these sets were also produced in other years, but all remained virtually the same as the original set, with only certain features updated.

Item #	Year	Description
0898-9	1951	Service Station Figures & Car Set
0912	1951	Farm Accessory Set
3606-7	1951	Fort Apache Stockade
3609-10	1951	Fort Apache Stockade
3931-2	1951	Farm Set
0796	1952	Airport & Hangar Set
3190MO	1952	Farm Animal Set
3449-50	1952	Service Station w/accessories
3509-10	1952	Fort Dearborn Stockade
3689-90	1952	Fort Apache Set
3670	1952	Kentucky Fox Hunt
3689-90	1952	Roy Rogers Rodeo
3696	1952	Lone Ranger Rodeo
3811-12	1952	Factory Set w/accessories (Pre-Fab)
3821-2	1952	School House w/accessories (Pre-Fab)
3831-2	1952	Airport w/accessories (Pre-Fab)
3841-2	1952	General Store Set (Pre-Fab)
3851-2	1952	Church Set (Pre-Fab)
3861-2	1952	Barn w/Silo and accessories (Pre-Fab)
3871-2	1952	House, Ranch Type Set (Pre-Fab)
3881-2	1952	Railroad Station Set
3889-92	1952	Service Station (Pre-Fab)

Service station attendants from the 1950s. (M. L. Smith collection, photo by M. L. Smith)

No. 3483 Super Station, as depicted in the 1973 Marx Toys Promotional Catalog.

No. 3382 Little Red School, 1956. (G. A. Whipkey photo collection)

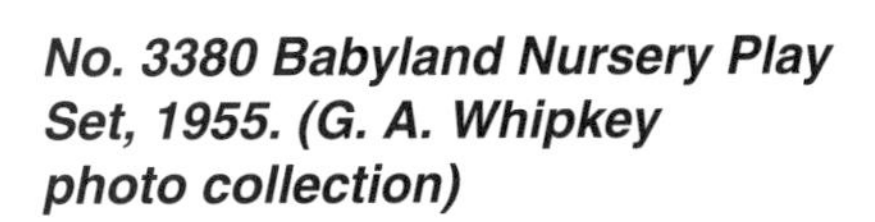

No. 3380 Babyland Nursery Play Set, 1955. (G. A. Whipkey photo collection)

***No. 3506 Three-Level Station, as depicted in the* 1973 Marx Toys Promotional Catalog.**

Marx Pet Shop box.

No. 4209-10 Pet Shop Play Set, 1953. (G. A. Whipkey photo collection.)

Pet Shop with dogs, birdcages and other accessories.

Item #	Year	Description
3925	1952	Lazy Day Farm Set (Wards)
3926	1952	Modern Farm Set (Wards)
3979-80	1952	Roy Rogers Ranch Set
4119-22	1952	Army Training Center
4144	1952	Army Training Center
4229-30	1952	Old Western Town Set
4257-8	1952	Roy Rogers Mineral City Western Town
4309-10	1952	Big Top Circus Set
4319-20	1952	Super Circus Set
4411-12	1952	Railroad Station w/accessories
4416	1952	Railroad Station w/lights
7009-10	1952	Tom Corbett Space Academy
7019-20	1952	Space Patrol Academy
7040	1952	Planet Patrol Space Drome
3459-60-62	1953	Service Station w/accessories
3464	1953	Happi-Time Service Station w/accessories
3504	1953	Fort Dearborn Stockade
3514	1953	Fort Dearborn Stockade w/shell shooting cannon
3612	1953	Fort Apache Stockade w/shell shooting cannon
771-2	1953	"Marxville" Dinner w/accessories
3781-2	1953	Fire House w/accessories
3893	1953	Service Station Take-Apart Set
3923-4	1953	Farm Set
3737-8	1953	Modern Farm Set
3940	1953	Happi-Time Farm Set
3949-50	1953	Cowboy & Indian Set
3990	1953	Happi-Time Roy Rogers Rodeo Ranch Set
4209-10	1953	Pet Shop Set
4709-10	1953	Medieval Castle Fortress Set
5424	1953	Truck Rail Terminal
7012	1953	Tom Corbett Space Academy
7014	1953	Rex Mars Planet Patrol
7024	1953	Rex Mars Space Port
7026	1953	Captain Space Solar Academy
0408MO	1954	Milking Cow Set
3114-MO	1954	Parade & Combat Soldiers Set
3127-8MO	1954	Captain Kidd w/Pirates
3134-MO	1954	Circus Figures Set
3359-60	1954	Zoo Set
3462/0740	1954	Service Station w/auto transport & accessories

***No. 3681 Fort Apache Play Set, as depicted in the* 1973 Marx Toys Promotional Catalog.**

Fort Apache set with metal log cabin, stockade fence, flag & pole, horses etc.

Item #	Year	Description
3614	1954	Fort Apache Stockade (Sears)
3721-2	1954	Police Station w/accessories (Pre-Fab)
3741-42	1954	Army Barracks w/accessories
3744	1954	Kiddie Speller Set
3856	1954	Chicken Coop Set
3894-5-6	1954	Assorted (Pre-Fab) Village Buildings
3909/10/11	1954	White House w/Presidents
3912/18/19/20		
3985-6	1954	Roy Rogers Double-Bar Rodeo Ranch Set
4145/46-8	1954	Army & Air Force Training Center
4158-9	1954	Army & Air Force Training Center
4256	1954	Silver City Western Town (Wards)
4302	1954	Super Circus Set
4306	1954	Super Circus Set
4409-10	1954	Railroad Station
4439-40	1954	Construction Camp
4705-6	1954	Prince Valiant Castle Set
4711-12	1954	Prince Valiant Castle Set
4713-4	1954	Military Academy
4715-6	1954	Military Academy w/6 generals
4819-20	1954	Fire House w/figures & accessories
4909-10-12	1954	U. S. Capitol Building
5421-2	1954	Spec. Truck Rail Terminal
7015-6	1954	Rex Mars Space Drome
7018	1954	Captain Space Solar Port
2694	1955	Noah's Ark w/animals
2901-2	1955	Statue of Liberty
2911-12	1955	Statue of Liberty
3016	1955	Religious Statuettes Set
3077	1955	Assorted American Heroes Set
3179-80	1955	Wild Animal Set
3315-16	1955	Nativity Stable Set
3369-70	1955	Nursery Set
3379-80	1955	Babyland Nursery Set
3453-4	1955	Cities Service Station
3466	1955	New Car Sales & Service Center w/lights
3479-80	1955	Turnpike Service Station Set
3518	1955	Davy Crockett Alamo Set
3520	1955	Davy Crockett Frontier Set
3529-30	1955	Davy Crockett at Alamo Set
3534	1955	Official Disney's Davy Crockett Alamo Set

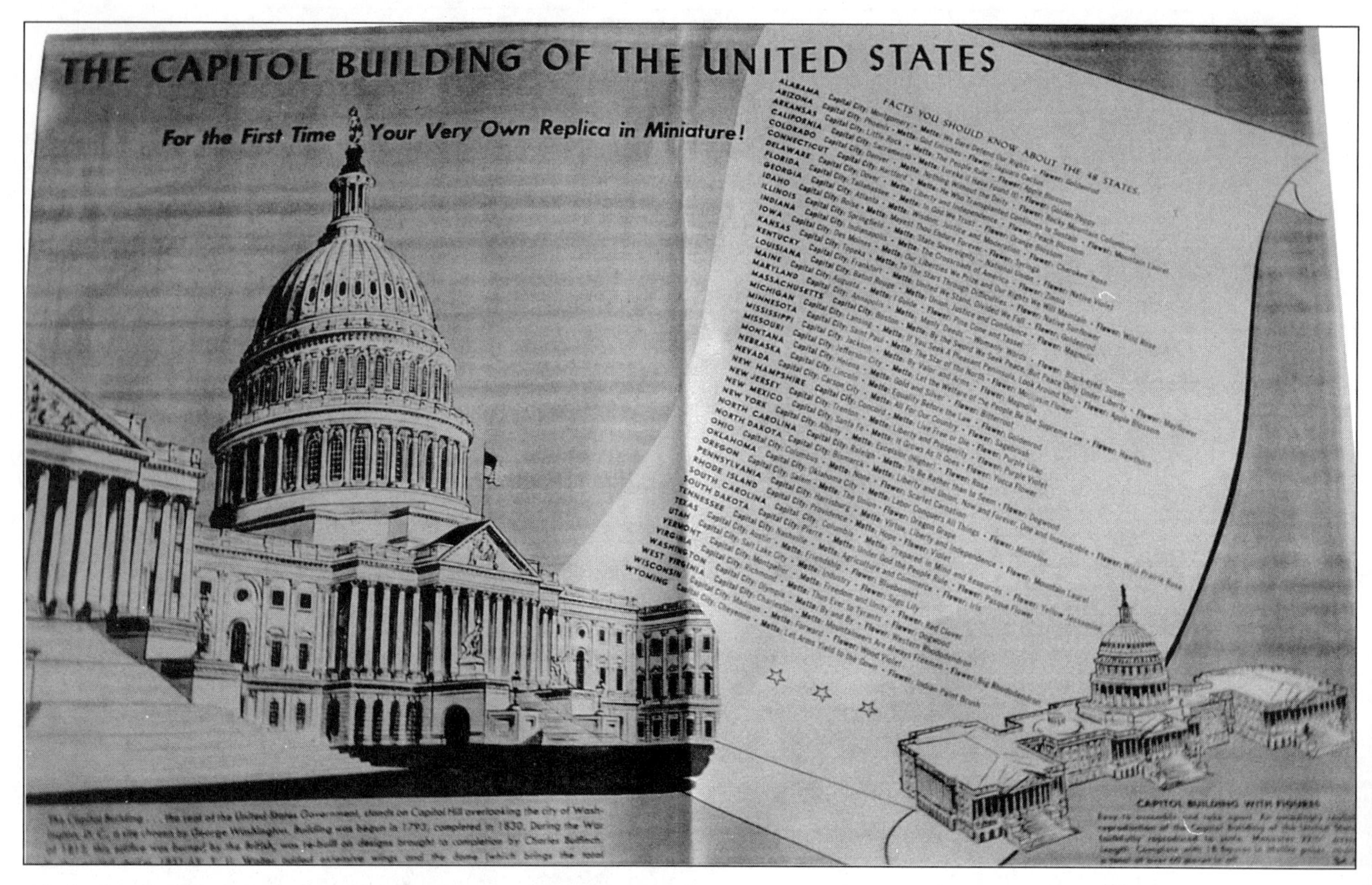

U. S. Capitol Building, 1950s Information Sheet. (M. L. Smith collection, photo by J. S. Smith)

U. S. Capitol Building, 1950s. (M. L. Smith collection, photo by M. L. Smith)

White House (front), 1950s/ 1960s. (M. L. Smith collection, photo by J. S. Smith)

White House (rear). (M. L. Smith collection, photo by J. S. Smith)

White House Information Sheet, 1950s/1960s. (M. L. Smith collection, photo by J. S. Smith)

Presidents of the United States on display.

The White House of the United States with 36 presidential figures.

Presidents of the United States on display.

No. 4820 Firehouse, 1954.
(G. A. Whipkey photo collection)

Item #	Year	Description
3539-40	1955	Davy Crockett Alamo Set
3544	1955	Official Disney's Davy Crockett Alamo Set (Sears)
3615-6	1955	Fort Apache Stockade w/Famous Americans
3944	1955	Happi-Time Farm Set w/new Chicken House
3992	1955	Roy Rogers Rodeo Ranch
4123-4	1955	Army Training Center
4149-50	1955	Armed Forces Training Center
4219-20	1955	Silver City Frontier Town
4441-2	1955	Construction Camp w/Friction Vehicles
4444	1955	Construction Camp w/Friction Equipment
7004	1955	Rex Mars Space Port
0765	1956	Wild Animal Set
0767	1956	Circus & Animal Figures Set
55/10	1956	Indians Set
55/11	1956	Combat Soldiers Set
55/14	1956	Robin Hood Set
55/16	1956	Indians Set
55/2	1956	Calvary Soldiers Set
55/3	1956	Robin Hood Set
55/6	1956	North American Wild Life Set
55/7	1956	Farm Animals Set
3191	1956	Pirates in Bag Set
3192	1956	Indians in Bag Set
3193	1956	Cowboys in Bag Set
3194	1956	Soldiers in Bag Set
3195	1956	Cadets in Bag Set
3196	1956	Soldiers in Bag Set
3197-8	1956	Sailors in Bag Set
3381-2	1956	Little Red School House w/accessories
3465	1956	New Car Sales & Service Station (34655-Spiegels)
3467-8	1956	Service Station w/accessories
3469-70-72	1956	Service Station w/accessories
3627-8	1956	Rin Tin Tin Fort Apache
4103-4	1956	Boy Scout Camp
4139-40-42	1956	Armed Forces Training Center
4268	1956	Silver City Western Town
4417-18	1956	Railroad Station w/voice box
4717-8	1956	Robin Hood Castle Set
4719-20	1956	Robin Hood Castle Set
4721-2	1956	Official Robin Hood Castle Set

Five-Star Generals of the U. S. Army, 1950s. (G. A. Whipkey collection, photo by M. L. Smith)

Astronauts - Rex Mars Space Figures, 1950s/1960s. (G. A. Whipkey collection. Photo by M. L. Smith)

Roy Rogers Play Set figures, 1950s. (G. A. Whipkey collection, photo by M. L. Smith)

Astronauts - Rex Mars Space Figures, 1950s/1960s. (G. A. Whipkey collection, photo by M. L. Smith)

Prehistoric Play Set Figures, 1950s/1960s. (G. A. Whipkey collection, photo by J. S. Smith)

Prehistoric Play Set Figures, 1950s/1960s. (G. A. Whipkey collection, photo by J. S. Smith)

Prehistoric Play Set Figures, 1950s/1960s. (G. A. Whipkey collection, photo by J. S. Smith)

No. 3414 Prehistoric Mountain Play Set, as depicted in the **1973 Marx Toys Promotional Catalog.**

Item #	Year	Description
5425-6	1956	Freight Terminal
0706	1957	Lassie Farm Figures Set (21 pieces)
0707	1957	Roy Rogers Cowboy Figures Set (27 pieces)
0708	1957	Lone Ranger Western Figures Set (27 pieces)
0709	1957	Rin Tin Tin Calvary Figures Set (26 pieces)
0710	1957	Tex Frontier Figures Set (34 pieces)
0711	1957	Captain Gallant Figures Set (22 pieces)
0712	1957	Armed Forces Figures Set (38 pieces)
0713	1957	Robin Hood Series Figures Set (22 pieces)
0714	1957	New Wild Animals Figures Set (26 pieces)
0715	1957	Boy Campers Figures Set (27 pieces)
54/1	1957	Calvary Figures Set (33 pieces)
54/10	1957	Cowboys & Indians Set (32 pieces)
54/11	1957	Soldiers Set (31 pieces)
54/12	1957	Soldiers Set (38 pieces)
54/16/17	1957	Wild Animals Set
54/18	1957	Prehistoric Set (35 pieces)
54/19	1957	Railroad Figures Set (30 pieces)
54/2	1957	Calvary Figures Set (30 pieces)
54/3	1957	Indians Figure Set (34 pieces)
54/6	1957	Wild Life Set (31 pieces)
54/7	1957	Farm Animals Set (47 pieces)
54/8	1957	Horse and Saddle Set (24 pieces)
54/9	1957	Cowboy Figures (38 pieces)
1025-6	1957	Wrecker Truck Set
2704-5	1957	Fort Dearborn Set w/Metal Fort
2706	1957	U. S. Military Post w/Metal Ports
2707	1957	Alamo Set w/Metal Alamo
3378	1957	Jungle Set
3389-90	1957	Prehistoric Play Set
3401	1957	Johnny Tremain Play Set
3404	1957	Revolutionary War Play Set
3455	1957	Allstate Service Station
3473-4	1957	Service Station w/accessories
3476	1957	Service Station w/service truck w/flashing light
3481-2	1957	Allstate Service Station w/friction cars
3485-6	1957	Service Station w/electric elevator
3491-2&D	1957	Allstate Service Station w/electric elevator

***No. 3492 Super Car City Station, as depicted in the* 1973 Marx Toys Promotional Catalog.**

o. 3326 Nativity, 1956. (G. A. Whipkey collection. . A. Whipkey photo collection)

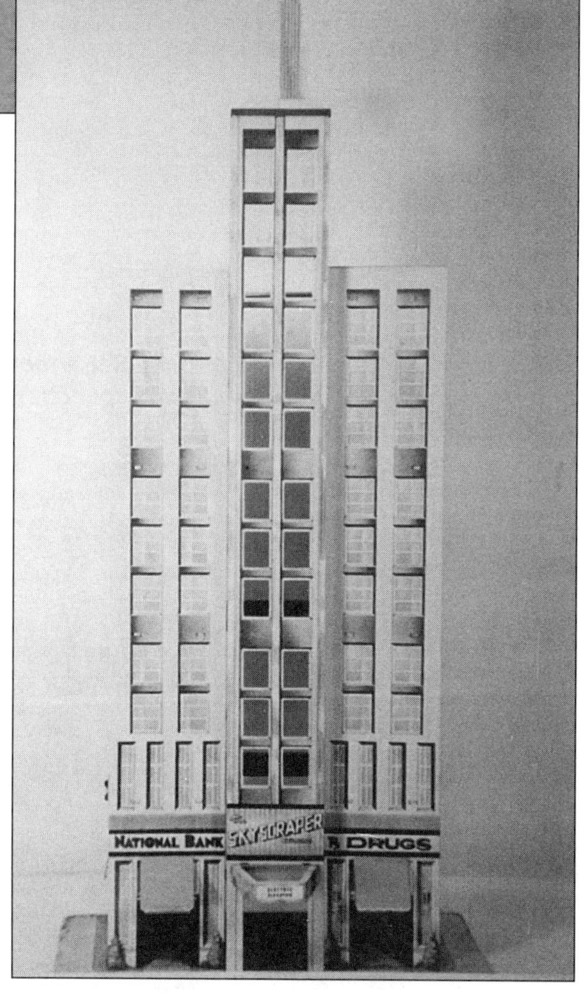

No. 5449-50 Skyscraper with elevator, 1957. (G. A. Whipkey photo collection)

Artwork for Project Mercury, Cape Canaveral Play Set, by Marx Toys artist Floyd "Joe" Chamberlain. (E. Chamberlain collection, photo by J. S. Smith)

Project Mercury Cape Canaveral Play Set artboard by Joe Chamberlain. (E. Chamberlain collection, photo by J. S. Smith)

Artwork for Prehistoric Monsters and Cavemen, by Marx Toys artist Floyd "Joe" Chamberlain. (E. Chamberlain collection, photo by J. S. Smith)

Item #	Year	Description
3647	1957	Fort Apache Stockade
3657-8	1957	Rin Tin Tin Fort Apache Set
3660	1957	Fort Apache Stockade
3675	1957	Fort Apache Play Set
3687-8	1957	Military Mobile Armored Combat Set
3689-90	1957	Allied Combat Set (Mobile S.L. Truck Set)
3705-6	1957	Jungle Jim Set
3927-8	1957	Lassie Farm Set
3939	1957	Modern Farm Set
3941-2	1957	Modern Farm Set
3493	1957	Happi-Time Farm Set w/chicken coop
3967-8-9	1957	Official Lone Ranger Ranch Set
3987-8	1957	Roy Rogers Rodeo Ranch Set
3995-6	1957	Bar "M" Ranch Set (Roy Rogers)
4102	1957	Armed Forces Training Center Set (32 pieces)
4133-4	1957	Army Training Center
4143	1957	Armed Forces Set w/guided missiles
4163-4	1957	Armed Forces Training Center w/Nike Base
4228	1957	Wyatt Earp Dodge City
4259	1957	Roy Rogers Mineral City
4260	1957	Western Town
4446	1957	Construction Camp Set
4723-4	1957	Robin Hood Castle Set
4778	1957	Indian Warfare Set
4779-80	1957	General Custer's Last Stand
5449-50	1957	Skyscraper w/elevator
5450M	1957	Skyscraper w/elevator & light (Wards)
54/107	1958	Wild Life Figures Set (31 pieces)
54/107	1958	Farm Animals Set (53 pieces)
54/108	1958	Horse & Saddle Set (27 pieces)
54/109	1958	Cowboy Figures Set (73 pieces)
54/118	1958	Prehistoric Set (16 pieces)
54/119	1958	Railroad Figures Set (30 pieces)
54/120	1958	Soldiers Set (68 pieces)
54/121	1958	Nike Rocket Launching Set
55/15	1958	Knights and Horses Set
54/103	1958	Indians Figure Set (60 pieces)
2658	1958	Army Combat Set
2660	1958	Cowboys & Indians Set
2664	1958	Satellite Launching Station
2801-2	1958	Zorro Rider & Horse Set

Item #	Year	Description
3388	1958	Prehistoric Times Play Set
3391-2	1958	Prehistory Play Set
3451-2	1958	Allstate Service Station
3457-8	1958	Service Station w/accessories
3475	1958	Service Station w/accessories
3477-8	1958	Service Station w/accessories
3483&D	1958	Service Station w/accessories (Mont.Wards)
3649	1958	Fort Apache Stockade
3677-8	1958	Fort Apache Play Set
3685-6	1958	Rin Tin Tin Fort Apache
3702	1958	Arctic Explorer Set
3703-4	1958	Jungle Set
3751-2	1958	Fort Mohawk Play Set
3753-4	1958	Zorro Play Set (Official Walt Disney)
3930	1958	Modern Farm Set
3940	1958	Lazy Day Farm Set
3948	1958	Happi-Time Farm Set w/Twin Silos
4151-2-3	1958	Armed Forces Training Center
4216	1958	Roy Rogers Mineral City
4226	1958	Wyatt Earp Dodge City
4227	1958	Roy Rogers Mineral City
4255	1958	Roy Rogers Mineral City
4261	1958	Roy Rogers Mineral City
4525-6	1958	Project Mercury Missile Base Set
4600	1958	Armed Forces Truck Set
4749-50	1958	Battleground Play Set
4752	1958	Army Battleground Play Set
R-4756	1958	Large Army Battlefield Set
4759-60	1958	Battle of Blue & Gray Set
4777	1958	Official Wagon Train Set
4800	1958	I.G.Y. Polar Satellite Base Set
443-4	1959	3-Stage Rocket Set
1526-7	1959	Rocket Launcher Set
2458-60	1959	Allstate Truck Set
2652	1959	Western Town Set
2654	1959	Army Combat Training Center
2656	1959	Cape Canaveral Missile Center Set
2703-4	1959	Space Rocket Target Set
2711-12	1959	Flying Saucer Set
2713-14	1959	Guided Missile Launcher Set w/figures
2741-2	1959	Tractor & Implement Set
2743-4	1959	Guided Missile Unit
2805-6	1959	Sleeping Beauty

Item #	Year	Description
3393-4	1959	Prehistoric Play Set
3408	1959	Revolutionary War Play Set
3430	1959	Service Station
3487	1959	Service Station w/Heliport
3488	1959	Spec. Service Station w/Parking Garage (Mont.Wards)
3489-90	1959	Service Station w/Parking Garage
3493-4	1959	Allstate Service Station
3680	1959	Fort Apache Play Set
3682	1959	Fort Apache Play Set
3707-8	1959	Alaska Play Set
3741-2	1959	Fort Pitt Play Set
3951	1959	Happi-Time Farm Set
3989	1959	Roy Rogers Ranch (Sears)
3997-8	1959	Rifleman Ranch Play Set
4131-2	1959	Army Training Center
4262	1959	Wells Fargo Western Town w/Dale Robertson
4263-4	1959	Wells Fargo Western Town
4304	1959	County Fair Play Set
4523-4	1959	Project Mercury, Cape Canaveral Set
4527-8	1959	Project Mercury Missile Base Set
4699-4700	1959	Medieval Castle Set
4701-2	1959	Ben Hur Play Set
4703-4	1959	Official Sleeping Beauty Castle Set
4708	1959	Medieval Castle Set
4725-6	1959	Medieval Castle Set
4731-2	1959	Marine Beachhead Landing Set
4745-6	1959	Battle of the Blue & Gray Play Set
4747-8	1959	Battleground Play Set
4788	1959	Official Wagon Train Play Set
4888	1959	Official Wagon Train Set
5185	1959	Rocket Launcher Set

Marx's extensive series of play sets proved very ·pular with children, and they were produced over ·any years. Records show that Marx reissued some of · most popular previous play sets with only minor ·anges or updates, but this reissued play set would ·ve a new item number assigned to it.

There are some play sets designated "BIG" or "Giant ·t." These play sets were not produced in a physically ·ger size, but merely offered more accessories or ·ssible more play set figures. For example, a Giant ·attleground play set would possibly offer more soldiers, cannons, and the like. Many popular TV show-related play sets seem very popular, and they command a higher price on the collectibles market (i.e. The Flintstones, Yogi Bear, Roy Rogers, Wagon Train, etc.).

The famous "Ben Hur" play set was very popular, as was "The Untouchables" play set. These play sets were not offered over an extended period of time, so their availability is limited, thus increasing their value. Play sets found intact today are scarce. Those play sets found in Mint-in-Box are even scarcer in the collectible marketplace.

If collectors prefer, there is today's Marx Toys, Inc., in Florida, which offers play sets manufactured from original Marx molds. In a recent Sears Wish Book catalog, several toy items, including play sets, were offered for sale. These play sets still feature basically the same figures and components, but sometimes are produced in a slightly different color than their original counterpart play sets. Some even offer a few different accessories. If you would like to obtain a new reproduction play set, check out Marx Toys online or obtain a copy of any popular toy collector magazine on the market for more information.

The following are descriptions of a number of popular play sets presented in a vintage 1964 Marx Toys Promotional Catalog:

Item #3936—Farm Set: Two-story lithographed steel barn (23" x 9" x 10-3/4") including a Hen House and Silo. Accessories include a tractor, farm vehicles, livestock, farm people, fence, and assorted farm equipment.

Item #3457—Marx Service Station: Lithographed steel, with accessories. Showroom window and manually operated elevator for Sky-View parking. Two plastic automobiles (4" long) with die cast wheels.

Item #3474—Day & Nite Service Station: Lithographed steel (15" x 26-1/4"), featuring a car wash, five plastic cars, operating lift, grease rack, and elevator for roof parking. Plastic gas pumps, five station workmen, tires, jacks and other station items. (Made in 1957/1964/1967)

Item #3495—Midtown Service Station: Lithographed steel (30-5/8" x 16-1/4" x 14") with electric elevator. Also includes accessories and five attendants. (Made in 1960/1964/1966)

Item #3501—(4 Level) Service Station and Parking Garage: Lithographed steel (30" x 24" x 16") with more than sixty plastic accessories, including vacuum-formed plastic ramps, auto hoist with elevator, washer unit, mechanical conveyor and nine cars, along with other service station accessories. (Made in 1962/1964)

Item #4756 U.S.—German Army Battleground Set: Features German figures in different poses; German field pieces; rolling tank, jeep, and half track; pontoon bridge; pellet-shooting howitzer; fences; wire entanglements; and all scale-size equipment needed for two opposing reinforced platoons.

Item #3528—Cape Kennedy Play Set: Atlas-type rockets with safe soft rubber tips fit into supplied gantries. Rockets were fired by a spring mechanism. Included Minuteman rockets as well as Moon Probe Flying Wheels. Lithographed metal Administration Building. Included missile base figures, helicopter, and spaceman's capsule.

Item #3675-78 (1957/1958), **Item #3680-1** (1957/1958/1959/1964/1967)—Fort Apache Play Set: Cowboys, Indians, cavalry, stockade, Indian village. Two shell-shooting cannons; lithographed steel HQ Building; and fifteen sections of interlocking stockade fence, with gate. This play set was produced with minor variations through the 1970s, and was one of the most popular of all play sets. Figures were solid colored.

Item #HK-7526—Miniature Fort Apache Play Set: Smaller version of the popular Fort Apache play set, featuring hand-painted figures and accessories (sixteen cowboys and ladies, and sixteen Indians).

Item #HK-6111—Miniature Battleground Play Set: Smaller version of the popular Battleground play set, featuring thirty-eight American soldiers, eight German soldiers, tanks, cannons, guns, motors, machine guns, jeeps, trucks, etc.

Item #4147—U.S. and Japanese Marines Battleground (Battle of Iwo Jima) Play Set: Included many accessories for recreating two battles. Two complete opposing platoons, supported by paratroopers, landing craft, spring-activated howitzers (with camouflage cover), rolling field equipment, tank stops, bunkers, palm trees, flags, mines, Marine and Japanese figures.

Item #4638—Beachhead Landing Set: Four rolling tanks, a squadron of planes (the lead plane fires rockets), paratroopers, landing craft, howitzers, and a reinforced platoon of U.S. combat soldiers (engaged in establishing a beachhead at Normandy). Defenders are a complete German fighting unit with German artillery, personnel carriers, camouflage net emplacement, and platoon of elite German soldiers.

Item #4804 (1963) /Item #4794 (1964)—S.A.C. Base: Lithographed steel control tower and building (17" x 9-1/4" x 15"). White plastic weather deck. Play set includes four F102 Delta Wing fighters, two B47 Bombers, three Nike Missiles with launcher, assorted trucks, equipment, and men.

Item #4657 (1962) **/Item 4658** (1964)—Civil War Centennial (Battle of the Blue & Gray) Play Set: Features two complete armies and four authentic miniatures of General Grant, General Lee, General Davis and Lincoln. Lithographed steel Civil War building, with white plastic porch and columns; battlefield equipment, assorted size tents, shell shooting mortar and cannon.

Item #7404—Medieval Castle With Moat and Base: Lithographed steel castle with plastic battlements mounted on a 22" x 32" vacuum-plastic 4" high base. Includes drawbridge across water-fillable moat. Features more than twenty-one Knights on foot, nine horses, catapults, spears, flags, and other accessories.

Item #HK7563—Miniature Knight and Castle Play Set: Minutely detailed, hand-painted replicas of the Knight and castle, featuring: castle, thirty-two Knight figures, eight horses, catapult, and accessories.

Item #HK7562—Miniature Knight and Vikings Play Set: Featuring sixteen Knights, sixteen Vikings, four

Flintstone Play Set Figures, 1960s. Traffic Cop, Barney Rubble, Fred Flintstone and Dino. (G. A. Whipkey Collection, photo by J. S. Smith)

Fred Flintstone, 1960s. (G. A. Whipkey collection, photo by J. S. Smith)

Barney Ruble, 1960s. (G. A. Whipkey collection, photo by J. S. Smith)

orses, a castle, an Invading Tower, and accessories. ach of the figures is break-resistant plastic, minutely etailed and hand-painted.

Item #HK6109—Miniature Blue and Gray Play Set: uthentic and minutely detailed hand-painted figures listoric Civil War), including twenty-six Blue soldiers, venty-eight Gray soldiers, and battleground accessories.

larx Toy Company Flintstones Play et—1960s

NOTE: Currently available are "new reproduction" ay sets which have been made from original Marx olds. A collector can easily locate individual collec-rs and dealers for these items on the Internet. Do a arch for "Marx Toys" to obtain more information.

Examining any of the current toy collector magazines will also yield information relating to the purchase of new sets made from the original Marx Toys molds.

If you are seeking any older original issue play set, here's one helpful hint to help you determine if it's an original item: Check over the exterior packaging for the Item Number, the Marx Logo, and an address (should be Marx Toy Co. New York, New York, or Glen Dale, West Virginia). Gaylord Whipkey said there were usually only two or three references (i.e. logo, address, or "Magic Marxie") on the original packaging box. In the 1999 Sears Wish Book, I noticed several Marx Toy Corporation toys featured. However you decide, it's a lot of fun just searching for the right Marx toy. If you're lucky, you'll meet a number of fellow Marx toy lovers along the way!

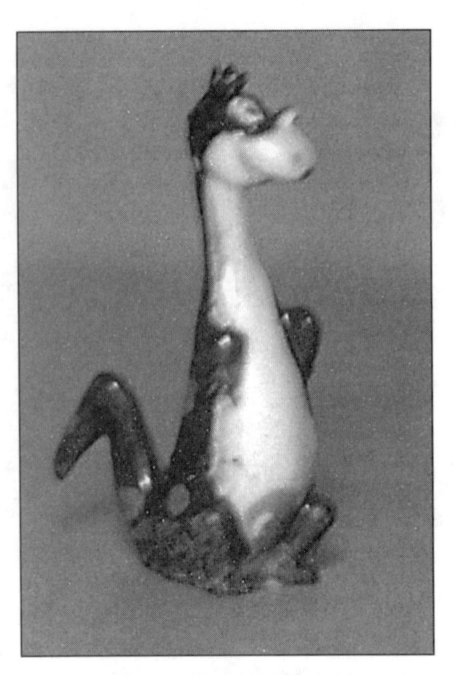

Dino, 1960s. (G. A. Whipkey collection, photo by J. S. Smith)

Saber Tooth Kitty, 1960s. (G. A. Whipkey collection, photo by J. S. Smith)

Traffic Cop, 1960s. (G. A. Whipkey collection, photo by J. S. Smith)

Traffic Cop and Worker, 1960s. (G. A. Whipkey collection, photo by J. S. Smith)

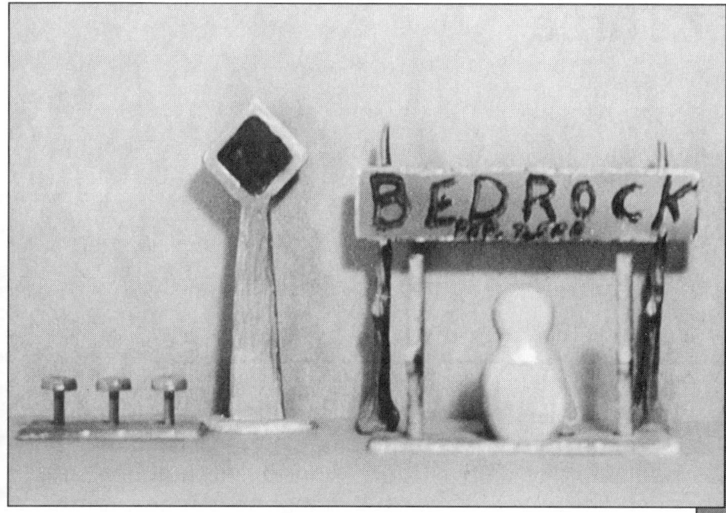

Prototype for Bedrock Service Station accessories, by modeler Gaylord A. Whipkey. (Gaylord A. Whipkey collection, photo by J. S. Smith)

Fred Flintstone Car, 1960s. (G. A. Whipkey collection, photo by J. S. Smith)

Action Carry-All Fort Apache Play Set, No. 4685, from the 1960s. (M. L. Smith collection, photo by J. S. Smith)

Chapter Three

Dollhouses

My research on Marx toys included a special—and somewhat personal—interest in the company's popular line of metal dollhouses, since that subject has not been treated in significant depth in other books on collectibles. Along with the black/white, color photographs and brief descriptions, this listing should help today's collectors and dealers more easily identify "true" Marx dollhouses and their numerous fine plastic accessories. This section also provides brief descriptions and/ or photographs of various dollhouse figures and play sets.

The Louis Marx Toy Company was considered by many to have created the finest and most detailed lithographed dollhouses and dollhouse plastic furnishings. Some collector reference magazines and books offer only limited information on these fine dollhouses. Although there were other manufacturers of lithographed dollhouses, none seem to match the excellence of the Marx Toy Company. Toy companies such as T. Cohn, Inc., Playsteel, Ohio Art, Wolverine, Meritoy, and Jayline were competitors who also offered lithographed items such as dollhouses and play sets.

In the course of my research with Gaylord Whipkey, I was able to date and identify several of the lithographed dollhouses in my collection. The Marx Toy Company produced numerous styles and types of dollhouses at the Glen Dale plant site in the late 1940s, and continued production until the late 1970s, possibly even into the early 1980s.

The Marx Toy Company's first dollhouse was small as were its household furnishings, but over the years Marx produced many different styles and sizes of dollhouses. Marx's two main competitors in the dollhouse market were the Wolverine Toy Company and the Ohio Art Company.

The exterior of Marx Toy Company dollhouses almost always displayed the company's logo (a circle containing the letters "Mar" and a "X" over the three letters, or Marx Toy Co. spelled out). No dollhouse displayed its assigned item number on the assembled dollhouse; only the Marx logo appears on each house. However, the cardboard packaging box displayed each dollhouse's assigned item number. Unless found intact (Mint-in-Box) today, it is difficult to determine a Marx Toy Company dollhouse's actual year of production. From a collector's perspective, at least, the Marx Toy Company creators made things more difficult by neglecting to display the assigned item number on each dollhouse. The result in that now, many years later, it is considerably more difficult to determine any dollhouse's true age. Many dollhouse styles remained basically the same over the years, with only minor updates to basic models. Nevertheless, each updated or modified version of an item received a new item number.

The Marx Toy Company facility in Glen Dale became more safety conscious in the late 1950s, 1960s, and throughout 1970s, with the introduction of rolled edges, and plastic inserts, windows, and doors. In 1972, the Marx Toy Company applied "Satin-Metal" flat-satin varnishing applications to dollhouses and service stations to provide a double protective coating and to enhance the depth and richness of the color finish.

While the production of the dollhouses themselves was ongoing from 1949 through the late 1970s, the manufacture of dollhouse furnishings and accessories similarly started in 1949, but continued only until about 1976. One of the first Marx Toy Company dollhouses sold for only $2.50, while the last of the dollhouse series—newer colonial styles with styrene roofs—sold for approximately $16 each.

Plastic Accessories for Dollhouses

The Marx Toy Company produced a "small scale" line of plastic furniture accessories starting in 1949, and subsequently introduced a larger scale lineup in 1950. Over the years (from 1950 until the mid-1970s), the Marx plant produced both small and large scales of furnishings. During some production years, both scales were produced. My research revealed that the small-scale line was apparently produced in larger numbers at the Glen Dale facility, with the larger scale furniture being produced mainly in the 1950s to early 1960s.

Plastic accessories for dollhouses were available in different room groupings in a variety of colors and price ranges. The first dollhouse furnishings produced in 1949 featured smaller accessories that were scaled approximately 1/2" to 1' scale. Most dollhouse furniture and accessories displayed either the Marx logo or a number on the bottom. But, there were some plastic

No. 6999, 1961. Mansion Series Dollhouse. (G. A. Whipkey photo collection)

No. 4055, 1975. Colonial Dollhouse with accessories and family, as depicted in the *1975 Marx Toys Promotional Catalog.*

1" Scale Dollhouse Furniture, Couch, and Chair from the 1950s/1960s. (M. L. Smith collection, photo by J. S. Smith)

1" Scale Dollhouse Bathroom from the 1950s/1960s. (M. C. Malone collection, photo by J. S. Smith)

1/2" Scale Dollhouse Dining Room Set. 1950s/1960s/1970s. (M. L. Smith collection, photo by J. S. Smith)

1" Scale Dollhouse Radio from the 1950s/1960s. (M. L. Smith collection, photo by J. S. Smith)

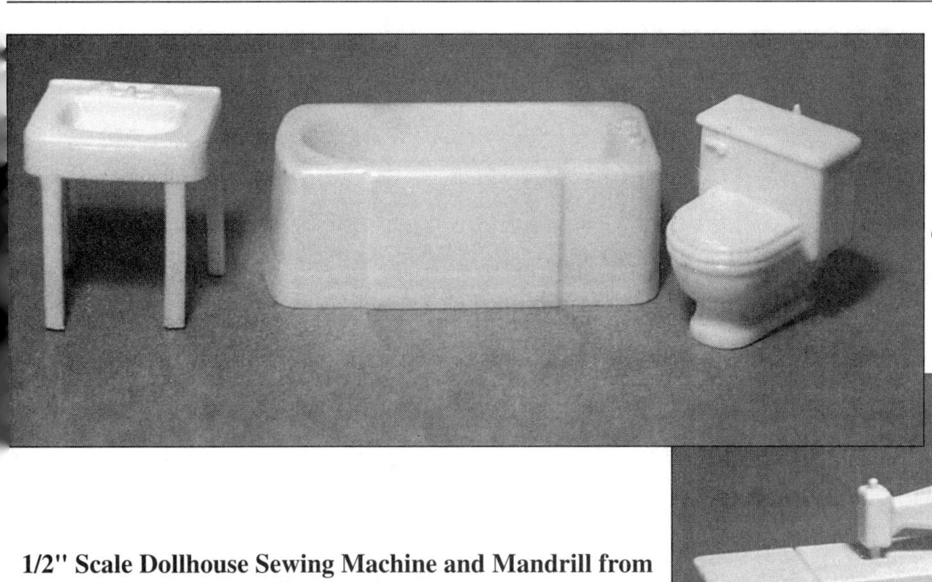

1/2" Scale Dollhouse Bathroom, 1950s/1960s/1970s. (M. L. Smith collection, photo by J. S. Smith)

1/2" Scale Dollhouse Sewing Machine and Mandrill from the 1950s/1960s. (M.L. Smith collection. Photo by J. S. Smith)

1/2" Scale Dollhouse Kitchen Table and Chairs, 1950s/1960s/1970s. (M. L. Smith collection. Photo by J. S. Smith)

" Scale Dollhouse Kitchen Set from the 950s/1960s. (M. L. Smith collection, photo by J. S. Smith)

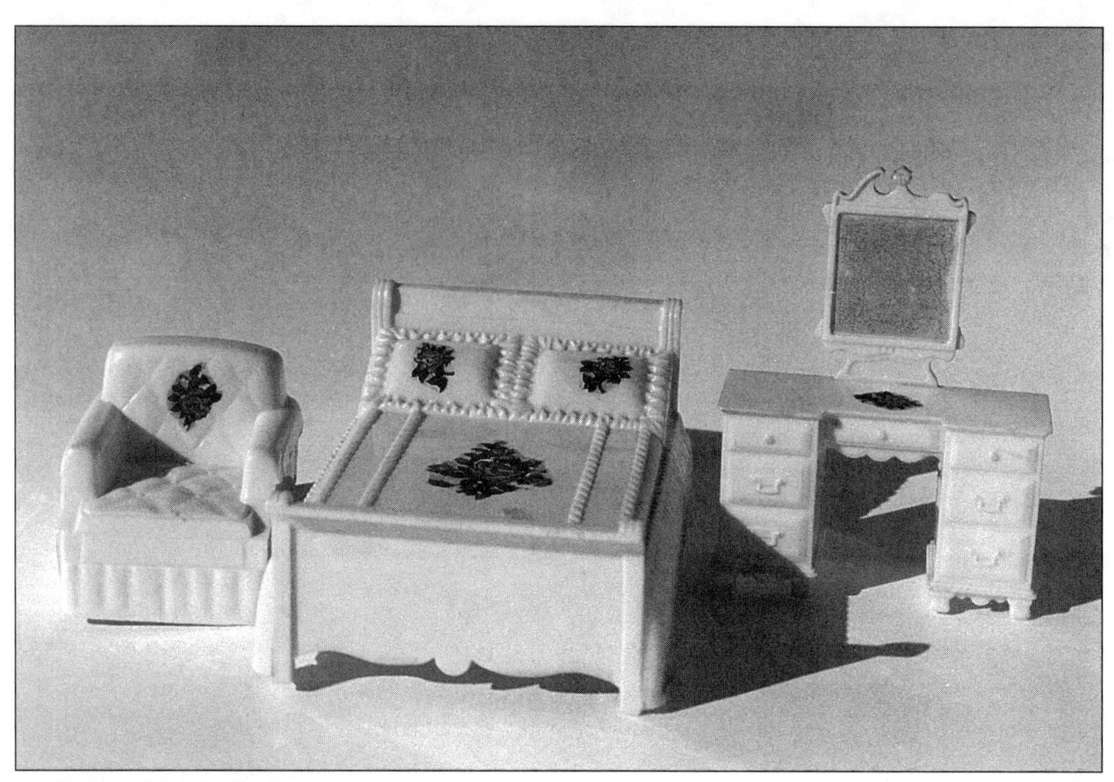

1" Scale Dollhouse Bedroom furniture with floral decals, from the 1950s. (M. L. Smith collection, photo by J. S. Smith)

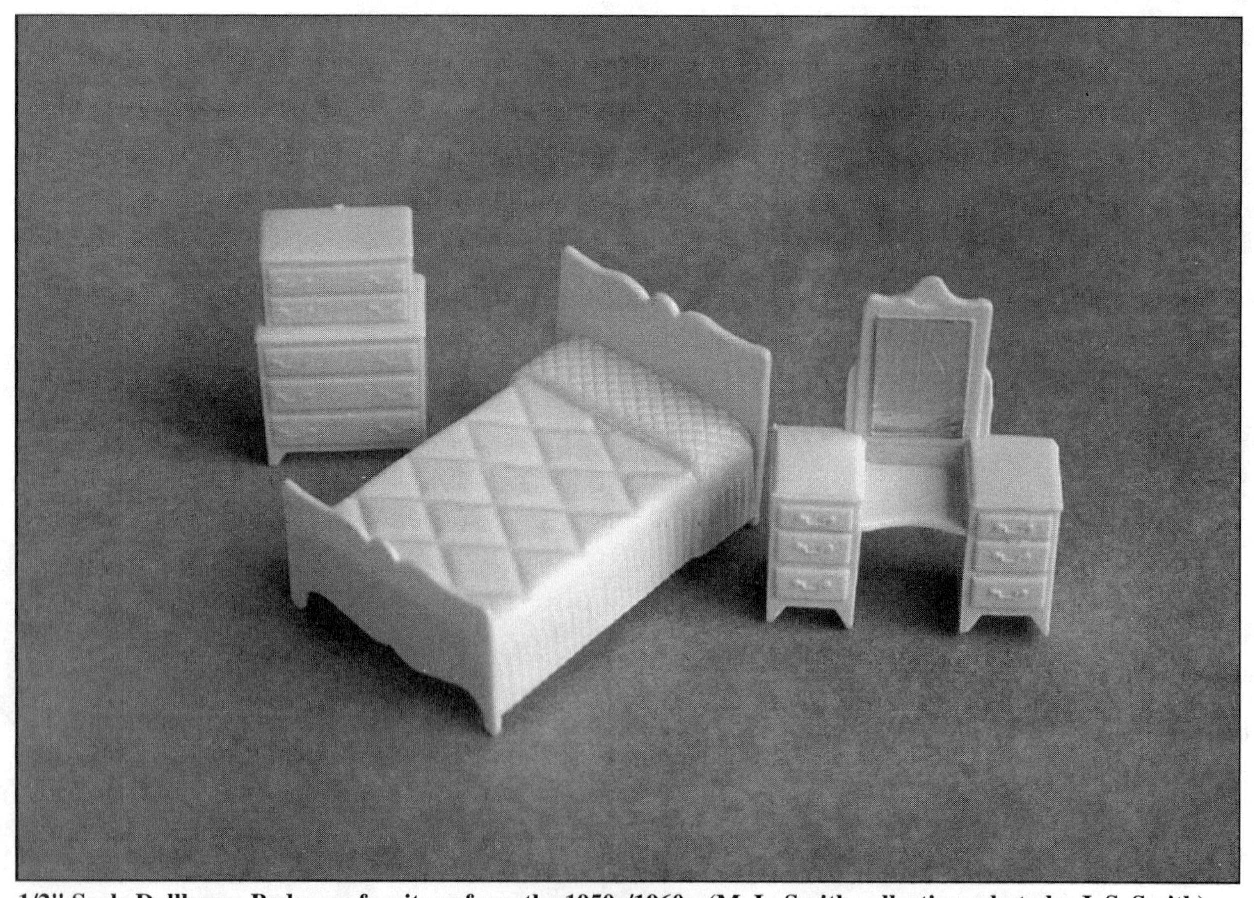

1/2" Scale Dollhouse Bedroom furniture from the 1950s/1960s. (M. L. Smith collection, photo by J. S. Smith)

items produced during the early years that bore neither an identification logo nor a number.

The many colors utilized in making plastic furniture and accessories included black, white, brown, tan, beige, ivory, yellow, pink, blue, green, gray, and red. The different room settings placed in each dollhouse were made in different colors, depending upon the dollhouse kit, although some earlier dollhouse accessories were made entirely of one color (i.e. mahogany brown or tan). For example, a kitchen set might be in ivory or white; a bath set in pink or ivory; and a bedroom in yellow, or possibly another color. Some dollhouse series featured different colored room accessories and dollhouse furnishings—one large-scale series even offered decaled items, such as a floral motif, on bedroom, living room, and patio furniture.

Finished sheets of molded dollhouse furniture and accessories traveled down the assembly lines and were gathered, separated, and sorted by the workers. Workers snapped off like types of furniture or accessories, and sorted the items into large bins. Different groups were then placed in designated dollhouses, or possibly separated by room group packages that could be sold separately. A package of the earliest room accessories cost only $ .98!

Gaylord Whipkey noted that the Marx Toy Company was an early recycler of unused plastic materials. When plastic shavings accumulated from the trimmed, finished sheets of plastic furniture and accessories, the shavings pile would be stored. Eventually, this stored plastic material would be re-melted, and then reprocessed into another piece of furniture or another accessory. Reusing the scrap plastic in molds saved both time and money for the Marx Toy Company.

Consumer demand for larger and more elaborate dollhouses ultimately led to the Marx Toy Company's production of larger scale dollhouses and dollhouse accessories. During most of its lifetime, the Marx Toy Company offered both large and small-scale dollhouses in different styles each year. Furniture and accessory scales (1/2" to 1'; 3/4" to 1' and 1" to 1') were produced each year to match the different dollhouse scales. The Marx Toy Company's play sets (i.e., Johnny West and Fort Apache series) used accessories in a scale or scales different from those used for the dollhouse furnishings.

Dollhouse Styles

Dollhouses produced at the Marx Toy Company, Glen Dale plant included not only the popular colonial style, but also ranch, split-level, and ultra-modern structures. These dollhouses featured anywhere from four to as many as seven rooms! Many Marx Toy Company dollhouses came complete with furnishings, but there were some models made that did not include accessories. However, dollhouse furniture and accessories were sometimes available in separate packages.

The colonial type of dollhouse proved, over time, to be the most popular style produced by the Marx Toy Company. All told, the firm produced dollhouses over a period of approximately thirty years.. Some dollhouse styles remained basically the same over their entire production run, but when they were updated or changed slightly, they were given a different item number. For example, item number(s) 4018, 4019, and 4020 (produced in 1949-1950) featured a two-story, five-room, basic dollhouse structure, with basically the same base model. These two-story, five-room structures were assigned a new item number each time they were offered with an altered or updated feature. By offering a new dollhouse feature such as a breezeway, patio, dormers, awnings, or the like, the Marx Toy Company would create a whole new series of dollhouses.

Two detailed and very elaborate colonial dollhouse models were the "Marx-a-Mansion" and the large mansion series, item numbers 6991, 6992, 6996, 6999-7000 (produced 1961 through 1969). These two-story "grand scale" dollhouses featured double-wing extension structures. They were approximately 45" long, 15" wide, and 19" deep, and exemplified the very best that the Marx Toy Company artists and modelers could create in terms of detail and accessories.

These dollhouses included a number of extras, such as upper level patios, awnings over the windows, twin dormers, a swimming pool with accessories, playground equipment (i.e., swing set, slide, sand box), patio sets, automobile, and even small green plastic shrubbery that could be placed by the front sidewalk. Item number 0260 Privet Hedge Set (1950) was a dark green, realistic-looking hedge that could be placed around the dollhouse and it even featured a gate. Item number 0270 Picket Fence Set was also offered the same year. Occasionally, a colonial series would feature a white roof with white railing positioned over the white plastic front door entrance. The upper level might feature red siding with white shutters (item #6999-7000), while the lower level of the dollhouse featured a white brick exterior with red shutters.

Some "mansion" dollhouse models offered slight changes in their exterior. For example, Item #6991-2 was similar to item #6999, but featured a white exterior, with green shutters and green front door. One model in the mansion series (item number 6992, produced in 1964) also featured a family of four (father, mother, son, and daughter) and dollhouse furnishings. Some dollhouse series in the 1950s even offered battery-operated lights and doorbells!

The ranch style dollhouse enjoyed many years of popularity among young homemakers. The first ranch-style dollhouse produced in the early 1950s was small. The early popularity of this dollhouse led to more elaborate ranch styles over the years.

The most elaborate of the ranch-style dollhouses were items number 5018 (produced in 1966 and 1971) and number 5025 (produced in 1965, 1966, 1968,

1964 Mansion Series Dollhouse (Front view), as depicted in the *1964 Marx Toys Promotional Catalog.*

1964 Mansion Series Dollhouse (Rear view), as depicted in the *1964 Marx Toys Promotional Catalog.*

No. 7008 in the Marx Mansion Series, with furniture and accessories, 1960s. (Gaylord A. Whipkey photo collection)

No. 7008 in the Marx Mansion Series, without extension, 1960s. (Gaylord A. Whipkey photo collection)

No. 4737 Ranch House with furniture and accessories, as depicted in the *1975 Marx Toys Promotional Catalog.*

No. 4737 Ranch House from the 1960s/1970s. (M. L. Smith collection, photo by J. S. Smith)

No. 5025 Dollhouse Packaging for Lift-Off Roof model. (Gaylord A. Whipkey photo collection)

No. 5025 1960s/1970s Dollhouse has Lift-Off Roof, and Rooster decal. (Gaylord A. Whipkey photo collection)

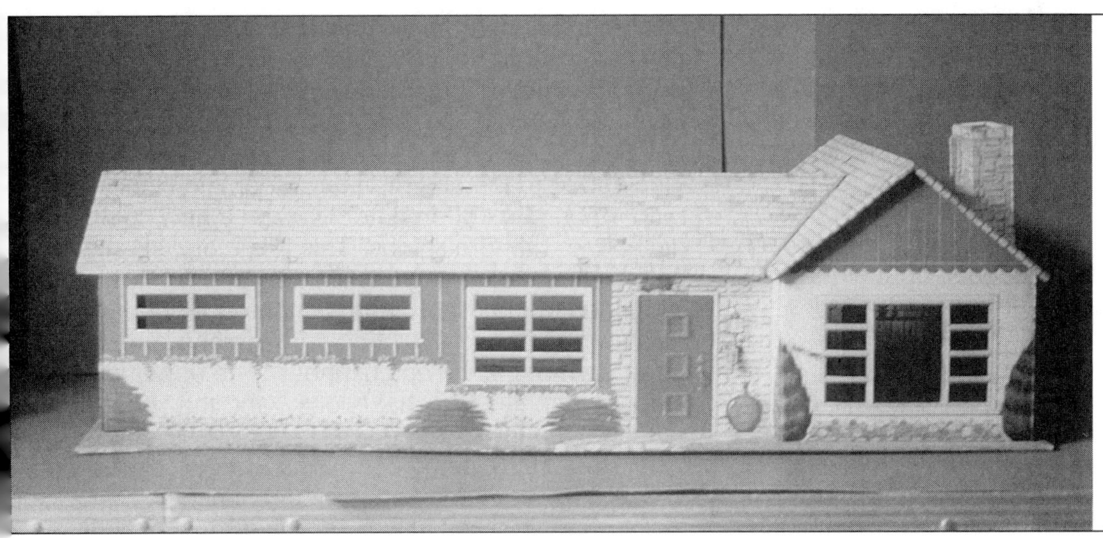

No. 4773 Modern "L" shaped Dollhouse with doorbell from the1950s/ 1960s. (M. L. Smith collection, photo by M. L. Smith)

No. 4861 Split-level "Modern" Doll-house (rear view), as depicted in the *1964 Marx Toys Promotional Catalog.*

No. 4861 Split-level Dollhouse from the 1960s/1970s, as depicted in the *1975 Marx Toys Promotional Catalog.*

1969, 1970, and 1971).This large contemporary dollhouse series measured approximately 32" long by 16" deep. These dollhouses featured a "lift-off" roof. The one-story, six-room house also had sliding patio doors at the rear of the house, and green plastic shrubbery displayed around the base.

Some ranch-style lift-off-roof models displayed a large black plastic "rooster" decal on the side chimney exterior. When the roof was positioned on these dollhouses, they were completely "under roof," with no open sides. The one hundred 153-piece furnishings included with item number 5025 were more than enough to keep any child gleefully occupied.

"L" shaped ranch house (item 4773-4, produced in 1957) was a large, single-story, five-room dollhouse. These "L" shaped ranch houses sometimes featured a doorbell, and a large patio area in the rear of dollhouse.

Another dollhouse series that enjoyed great success was the modern split-level: item numbers 4861, 4862, 4863, 4864, 4865, and 4866, produced from 1958 through 1973. These were large dollhouses, measuring approximately 29-1/2" long, 16" wide, and 14" high. As produced in 1971 and 1973, this dollhouse series also offered hand-painted family figures. Accessories included furniture, playground, patio and pool items, and, in some kits, a separate lithographed metal pool!

Many unusual metal and non-metal dollhouses made by the Marx Toy Company deserve recognition and description. These detailed and colorful dollhouses were very popular with children. One such dollhouse was item number 4650) "Corrugated" Carry Case Dollhouse with vinyl handle (produced in 1968, 1969, 1970, and 1972). When opened, it transformed into a two-story, four-room house. Each room's colorful lithographed decor appeared on paper on the interior and the exterior of the carrying case. This dollhouse included two dozen accessories, and a family of four. The closed case measured 7" x 14-3/4" x 17", and, when open, the case even displayed a patio area!

Item number 4002 Fantasy Dollhouse (produced in 1971, 1972 and 1973) was 11-3/4" long, 9-1/4" wide, and 10-5/8" high, and featured a two-story, three-room house when opened. This dollhouse included a family of five small, round, easily handled figures, along with an assortment of house furniture.

Another similar, but nevertheless slightly different dollhouse, was item number 4006, the Disney all-steel lithographed "Carryall" Dollhouse (produced in 1972 and 1973). This whimsical house was designed for Mr. and Mrs. Mickey Mouse and Mr. and Mrs. Donald Duck, and it came complete with house furnishings and a car. When the dollhouse opened, it measured approximately 11-3/4" x 10-1/2" x 9-1/4". This Disney-theme house was a two-story, three-room (living room, dining room, and bedroom) dollhouse.

Item number 6990HK "Mountain House" dollhouse (produced in 1975) measured 12-1/2" high, 1' long, and 9" high, and it featured a new look. This modern, all-plastic constructed "A-Frame" house sported windows that moved up and down, and also included a boat with fishing pole, one fish, and a boat motor. Two detailed, four-inch poseable dolls and house furnishings added to the charm of this Mountain House.

In 1974, Marx offered item 4001—a new colonial dollhouse with furnishings. This two-story, six-room dollhouse measured approximately 24-3/4" long, 8" wide, and 16-1/4" high, and it featured an upper patio with awning. It had a light-colored styrene roof, inserts, three dormers, and two chimneys. The upper level exterior displayed a "shake look," and the lower level reflected a brick exterior.

In 1974-1976, item 4031, another new colonial dollhouse, replaced many of its older cousins in the colonial series. This was a two-story, five-room dollhouse in lithographed plate, and it had a styrene roof, plastic inserts, and a bay window. In 1975 and 1976, this item was offered with dollhouse furniture and accessories. This dollhouse measured approximately 18" long, 8" wide, and 16-1/4" high.

Item numbers 2000/MO, 2007, and 2010 ultra-contemporary or "Imagination" Dollhouses (produced in 1968, 1969, 1970 and 1971), offered something different for young homemakers—a "see-through" dollhouse. A young girl could let her imagination go wild with unlimited possibilities in arranging rooms. She could set up the kitchen, bedroom, living room, or any other room anywhere she liked! This dollhouse featured transparent floors and walls made of high-impact, brightly colored, transparent plastic components. When assembled, dollhouses in this series displayed an "open room" concept, with no outside walls. Approximate size of the two-level (1970 and 1971) or three-level (1968 and 1969) house was 36" long and 19-1/2" high, with floor dimensions of 8-1/4" x 13-1/4". Each of the three dollhouse models also featured an upper patio area.

This dollhouse series included ultra-modern appearing furniture made of plastic, other accessories, and four or more family member figures (in standing or sitting poses). One of the dollhouses even included a hand-painted family of four. Many of the furniture pieces were interchangeable. For example, a dresser or buffet could be rearranged with other pieces to become another piece of furniture). Accessories included table and floor lamps. This beautiful and "futuristic" dollhouse's production ceased after approximately four years. Gaylord Whipkey commented that he helped with the creation of this dollhouse, and that he was disappointed when production ceased. Information on this unique dollhouse is quite limited—Gaylord had only one photograph of this dollhouse, and it was very dark. The other information presented here came from the Marx Toys Promotional Catalog, which carried an advertisement for the item. The advertisement

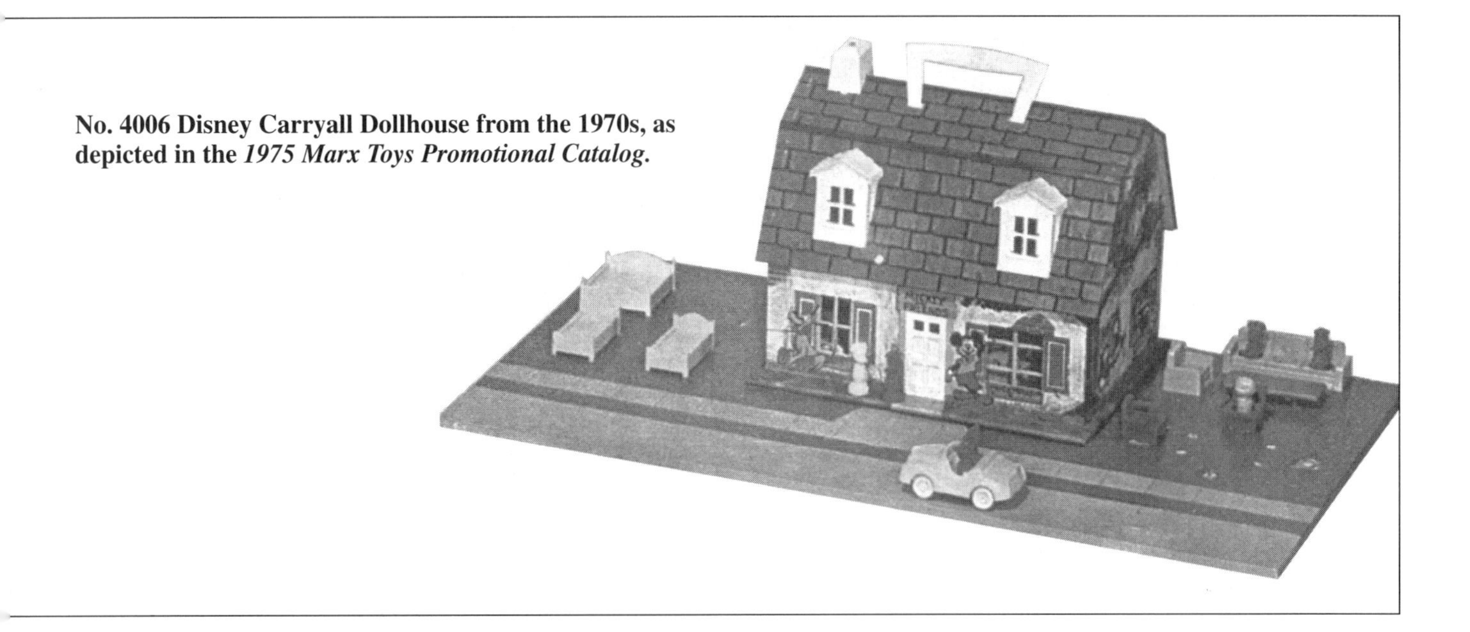

No. 4006 Disney Carryall Dollhouse from the 1970s, as depicted in the *1975 Marx Toys Promotional Catalog.*

No. 6990HK Mountain House from 1975, and No. 4001 New Colonial Dollhouse with Furnishings from 1974. Both were pictured in the *1974 Marx Toys Promotional Catalog.*

No. 2000/MO, 2007, 2010, produced from 1968 through 1971. Known as the "Imagination Dollhouse." (Gaylord A. Whipkey photo collection)

No. 5018 Dollhouse with Lift-Off Roof from the 1960s/1970s. (Gaylord A. Whipkey photo collection)

No. 4861 Split-level "Modern" "Dollhouse (front view), as depicted in the *1964 Marx Toys Promotional Catalog.*

No. 4002 Fantasy Carryall Dollhouse from the 1970s, as depicted in the *1975 Marx Toys Promotional Catalog.*

offered only an artist's outline of the dollhouse. What an exceptionable and unique dollhouse this must have been!

During the last few years of operation at the Glen Dale plant, production of dollhouses slowed. Dollhouse styles in production were limited, and sometimes included only one or two models. The company no longer offered a large variety of dollhouse styles. The once great era of mass production of numerous and varied types of lithographed dollhouses by the Marx Toy Company had come to an end.

These once popular and likely very "played with" dollhouses are scare in today's collector market. If you can find one in it's original packaging, or one in "mint" or "good" condition, consider buying it. Cherish and preserve this small representation of Louis Marx's fine toy craftmanship. These dollhouses are also great for displaying not only the wonderful dollhouse people, furniture, and accessories that the Marx Toy Company produced, but also similar items made by other companies, as well.

Inspection Guidelines for Marx Dollhouses

Following are a few important things to look for when considering the purchase of a Marx dollhouse:

1. Look over the entire dollhouse's exterior closely, and locate the Marx logo.

2. Look for signs of surface rust on the interior and exterior sides. There are some good dollhouses with small rust areas that may be tolerated and enjoyed as much as the "mint" ones. Remember that surface rust cannot be removed easily without possibly damaging the original lithographed image.

3. Check to make sure that all room dividers and connecting metal tabs are present in any dollhouse.

4. Look for any "open slot or hole" areas that may appear on the roof, side, or bottom areas of a dollhouse. These open areas might suggest that one or more of the following is missing:

a) a chimney, window, carport awning, set of front steps, support post(s) or column(s), plastic window pieces, or doors. Note: Early dollhouse models had "cut-out" windows that appeared on the metal exterior sides. Plastic insert windows, offered in the late 1950s through the 1970s, help to promote safety for youngsters handling the dollhouses.

5. Look for any warped or dented areas on the dollhouse exterior and interior sides. Sometimes, the metal roof and side(s) appears "bent" out of shape, and the component may not go back into its original shape.

6. Any "played with" dollhouse will show indications of wear, and possibly a missing piece or two. But, it possibly can be purchased at a much cheaper price than a "mint" condition item, so don't rule these minor flawed dollhouses out! These dollhouses would provide a good way to display your collectible plastic accessories. A set of missing steps can be tolerated if few or no other faults, or rust, appears on the dollhouse.

7. Ask about the age of the dollhouse. Any collector appreciates knowing this information. Many series models changed little over the years from their original style, but, when updated, they do show different assigned item numbers on the packaging.

8. Consider bargaining with the dealer or individual selling any dollhouse. If there are any noticeable flaws, remember to point these out to the dealer before determining a final price.

9. A dollhouse in good shape, with no missing pieces, or a dollhouse in Mint-in-Box condition will cost more, but remember that they are very hard to find. It all depends on what you want, and what you are willing to pay.

10. Dollhouses found with all their original packages may be rare, but such items do occasionally become available. If you live in the Ohio Valley area, try locating a former employee(s) of the Marx Toy Company's Glen Dale plant. He/she might be able locate one just by talking to someone. Many people living in the Ohio Valley either worked for, or had relatives and friends working for, the toy plant when it was in operation. Former employees can often help to locate a dollhouse with little or no wear. Also, some dealers in Marx Toys items may possibly be able to help you.

NOTE: One way to maintain your dollhouse's finish is to carefully clean all surfaces of the dollhouse using a soft cloth which has been slightly dampened with a mild soap and water. Very gently go over the surfaces with this damp cloth, then dry thoroughly with a clean cloth. Apply a very thin coat of paste wax in a small, obscure area (it's important to test an area first—don't proceed if litho image starts to come off!), then allow the area to dry for approximately 5-10 minutes. Next, proceed to gently rub the wax off all surfaces, using a soft cloth. The applied wax coating will help to preserve the lithographed finish on the dollhouse.

Chapter Four

Dollhouse Figures (Dolls)

The Marx Toy Company produced dollhouse "People" in 1951, 1954, 1960, 1961, and from 1964 through 1976. Item numbers produced changed only slightly over the years, with most family sets consisting of four figures (father, mother, sister, brother, and possibly a toddler or baby). Item No. 0890 Dollhouse People, produced in the early to mid-1950s were not mounted on a base, but were made of a slightly heavier rubber or plastic, and could stand without a base. Later issues in the series featured harder, lighter-weight plastic dollhouse figures that were produced with a base for better placement in the dollhouses.

These hard plastic, highly detailed figures were generally white or light-colored, and were approximately 1" to 3" (60mm) in height. Most figures were mounted on a square base, with the type of figure (ie., Sister) identified on the bottom of the base. Some figures could be painted with paint from a Hobby Color Paint Set (item number 398), which was offered by the Marx Toy Company for $ .69 in 1950s.

Dollhouses that included playground and pool equipment sometimes included a few extra figures, such as a woman in a bathing suit lying on a sun lounger, or children on a swing set or playing on playground equipment.

1950s-1960 Marx Toy Company Dollhouse Figures

The initial Series 0893 Dollhouse Children in 1951 and 1954 cost $ .10 each. This series featured 12 different figures:

- Three young boys and one girl in different baseball poses: two with catcher's mitts, one swinging a baseball bat, and one pitching a ball.

No. 0893 Dollhouse Children Series from the 1950s. (M. L. Smith collection, photo by J. S. Smith)

• One young girl with arms stretched upward.

• One young girl in a pretty off-the-shoulder play ress, holding what appears to be a handful of clay. he is in a sitting pose, with legs crossed (probably sat n a swing or on a bench).

• One young girl sitting with a small (separate) pet.

• One small boy in pajamas, brushing his teeth while olding a toothbrush in one hand and a tube of tooth- aste in the other hand.

• One baby, crawling and wearing a diaper and ocks.

• One toddler with toy blocks and carrying a small oll and with pants slighting drooping in rear (letters howing on blocks are "W", "L" on front side and "T", <" on back side).

• One small toddler in a sunsuit and in a crouched osition playing with sand bucket and shovel.

• One nurse (nanny) standing with an outstretched and.

The 1954 Series 0890 Dollhouse People cost $ .15 ach. This series featured four figures:

• Father in dress suit (left hand extended for hand- hake and right hand in side pant's pocket).

• Mother in dress (her right hand up and placed ehind right side of head and her left hand is down gainst front of apron).

• Son with casual sweater vest over shirt and wearing cuffed pants (his hands are in each pants pocket).

• Daughter in jumper-type dress with short-sleeved blouse (arms slightly extended upward, wearing bobby socks and bow in hair).

These dollhouse figures featured the same series number(s) as the famous Marx Miniature Sculptured Figures' series offered in the early to mid-1950s. Not much information has surfaced on the following two item numbers except for that information noted on the Marx Item Listing, dated 10/73, for Item 0999 Dollhouse Family, non-poseable (produced in 1960), and item 2702 Dollhouse Figures (produced in 1961).

Many family figures produced in the 1960s through 1976 probably changed little from the earlier dollhouse figures. The later figures were slightly smaller than the early to mid-1950s series. These later series were also produced in a harder form of plastic, and came with a base for easier placement. Numerous other plastic figures were produced, including assorted dollhouse, playground, and pool figures that were featured in selected dollhouse kits.

In 1975, the Marx Toy Company offered a new and different type of dollhouse, item 6990HK "Mountain House A-Frame." It included two unique and different 4" poseable dolls (two female figures whose positions

No. 0890 Dollhouse People Series from the 1950s. (M. L. Smith collection, photo by J. S. Smith)

could be changed). One woman doll featured long dark hair, and wore slacks and a long-sleeved plaid shirt. The other woman doll had long light hair, and wore a long, light-colored dress.

Young Girl/Sister from the 1960s. (M. L. Smith collection, photo by J. S. Smith)

Guidelines for Buying Plastic Figures and Accessories

1. Doll house plastic figures and accessories can be found in a wide range of condition and price. Look for clean and near-mint items.
2. Generally, most items are found separately, but sometimes an entire set can be found for one price. Examine each item carefully, checking for any broken, warped, or missing pieces.
3. Items found in "Near Mint" or "Mint-in-Box" condition will bring the highest prices. Other plastic items with only a minor flaw (i.e., slight warp or a surface scratch) may be bought at a reduced price.
4. Be prepared to bargain with any dealer or individual selling an accessory item.
5. Ask the dealer or individual selling any dollhouse accessory item for the approximate production date (i.e. 1950s, 1960s, or 1970s).
6. Remember, there were three scales of furniture produced to "fit" different dollhouses, and the various scales were produced from 1949 through 1976. Scales produced by the Marx Toy Company in Glen Dale were approximately 1/2" to 1'; 3/4" to 1'; and 1" to 1'.
7. Look for the Marx logo on each item. Also, remember that not all items displayed the classic Marx logo—some had numbers, and there were even some with no logo or numbers at all.
8. Be sure that the original packaging is available when buying anything advertised as "Mint" or "Mint-in-Box." Check for the assigned item number, which normally would be printed on the sides or end flaps of the box.
9. Dollhouse accessories came in many colors, but some sets of furnishings were available in only one color (i.e., ivory, white, or mahogany).
10. Remember: "Buyer Beware" when purchasing any old item!

NOTE: To clean any plastic furniture piece or dollhouse figure, use a soft cloth dampened with mild soap and water. Dry the item thoroughly.

Dollhouse Collecting: What You Want to Collect, and What It's Worth

Acquiring any vintage Marx dollhouse furnishings or figures all depends on what you want; what you'll be happy with; and what you are willing to pay for it! Prices on dollhouses and their accessories may vary—slightly or greatly—from one dealer to another, and from one area to another. Some dealers and individual collectors will not lower their asking price for any original Marx item. Perhaps you might consider your search for these old dollhouses and their numerous accessories as something of an adventure! I truly enjoy the challenge of seeking out new shops and places in hopes of finding even one small accessory to add to my collection. I've collected several old dollhouses, some of which are in excellent shape, while a couple others show a bit of wear. In my collection there are also many accessories ranging from Mint to those having only a slight flaw. I love all the items!

Approximately 150,000 dollhouses were produced annually by the Marx Toy Company at the Glen Dale plant, and the steel sheets used in making of these dollhouses was easily supplied by area steel mills.

'hese are amazing production numbers. Where did ey all go, you might ask? Well, many were just played to death," such as the one I shared with my ree sisters in the mid-1950s. Most were likely just ossed out when a young girl outgrew the plaything. 'hankfully, some individuals had the foresight (or a arent) to store away their dollhouses, and some of ese treasures are now being rediscovered in today's ollector market. Perhaps, stored away in the attic of omeone you know or come across, there is still nother old Marx Toy Company dollhouse waiting to be ediscovered! These toy treasures might be found at ntique shops, flea markets, yard sales, or even in a iend's basement or attic. The cost of buying one might ary from as little as $5.00 to well over $75.00-100.00, or more, depending upon it's age, condition, nd packaging.

Think about it...twenty to thirty years later, some of s so-called "Baby Boomers" are still busy "playing house" or "building erector sets!" Of course, it's fun to recall past days of playing with our favorite toys. And, it's quite a treat to find even one of these wonderful toys at an antique dealer, flea market, or even a garage sale. Our precious collections, and the enjoyment we receive from them, are hard to put a price on.

Only today can we fully appreciate the Marx Toy Company's contribution to fine workmanship and durability in making toys. The Company built lasting value into each and every dollhouse, piece of dollhouse furniture, and accessory item, as well as all the other Marx toys it produced. The toys were sturdy, rugged and made to be played with—not once, but over and over again. Our younger generation can still play with these dollhouses and furnishings, and they can still enjoy any of the other toys produced by the Marx Company. If a new collector is fortunate, he or she may discover what we "Baby Boomers" did: That the Marx Toy Company's dollhouses and accessories have truly withstood the test of time!

Chapter Five

Marx Toy Company Lithographed Dollhouses and Dollhouse Accessories

---

(Manufactured at the Glen Dale, West Virginia plant)

Item #(s)	Year(s)	Description
0300B/C	1949	Dollhouse living room furniture
0310B/C	1949	Dollhouse dining room furniture
0315	1949	Dollhouse utility room accessories
0319/B	1949	Dollhouse assorted furniture set
0320B/C	1949	Dollhouse kitchen furniture
0330B/C	1949	Dollhouse bedroom furniture
0340B/C	1949	Dollhouse bathroom furniture
0350B/C	1949	Dollhouse nursery furniture
0360	1949	Dollhouse patio furniture set
0391	1949	Dollhouse playground equipment set
0395	1949	Dollhouse assorted furniture, with Cadillac automobile
4079-80	1949	Dollhouse with furniture
0186-MO	1950	Dollhouse, mini tableware
0188-MO	1950	Dollhouse, mini appliances
0800	1950	Dollhouse large living room furniture
4019-20	1950	Dollhouse, colonial—two-story, five rooms
4089-90	1950	Dollhouse with breezeway and furniture

Item #(s)	Year(s)	Description
5049-50	1950	Dollhouse, large, with furniture—two-story, six rooms, patio, gray shingle roof, red/white striped awnings over all windows, red exterior siding w/white shutters, and white siding w/red shutters, red door
5051-2	1950	Dollhouse
5053	1950	Dollhouse, extra large, complete (Montgomery Wards)
5054-6	1950	Dollhouse, extra large, complete
5058-9-60	1950	Dollhouse, large
0810	1951	Dollhouse large dining room furniture
0893-94	1951	Dollhouse family figures, assorted
4021-2 & D	1951	Dollhouse, colonial, with awning and furniture—two-story, five rooms
0891	1952	Dollhouse, people, assorted
4025-6	1952	Dollhouse with breezeway and furniture
4027	1952	Dollhouse with breezeway and awnings
4052	1952	Dollhouse, colonial, with furnishings—two-story, six rooms, patio, green roof, single wing extension, white exterior with light green shutters
3791-2	1953	Dollhouse, "L"-shaped ranch house, with accessories—one-story
3799-3800	1953	Dollhouse, colonial—two-story, five rooms
3801-2	1953	Dollhouse, colonial, with accessories—two-story, five rooms
4050	1953	Dollhouse with furniture and sedan
4050MW	1953	Dollhouse with furniture and sedan (Montgomery Wards)
4071-2	1953	Dollhouse with carport and playground
4759-60	1953	Dollhouse, ranch—one-story
4769-70	1953, 1959	Dollhouse, "L"-shaped ranch, with furniture, patio/playground area—one-story, five rooms, gray roof, red door, red siding and green siding/white brick on exterior
4772	1953	Dollhouse, "L" shaped ranch, with furniture and car—one-story, five rooms
0370	1954	Dollhouse playground equipment set
0820	1954	Dollhouse large kitchen furniture
0830	1954	Dollhouse large bedroom furniture
0840	1954	Dollhouse large bathroom furniture
0850	1954	Dollhouse large nursery furniture
0860	1954	Dollhouse large patio furniture
0890	1954	Dollhouse family figures assortment
4023	1954	Dollhouse, colonial, with carport and furniture (Montgomery Wards)— two-story, five rooms
4092	1954	Dollhouse, colonial, with breezeway—two-story, six rooms
4093	1954	Dollhouse, colonial, with breezeway and playground—two-story, six rooms
4739-40	1954, 1959	Dollhouse, ranch—one-story, four rooms, one wing extension, patio with green awning, light yellow or beige shingle roof, gray front door; light blue siding with gray shutters on exterior

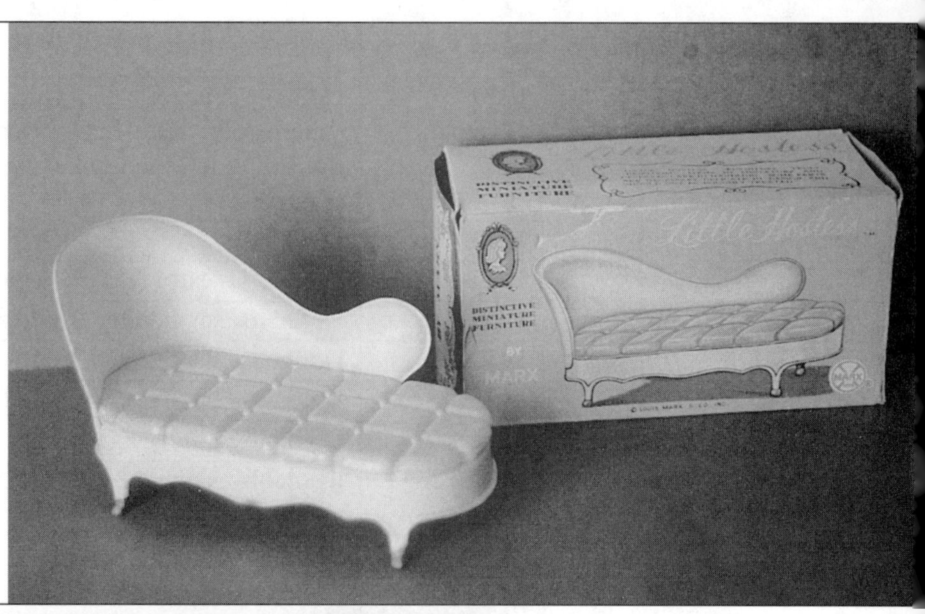

No. 8958 Little Hostess Chaise Lounge with original packaging, from the 1960s. Produced in Hong Kong facility. (M. L. Smith collection, photo by J. S. Smith)

No. 8972 Little Hostess Night Table and Occasional Chair, with original packaging, from the 1960s. Produced in Hong Kong facility. (M. L. Smith collection, photo by J. S. Smith)

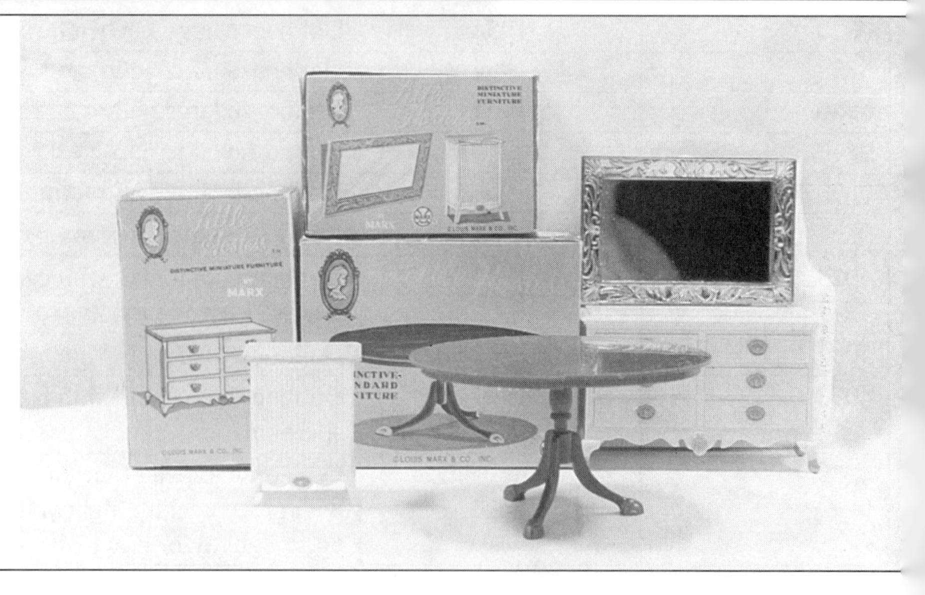

Marx Little Hostess furniture, clothes hamper & mirror, double dresser, and oval dining table.

Item #(s)	Year(s)	Description
4739/0275	1954	Dollhouse, ranch, with playground equipment—one-story
4742	1954	Dollhouse, ranch, with furniture—one-story
4815-6	1954	Two-car garage
4825-26	1954	Two-car garage with cars—one-story garage for two cars; red roof and white exterior siding; overhead garage door has red plastic handle and can be rolled up to open and rolled down to close; two plastic cars; red garage floor; lantern centered over outside garage door; windows have flower boxes printed on exterior sides
5070	1954	Dollhouse, large, with furniture
4028	1955	Dollhouse, Happitime, with lights and doorbell—two-story
4028L	1955	Dollhouse with lights and doorbell—two-story
4029	1955	Dollhouse
4109	1955	Dollhouse assorted rooms
4111	1955	Dollhouse assorted rooms
6083-R	1955	Dollhouse, large colonial, with furniture—two-story, five rooms
6085	1955	Dollhouse, large colonial, with awnings and accessories—two-story, five rooms
0819	1956	Dollhouse—six rooms, assorted furniture
4036	1956	Dollhouse, colonial, with furniture—two-story, five rooms
4039-40	1956	Dollhouse, colonial —two story, five rooms
4041-2	1956	Dollhouse, colonial, with breezeway and furniture—two-story, six rooms
4095	1956	Dollhouse with utility room and breezeway
4112	1956	Dollhouse single bed
4113	1956	Dollhouse rocking chair
4114	1956	Dollhouse vanity with bench
4115	1956	Dollhouse bunk beds with ladder
4116	1956	Dollhouse extension table with two chairs
41118	1956	Dollhouse furniture set
0278-9	1957	Dollhouse accessory set
4018 & D	1957	Dollhouse, colonial, with furniture—two-story, five rooms, green roof, exterior with white siding on upper level and red brick lower level
4023	1957	Dollhouse, colonial, with furniture (Sears)—two-story, five rooms
4024	1957	Dollhouse, "Disney" house, with furniture and figures
4034-4	1957	Dollhouse, colonial, with breezeway and furniture—two-story, six rooms
4045	1957	Dollhouse, colonial, with breezeway and awnings—two-story, six rooms
4054	1957	Dollhouse, colonial, with furniture and picture window—two-story, six rooms, patio
4097	1957	Dollhousc, colonial, with breezeway and furniture—two-story, seven rooms, gray shingle roof, awning over upper patio, white round window located over front door; white exterior with green shutters, gray front door

Item #(s)	Year(s)	Description
4737-8 & D	1957	Dollhouse, ranch-style, with furniture—one-story, four rooms, patio with gree awning, light gold/beige roof, light blue exterior siding w/ white front door
4773-4	1957	Dollhouse, "L"-shaped ranch, with furniture—one-story, five rooms
5083-4	1957	Dollhouse, large colonial, with furniture—two-story
6089-90	1957	Dollhouse, large colonial, with furniture—two-story
4015-6	1958	Dollhouse, colonial, with furniture—two-story, five rooms
4038	1958	Dollhouse, colonial, (Sears)—two-story, five rooms
4053	1958	Dollhouse, colonial, with twin dormers—two-story, six rooms, one wing extension, patio, green shingle roof, twin dormers, white exterior siding with red shutters, white door, small white round window located over front door.
4056	1958	Dollhouse, colonial, with breezeway and pool—two-story, seven rooms, patio, white exterior siding with green shutters, green roof, small white round window located over front green or gray door. (Some models offered furniture and electric light.)
4861-62	1958-1960, 1964	Dollhouse, split-level, w/pool—two-story, 4863-4864-5-6 (1965, 1968-1970) five rooms, white shingle roof, white shutters, gray 1971-1973* or light green siding on upper level, white brick lower level, white front door with steps and white hand rails. Some models offered a pool and pool accessories. (Note: These model years included hand-painted family figures.)
5086	1958	Dollhouse, large colonial —two-story
4010	1959	Dollhouse with patio and swimming pool set
4012	1959	Dollhouse, "Early American" house, with accessories
4042	1959	Dollhouse, colonial —two-story, six rooms, one wing extension, gray shingle roof, green siding and white shutters on upper level of exterior, white siding with green shutters on lower level
4043	1959	Dollhouse, colonial, with breezeway and furnishings—two-story, six rooms, gray shingle roof, green siding and white shutters on upper level of exterior, white siding with green shutters on lower level
4048/49	1959	Dollhouse, southern colonial (Sears)— two-story, five rooms, gray roof, twin red brick chimneys, red brick exterior with four white columns on a white base in front of house, white filigree plastic railing trims, roof with trim over door entrance and columns, white hanging lantern over front door entrance, white base under columns
4055	1959	Dollhouse, colonial, with breezeway and pool—two-story, six rooms
4057-8	1959	Dollhouse, southern colonial mansion—two-story, five rooms
4060	1959	Dollhouse, colonial, with furniture— two-story, five rooms
4775-6	1959	Dollhouse with double wings and twin dormers—two-story, seven rooms, twin chimneys, red roof, white exterior siding with white shutters, yellow or gold-colored front door, white plastic windows
4863	1959	Dollhouse, split-level—two-story, five rooms, white roof, light gray or green upper level exterior siding with white shutters, white lower level siding, front steps

Item #(s)	Year(s)	Description
0999	1960	Dollhouse family—plastic, non-poseable.
4046	1960	Dollhouse, colonial, with family room—two-story, six rooms
2702	1961	Dollhouse figures
4064	1961	Dollhouse, colonial, with bay window—two-story, five rooms
4067	1961	Dollhouse, colonial, with family room extension—two-story, six rooms
4069	1961	Dollhouse, colonial, with car port—two-story, five rooms
4074	1961	Dollhouse, colonial, with bay window—two-story, five rooms
4076	1961	Dollhouse, colonial —two-story, five rooms
4078	1961	Dollhouse, colonial, with furniture (made for supermarkets)—two-story, five rooms
4868	1961	Dollhouse, split-level
6996	1961	Dollhouse, large dream house—two-story, seven rooms, double wing extensions, patio upper left, white weather vane over right extension roof, twin dormers, gray roof, light green or gray awning over upper three windows, white plastic roof with decorative white plastic railing over front door entrance, red siding on exterior with white shutters upper level, white brick with red shutters on lower level
6999-7000	1961	Dollhouse, "Marx-A-Mansion" dream house—two-story, seven rooms, double wing extensions, gray roof, patio upper left wing extension, red siding on exterior with white shutters on upper level, white brick with red shutters lower level, white plastic roof with decorative white railing over front door entrance, gray awnings over second floor windows. (Some models offered twin dormers and house furnishings, including swimming pool accessories, swing set, slide, sand box, patio set, red car, and green plastic shrubbery along front sidewalk. One model was a two-story house with six rooms and one wing extension, and had a "Black Rooster" decal or plastic device mounted on the white chimney on right side of house.)
0818	1962	Dollhouse assorted furniture for four rooms
4071-2	1962	Dollhouse, colonial —two-story, five rooms
4073	1962	Dollhouse, colonial —two-story, five rooms
4771	1962	Dollhouse, colonial, with breezeway and shelter—two-story, six rooms, one wing extension, green roof, green awning over upper patio. red upper level exterior with white shutters, lower level light colored brick with white plastic front door and white plastic bay window, white siding on extension with white shutters and white weather vane on roof
6995	1962	Dollhouse, new colonial mansion, with voice—(not produced)
6997-8	1962	Dollhouse, colonial mansion—two-story, six rooms
7005-6	1962	Dollhouse, colonial mansion—two-story, six rooms
4051MO	1963	Dollhouse, colonial, with plastic awnings (Montgomery Wards)—two-story, five rooms
4091	1963	Dollhouse, colonial (special for Mutual)—two-story
4094	1963	Dollhouse, colonial (Sears)—two-story

Item #(s)	Year(s)	Description
4796	1963	Dollhouse, colonial, with breezeway—two-story, seven rooms, twin dormers, twin chimneys, gray roof, blue or gray upper level exterior siding with white shutters, white lower level siding, white plastic front door, bay windows
4798	1963	Dollhouse, large, double wing, twin dormers—two-story, seven rooms, red roof, light gray or green awnings over three windows, yellow upper level exterior siding with white shutters, white lower level exterior with yellow shutters, white front door.
6990	1963	Dollhouse, country, split-level
6991-2	1963	Dollhouse, large colonial mansion— two-story, seven rooms, gray roof, white exterior with green shutters and green front door, green awnings over three windows
6994	1963	Dollhouse, large colonial mansion, with furniture—two-story, six rooms, gray roof, red siding on upper level exterior with white shutters, white siding on lower level exterior with red shutters, yellow front door, yellow awnings over upper level windows
R-4768	1963	Dollhouse (Eaton's) with breezeway
4017	1964	Dollhouse (Sears)
4018B	1964	Dollhouse with furniture—two-story, five
4030	1964	Dollhouse, no accessories
4047	1964	Dollhouse (Sears)
4051	1964	Dollhouse, colonial —two-story, six rooms, open patio, green roof, yellow upper level exterior siding with white shutters, white brick lower level, green awning over patio, white front door
4053	1964	Dollhouse, colonial, with awnings (Sears)—two-story
4063	1964	Dollhouse with breezeway (Montgomery Wards)—two-story, seven rooms, patio, red roof, light green or gray exterior siding, green shutters, yellow awnings over windows, small white round window over green front door entrance
4072B	1964	Dollhouse, colonial, with furniture and carport—two-story, five rooms, simulated wrought-iron look on exterior front post and chain
4738	1964	Dollhouse, ranch-style—one-story, five rooms, patio, white exterior, green awning over patio, single wing extension, yellow/beige shingle roof
4872	1964	Dollhouse (Sears)
6992	1964	Dollhouse, large, colonial mansion w/family of four and furniture—two-story, seven rooms, patio, simulated wrought-iron look on front entrance door area
4018-19-20	1965, 1968	Dollhouse, colonial, with 1969-1970, furnishings—two-story, five rooms, green roof, 1972-1973white exterior siding with green shutters on upper level, red brick lower level. (Some 4018 models have red siding w/white shutters on the upper level, and a white brick lower level.)
4033	1965	Dollhouse furniture set
4036	1965	Dollhouse accessory set

Item #(s)	Year(s)	Description
4077	1965	Dollhouse, colonial, with carport and furnishings—two-story, five rooms, blue exterior siding with white shutters on upper level, white brick on lower level, blue front door, black simulated wrought-iron posts by carport and railing at front of house, gray roof, carport roof extends from left of house to approximately middle of front of house
4080	1965	Dollhouse, colonial (SEARS)—two-story, six rooms, patio, gray roof, green exterior siding with white shutters on upper level, light gray or white brick lower level
4086	1965	Dollhouse (SEARS)—two-story, seven rooms, twin dormers, double-wing extensions, gray shingle roof, blue exterior siding with white shutters on upper level, blue/white siding on lower level, white plastic bay windows, windows, and front door.
4028	1966	Dollhouse, colonial, with breezeway (Sears)—two-story, six rooms, one wing extension with white siding and red shutters, gray shingle roof, red siding on exterior with white shutters upper level and white brick on lower level, white front door
4058	1966	Dollhouse with furniture (Sears)—two-story, seven rooms, patio, red roof, white or light green siding on exterior with green shutters, dormer extension shows three windows under one red roof, one wing extension white with brick exterior and red roof with white weather vane, small white round window located over front door entrance, green front door with white plastic roof, white posts and railing
4071	1966	Dollhouse with pool and accessories
4088	1966	Dollhouse with talking unit—(not produced)
5018	1966, 1971	Dollhouse, contemporary, removable roof, with furnishings, one-story, six rooms, gray roof, no open sides (roof lifts off), sliding patio doors in rear of house, green plastic "snap on" shrubs around outside of house, light tan siding on exterior with lower gray or white areas, white plastic windows and patio doors
5025	1966, 1968	Dollhouse, contemporary, removable 1969, 1970 roof, with 153-piece furnishings—one story, six room, gray roof, no open sides (roof lifts off), sliding patio doors at rear of house, green plastic "snap on" shrubs around outside of house, light tan exterior siding with lower gray or white brick areas, white plastic windows and door, large black plastic "rooster" mounted on side chimney
4029	1967	Dollhouse—two-story, five rooms, twin dormers, gray roof, green exterior siding with white shutters upper level, white siding lower level, white plastic bay window and front door
4032	1967	Dollhouse furniture set (MONTGOMERY WARDS)
4054	1967	Dollhouse, colonial —two-story, six rooms, patio, green roof, green awnings over upper windows, white plastic bay windows, windows and door, white siding with green shutters on upper level, red brick with green shutters lower level, awning over patio
C-4072	1967	Dollhouse, colonial —two-story, five rooms, gray roof, blue exterior siding with white shutters upper level, white brick lower level, roof over carport extends around front of house, lack simulated wrought-iron posts and rail trim

Item #(s)	Year(s)	Description
4076	1967	Dollhouse, colonial, with columns (Sears)—two-story, five rooms, gray roof, green exterior siding with white shutters on upper level, white siding on lower level, black simulated wrought-iron posts
4087	1967	Dollhouse (Sears)—two-story, seven rooms, double wing extensions, gray roof, white exterior siding with green shutters on upper level, red brick lower level, patio, white plastic door, windows, bay windows, twin dormers; furniture included
2000/MO	1968, 1969	Dollhouse, ultra contemporary
2007	1970, 1971*	(Imagination)—two- or three-levels, upper 2010 level patio, "Open Rooms Concept" with no outside walls. When snapped together, forms three basic modules. Made of high-impact transparent plastic components. (*1971 dollhouse is two-level and includes hand-painted family of four.)
4053MW	1968	Dollhouse, colonial (Montgomery Wards)—two-story, five rooms
4055	1968, 1969	Dollhouse, colonial —two-story, six rooms, 1970, 1971, covered patio, family of four and furniture 1972, 1973 included, green awning over patio, green roof, white exterior siding with green shutters on upper level, red brick lower level with green shutters, operating double-hung white plastic windows and opening front door, 3-D bay window
4057	1968	Dollhouse, colonial, with pool—two-story, five rooms, green roof, white exterior siding with green shutters on upper level, red brick with green shutters on lower level, 3-D bay window, white front door
4079 & MO	1968, 1969	Dollhouse, colonial, with carport and (1970, 1971*), furnishings—two-story, five rooms, gray roof, (1972, 1973**) blue exterior siding with white shutters on upper level, white brick lower level, operating double-hung windows, front door, 3-D bay window. (*1971 with family of four hand-painted figures.) (**1973 with family of three hand-painted figures.)
4650	1968, 1969	Dollhouse, "corrugated" carrycase 1970, 1972 with vinyl handle—two-story, four rooms, room decor printed on corrugated board, "Closed for the teeny-bopper go-go set." Two dozen pieces of accessories and furnishings, family of four included, patio area shows when opened, fully colored decor inside and outside
4737	1968, 1969	Dollhouse, ranch, with furniture—one-story(1970*, 1971*), four rooms, gray roof, white exterior siding (1972*, 1973*) with gray or green shutters, gray or green siding on right side. (1970 through 1973 featured playground area, children, swing set, and metal awning over patio.)
6992	1968, 1969	Dollhouse, large colonial mansion, with furniture, patio, and twin dormers— two-story, seven rooms, simulated wrought-iron entranceway trim, gray roof, white exterior with green shutters on upper level, green shutters and green front door lower level, green siding with white on right extension
0818	1969	Dollhouse assorted rooms of furniture for six rooms—nursery, bedroom, kitchen, bathroom, dining room, and living room

Item #(s)	Year(s)	Description
4022	1969, 1970	Dollhouse, colonial—two-story, five rooms, 1972, 1973 gray roof, green or blue exterior with white shutters on upper level, white brick on lower level, 3-D bay window, white plastic front door opens
4045 & D	1969	Dollhouse, colonial, with breezeway and patio furnishings—two-story
059	1969	Dollhouse (Montgomery Wards)
4090	1969, 1970	Dollhouse, modern colonial, with 1971 wing and roof extension—two story, six rooms, brown shingle roof with a soft brown shingle effect (Colonial motif blends with the Williamsburg-type green shakes on the upper story), lower and upper patios, moveable windows and front door, picture window, family of four, furniture, and 3-D plastic chimney
4660	1969	Dollhouse, "Blondie" Dollhouse
5072	1969	Dollhouse
6976 & MO	1969	Dollhouse (Montgomery Wards)—two-story
3726	1971, 1972	Dollhouse, carryall—steel with vinyl handle, two-story, five rooms and garage, two cars and furniture included, family of four small, round, figures
4002	1971, 1972	Dollhouse, fantasy house—two story, three 1973 rooms, family of five small, round, easily handled figures, family auto and furnishings
4061	1971	Dollhouse, colonial, with patio—two-story, six rooms, includes family of four, working double-hung windows and front door
6981	1971, 1972	Dollhouse, large estate colonial, with 1973* furniture—two-story, six rooms and patio. (*1973 includes family of four.)
4006	1972, 1973	Dollhouse, Disney carryall—two-story, three rooms, lithographed steel with vinyl handle. For Mr. and Mrs. Mickey Mouse and Mr. and Mrs. Donald Duck. Includes furnishings and car
4065 & MO	1972	Dollhouse, longview
4001	1974	Dollhouse, colonial, with family of four—two-story, six rooms, light-colored roof, shingled exterior look with white shutters and windows, double-hung operating windows, 3-D bay window, white front door opens, awning over right upper patio, two chimneys and three dormers on roof
4031	1974, 1975	Dollhouse, colonial —two-story, five rooms, 1976 Styrene roof and inserts, light-colored roof, dark upper level siding with white shutters, light-colored lower level exterior, 3-D bay window, windows and operating front door
6990HK	1975	Dollhouse, mountain house—two-story "A"-frame, all Styrene, moveable windows, two poseable dolls, furnishings include boat, fishing pole, fish, boat motor, and room furniture

iscellaneous Furniture Items:

Little Hostess Chaise Lounge: (Produced in Hong Kong.) Approximately 1'- 1" scale for dollhouses. Chaise ounge is cream with gold details and has pink "tufted"-look seat covering. Warning on box indicates that item is ery fragile, and will not withstand rough handling.

Little Hostess Night Table and Occasional Chair: (Produced in Hong Kong.) Approximately 1" - 1' scale for dollouses. Occasional Chair is ivory with gold details, pink arm rests, back pad, and seat. Night Table is cream with old detailing. Warning on box indicates that item is very fragile, and will not withstand rough handling.

Chapter Six

Marx Toy Company Miniature Sculptured Figures

Item #	Year	Description
0398	1950s	Hobby Colors Paint Set
0726	1950s	Birds (8)
0893	1951/1954	Dollhouse People Series (4)
0832	1952	Frontiersmen Series
0834	1952	American Indian Series
0858	1952	Wild Animals Series (6)
0862	1952	Farm Animal Series
0864	1952	Farm Animal Series
0879	1952	Western Animal Series
0882	1952	Freight Station Workers Series
0884	1952	Farm People Series
0990	1952	Soldiers in Training Series
0992	1952	Medical Soldiers Series
0994	1952	World War II (1941-1945) Combat Soldiers Series
0996	1952	Marching Army Band Series
0998	1952	Sailors Series
0805	1953	Champion Show Dog Figures Series
0812	1953	Famous Comic Figures
0828	1953	Pirates Series TV Personalities
0829	1953	Walt Disney Series
0835	1953	American Indian Series (new)
0846	1953	Knights in Armor Series
0848	1953	Horses in Armor Series
0872	1953	Western Cowboy Figures Series

Famous *Marx Miniature Sculptured Figures Catalog* cover (front and back), from the 1950s. G. A. Whipkey collection.

No. 0890 Dollhouse People series from the 1950s. (M. L. Smith collection, photo by J. S. Smith)

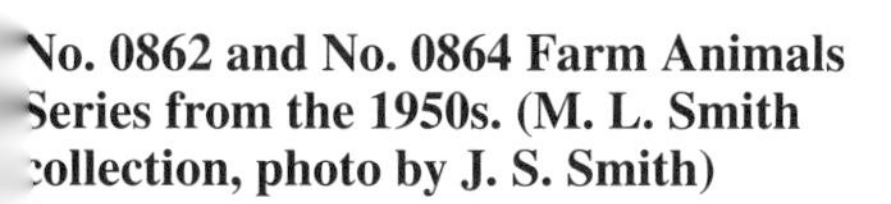

No. 0862 and No. 0864 Farm Animals Series from the 1950s. (M. L. Smith collection, photo by J. S. Smith)

Item #	Year	Description
0968	1953/1954	War of 1812 Soldiers (1812-1814) Series
0900	1953	Sports Figures Series
0904	1953	Spacemen with Helmets (Rex Mars Figures) TV Personalities
0981	1953	Marching Soldiers Series
0982	1953	Union Soldiers Civil War (1861-1865) Series
0983	1953	Confederate Soldiers Civil War (1861-1865) Series
0984	1953	Revolutionary War Soldiers (1775-1783) Series
0989	1953	World War I (1917-1918) Series
0991	1953	West Point Cadets Series
0993	1953	Marines Series
T-152	1953	Put-To-Gether English Soldiers Set
0827	1954	Walt Disney Series
0837	1954	Prince Valiant Series
0838	1954	Royal Canadian Mounted Police Series (4)
0866	1954	Roy Rogers Series TV Personalities (6)
0869	1954	Lone Ranger Series TV Personalities
0868	1954	Rodeo Figures Series
0890	1954	Dollhouse People Series (4)
0918	1954	English Royalty Series
0920	1954	Winston Churchill
0934	1954	The Presidents of the United States Series (33)
0943	1954	Inauguration Series
0950	1954	American Heroes Series
0970	1954	Spanish-American War (1898) Series
0975	1954	English Guards Series
T-154	1954	Put-To-Gether Cowboys & Horses Set
0760	1955	Super Circus Series TV Personalities
0811	1955	Howdy Doody Series TV Personalities
0916	1955	Religious Figures Series
0969	1955	Mexican War Soldiers (1846-1848) Series
0782	1956	Railroad People Series (10)

No. 0805 Champion Dog Figures from the 1950s. (M. L. Smith collection, photo by J. S. Smith)

No. 0805 Champion Dog Figures from the 1950s. (M. L. Smith collection, photo by J. S. Smith)

No. 54/6 Badger. Wildlife Series from 1957. (M. L. Smith collection, photo by J. S. Smith)

No. 0894 Revolutionary War Soldiers Series from the 1950s. (G. A. Whipkey collection, photo by J. S. Smith)

No. 0894 Revolutionary War Soldiers Series from the 1950s. (G. A. Whipkey collection, photo by J. S. Smith)

No. 0866 Roy Rogers Series TV Personalities from the 1950s. (G. A. Whipkey collection, photo by J. S. Smith)

No. 0916 Religious Figures from the 1950s. (G. A. Whipkey collection, photo by J. S. Smith)

Chapter Seven

Women Figures & Sindy Doll

The Marx Toy Company manufactured many figures of women over its years of operation. Some memorable (small figure) items are the American Beauties (eight in different poses), Bathing Beauties (some were introduced in Dollhouse kits which offered pool and accessories), and ones referred to as "Nudies" (nude ladies in various poses). These "Nudies" figures were small, and a soft-pinkish color. It was rumored over the years that Louis Marx kept many of these American Beauties and Nudies in his oversized suit pockets and that he handed them out to his associates, friends, and/or customers. The detailing on each figure is excellent, and these items are highly sought after in today's collector market.

Campus Cuties—1964

(two series produced)

In 1964, the Marx Toy Company introduced Item Number 2018, the "Campus Cuties" series from "Smith, Skidmore, and Southern Cal." These 6" figures were made in two separate series, and were manufactured of solid plastic in a soft beige color. Each figure's dress reflected the latest fashions, and she was named according to her activity.

Series 1	**Series 2**
Shopping Anyone?	*Belle of the Ball*
Stormy Weather	*Bermuda Holiday*
Lodge Party	*Day at the Races*
Dinner For Two	*Night at the Opera*
On The Beach	*Our Girl Friday*
Nitey-Nite	*Saturday Afternoon*
Lazy Afternoon	*Touch of Mink*
On The Town	*Twist Party*

Look for the following on each character: On the underside of each figure is information describing that figure, which includes the title (i.e. "Stormy Weather") Campus Cuties T.M. Copyright MCMLXIV, Louis Marx & Co., Inc.

Sindy Doll

In 1978, the Marx Toy Company offered a beautiful doll called the "Sindy Doll," Item #1000. This lovely doll must have enchanted many young girls in hours at play. Numerous accessories and clothing were also available. Sindy stood approximately 11" tall, and featured flexible hands at the base of each arm. The doll's head and upper torso turned. The Sindy Doll's legs were straight, and could only be moved back and forth. Her lovely blonde hair was matched with large blue eyes. (Marx Toys Company also produced a black Sindy doll.)

Some of her appropriately scaled accessories included Item #1232 Wardrobe; Item #1233 Vanity; Item #1231 Bed; Item #1234 Bedside Table w/working light; Item #1236 Dining Room Breakfront; Item #1235 Dining Table w/four chairs and accessories; Item #1239 Refrigerator; Item #1246 Sink; Item #1238; Item #1237 Wall Oven; Item #1240 Bathtub; Item #1241 Washstand; Item 1244 Loveseat; Item #1245 Armchair; Item #1242 Music Center w/real AM radio; Item #1601 Scenesetter (four highly-detailed room layouts set the scene for Sindy's World, Bedroom, Dining Room, Kitchen & Den); Item #1150 "Let's Get Married" Sindy Doll;

Sindy's outfits, Item #1110 Outfit Assortment included: Let's get our beauty sleep; Let's go shopping; Let's have a dinner party; Let's take it easy; Let's go to the ballet; and Let's go riding (hat included with horse) outfits. Item #1200, Sindy's Horse, was jointed for easy posing, and came with curry-comb and brush, trophy, bucket, broom, hay bag, and hat.

Marx Bathing Beauties from the 1950s. (G. A. Whipkey collection, photo by J. S. Smith)

Marx Nudes from the 1950s. G. A. Whipkey collection. (Photo by J. S. Smith)

Marx American Beauties (set of eight) from the 1950s. (G. A. Whipkey collection, photo by J. S. Smith)

Marx American Beauties (set of eight) from the 1950s. (G. A. Whipkey collection, photo by J. S. Smith)

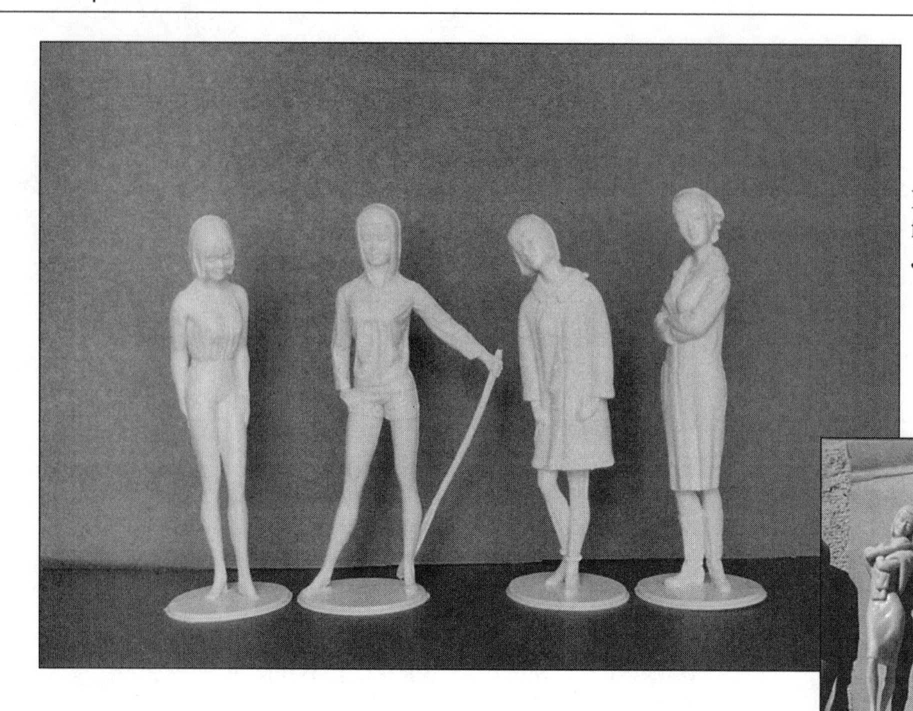

No. 2018 Campus Cuties, Series 1 (Set of eight), from 1964. (G. A. Whipkey collection, photo by J. S. Smith)

Campus Cuties (20).

No. 2018 Campus Cuties, Series 1 (Set of eight) from 1964. (G. A. Whipkey collection, photo by J. S. Smith)

No. 1000 Sindy Doll, from 1978, as depicted in the *1978 Marx Toys Promotional Catalog.*

No. 1150 "Let's Get Married" Sindy Doll from 1978, as depicted in the *1978 Marx Toys Promotional Catalog.*

No. 1601 Scenesetter for Sindy Doll from 1978, as depicted in the *1978 Marx Toys Promotional Catalog.*

Chapter Eight

Johnny West Series Figures

Among the numerous play sets, the Johnny West Series was probably the most popular. This western line featured figures and many accessories for both boys and girls to enjoy. These durable Western figures and accessories were enjoyed by countless youngsters in the mid-1960s through the 1970s. Some of the characters offered were: Johnny West, Jane West, Janice West, Jamie West, and Josie West. Other notable figures were Geronimo, Fighting Eagle, Captain Maddox and many others. Many horses were also offered,

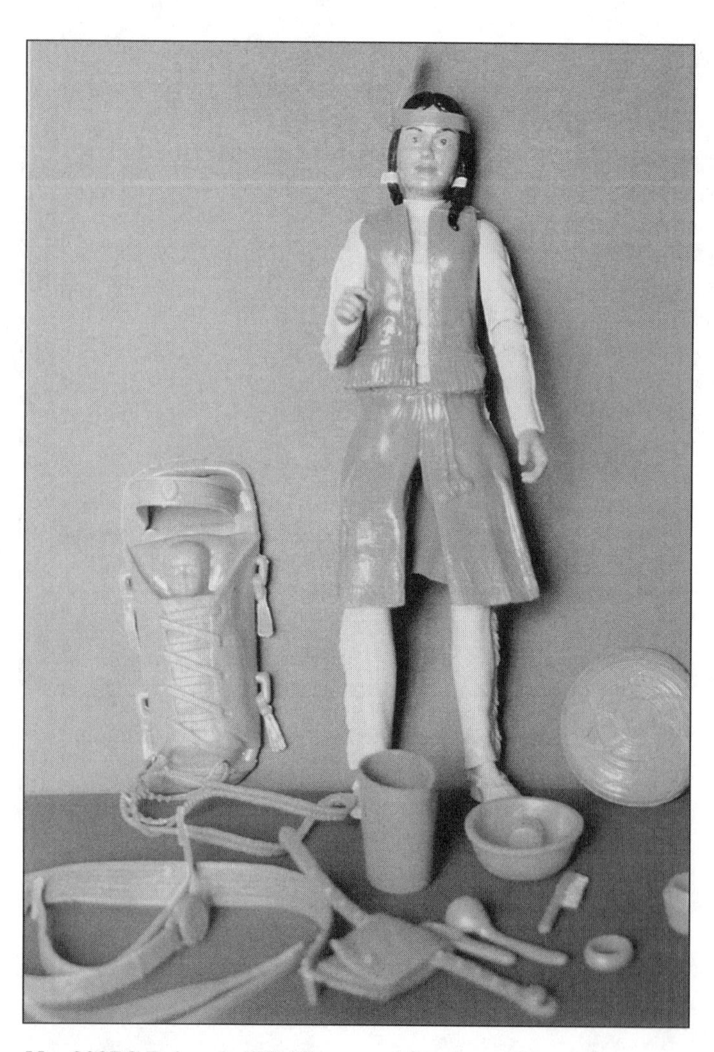

No. 2097C Princess Wildflower, with accessories. (G. A. Whipkey collection, photo by J. S. Smith)

No. 1067B Josie West and No. 1863 Fighting Geronimo. (M. L. Smith collection, photo by J. S. Smith)

including Thunderbolt, Thundercolt, Flame, Pancho, and Comanche.

This extensive line of toys was very authentic looking to the smallest detail. The horses, wagons, and all of the accessories created by the Marx Toy Company artists and modelers were very realistic. The figures, and even one of the horse series models, were jointed, and easily posed.

The Johnny West series also included many covered wagons, buckboards, and even a Johnny West jeep! Many figures came with numerous accessories to compliment the figure(s). Very popular items, other than the figures, were animals: #2081 Flame, The Pranching Horse; #1061 Pancho Horse; #2031 Thundercolt; #1861B Comanche, The Articulating Horse; #2029A "Flick" Shepherd Dog; #2029B "Flack" Setter Dog; and #2033 Buffalo. These figures were very detailed and were offered with numerous accessories.

Best of the West buckboard with horse and harness.

No. 4424C Buckboard and Horse from 1975, as depicted in the *1975 Marx Toys Promotional Catalog.*

No. 2062 Johnny West. (G.A. Whipkey collection, photo by J. S. Smith)

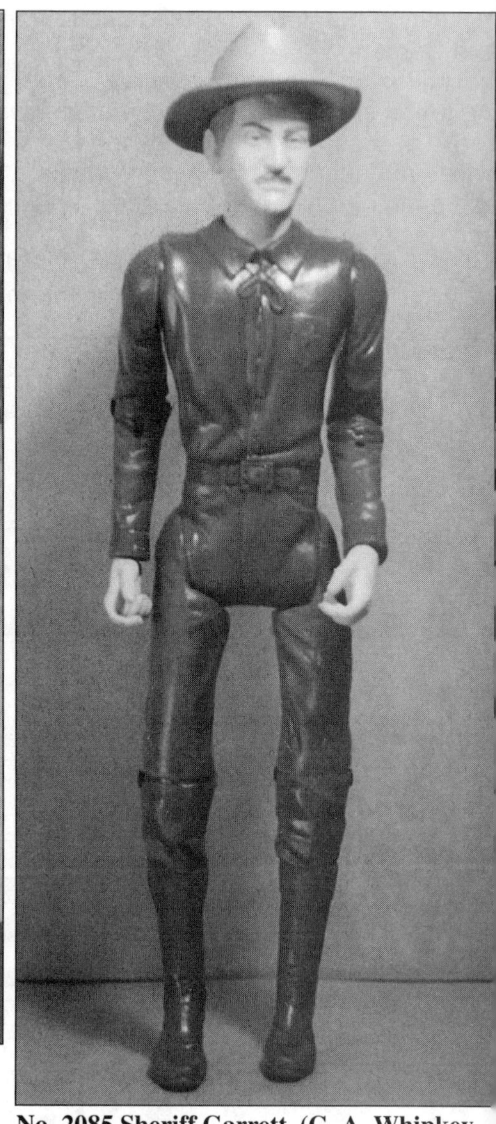

No. 2085 Sheriff Garrett. (G. A. Whipkey collection, photo by J. S. Smith)

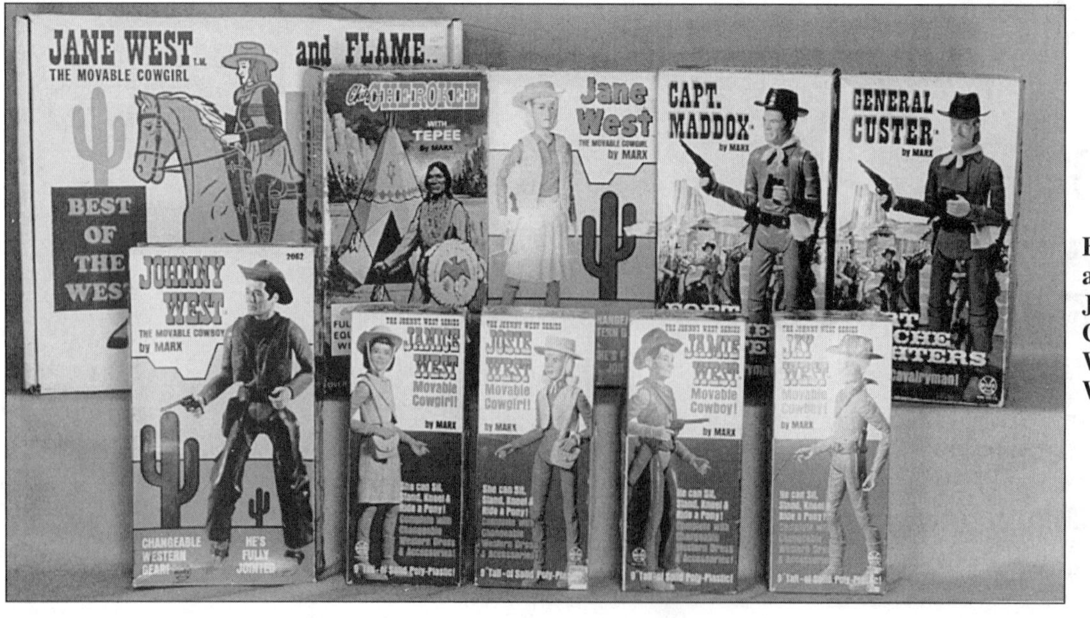

Best of the West, Jane West and Flame, Cherokee Tepee, Jane West, Capt. Maddox, General Custer, Johnny West, Janice West, Josie West, Jamie West, Jay West

No. 1062A James West and No. 1062B Jay West. (G. A. Whipkey collection, photo by J. S. Smith)

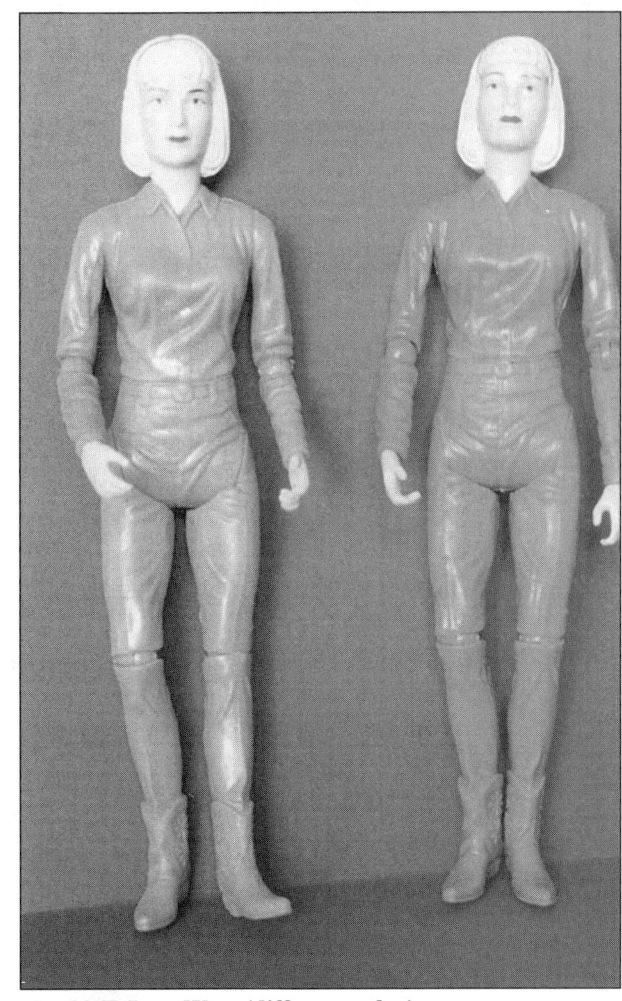

No. 2067 Jane West (different color). (G. A. Whipkey collection, photo by J. S. Smith)

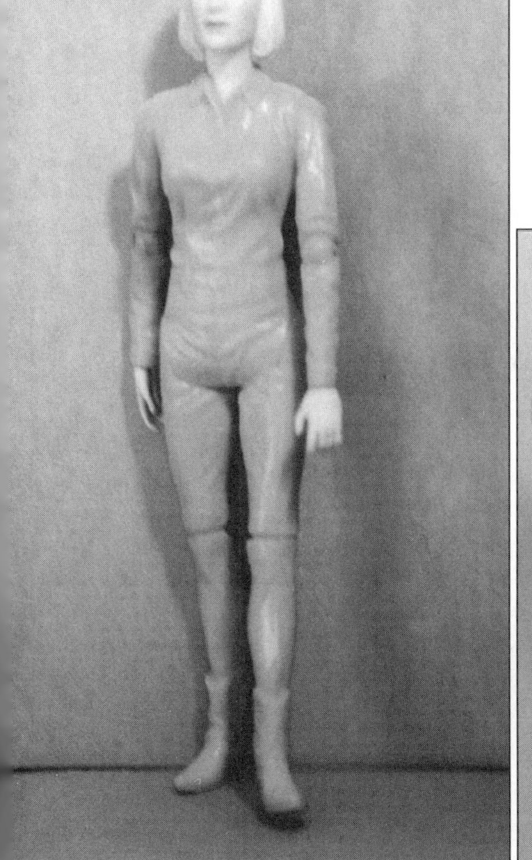

No. 2067 Jane West. (G. A. Whipkey collection, photo by J. S. Smith)

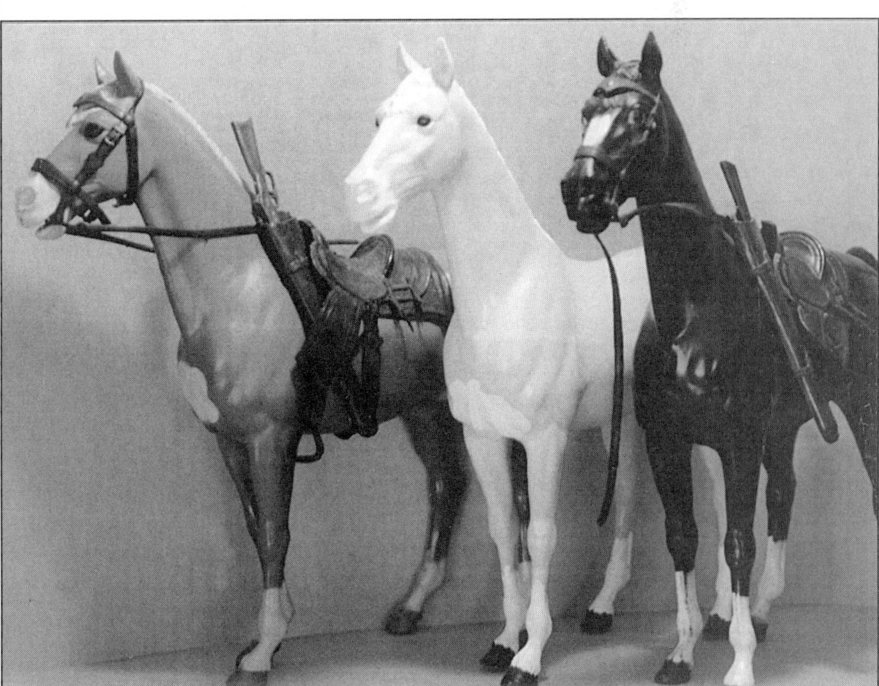

No. 2061 Thunderbolt. (G. A. Whipkey collection, photo by J. S. Smith)

5062C—JOHNNY WEST "QUICK DRAW" (NEW)
Multi-color clothing; button at rear raises arm and "shot is fired," must be manually lowered. Same accessories as 2062C.
PACKED: 12, wgt. 18 lbs., cube 1.76

5072C—SAM COBRA "QUICK DRAW" (NEW)
Button at rear of figure raises arm and "shot is fired," must be manually lowered. Same accessories as 2072C.
PACKED: 12, wgt. 18 lbs., cube 1.76

1061C—PANCHO ASSORTMENT
Welsh pony, 12½" long for West kids.
PACKED: 12, wgt. 15 lbs., cube 3.86

1062C—JOHNNY WEST BOYS ASST.
Each with 11 pieces clothing, gear.
PACKED: 12, wgt. 8 lbs., cube .70

1067C—JOHNNY WEST GIRLS ASST.
Both with 10 pieces clothes, accessories.
PACKED: 12, wgt. 7½ lbs., cube .71

1861C—COMANCHE HORSE
Has 13 hinges, poseable, accessories.
PACKED: 12, wgt. 23¼ lbs., cube 5.01

1863C—GERONIMO INDIAN
36 pieces ceremonial trappings, fit-on clothes.
PACKED: 12, wgt. 19 lbs., cube 1.70

1864C—FIGHTING EAGLE
With 3 dozen pcs. ceremonial gear.
PACKED: 12, wgt. 18 lbs., cube 1.76

1865C—CAPTAIN MADDOX
Cavalry figure with 24 accessories.
PACKED: 12, wgt. 16¼ lbs., cube 1.70

1866C—GENERAL CUSTER
Cavalry hero with 24-piece dress and field garb.
PACKED: 12, wgt. 16¾ lbs., cube 1.75

2036C—BUCKSKIN HORSE
Moving head, 15" long, accessories.
PACKED: 6, wgt. 13 lbs., cube 3.04

2057C—JED GIBSON (NEW)
In cavalry uniform with 5 cavalryman accessories, also 8 pcs. of hunter scout clothing and pelts.
PACKED: 12, wgt. 15 lbs., cube 1.76

2061C—THUNDERBOLT HORSE ASST.
Universal horse, 14½" long, asst. colors.
PACKED: 12, wgt. 23¾ lbs., cube 5.96

2062C—JOHNNY WEST
With 21 pieces clothing, weapon, utensils.
PACKED: 12, wgt. 16¼ lbs., cube 1.77

2063C—CHIEF CHEROKEE
With 3 dozen pcs. ceremonial gear.
PACKED: 12, wgt. 18 lbs., cube 1.76

2067C—JANE WEST
27 pieces accessories, costumes, utensils.
PACKED: 12, wgt. 16¼ lbs., cube 1.82

2071C—SMOKE CLOUD HORSE ASST.
Indians' 14½" horse, plus trappings.
PACKED: 12, wgt. 20¾ lbs., cube 5.96

2072C—SAM COBRA
Complete array of 25 sinister accessories.
PACKED: 12, wgt. 15 lbs., cube 1.73

2085C—SHERIFF GARRETT
With 21 clothing, weapon and utensil pieces.
PACKED: 12, wgt. 15 lbs., cube 1.70

2097C—PRINCESS WILDFLOWER
Comes with 22 pieces wardrobe, jewelry, utensils.
PACKED: 12, wgt. 15 lbs., cube 1.72

Page from the *Marx Toys 1975 Promotional Catalog* featuring Johnny West figures and accessories.

Page from the *Marx Toys 1975 Promotional Catalog* featuring Johnny West figures and accessories.

Chapter Nine

Marx Toys Listing

(Glen Dale, West Virginia plant)

The Marx Toys Listing which follows was initially prepared by Gaylord "Andrew" Whipkey in October, 1973. He prepared this list knowing that "someday, somewhere down the line" people would be interested, and he was right. It is from his loving dedication to preserving the Marx toys' history that this listing is made available. We both felt that this listing would better inform any toy collector in learning about a toy item number and year of production.

Early in March of 1995, Gaylord and I decided to combine our information on the value of various toys. Our information, as well as the input collected from area toy collectors and dealers, is reflected in the value guide listings incorporated with the original toy list. The listing and value guide covers many of the wonderful Marx toys made during the late 1940s through 1970s.

I have never met an individual as knowledgeable on the topic of Marx toys as Gaylord Whipkey. He truly was a walking encyclopedia of Marx Toy Company history. Sadly, Gaylord passed away a few years ago, and did not live to see this book become a reality.

Please keep in mind, when referring to this listing, that the values suggested are for toy items in the "good to excellent" condition. Remember, too, that condition is very important in ascertaining the value of any toy, and that mint condition or MIB (mint in box) items will command higher prices. Some toy collectors won't mind if a toy has a small flaw, missing part, or scratch, whereas others want only mint toys. It all comes down to what you're looking for, and what you're willing to pay once you locate it.

If you are a computer user, you may be interested in checking out Marx toys items on the Internet. Two sites of particular interest are:

www.marxtoys.com

www.vintagetoyroom.com

Or, you might possibly want to check with the International Toy Collectors Association (ITCA) .

Remember, these values are only a guide. Item values may range due to demand and region, as well as condition, so don't forget to do a little homework before buying or selling an item.

MARX TOYS LISTING

Prepared by G. A. Whipkey, 10/73

ITEM DESCRIPTION	ITEM NO.(S)	YEARS	PRICE VALUE GUIDE
ACTION CARRY-ALL BOOT CAMP	4645	1968-69/72-73	150.00-200.00
ACTION CARRY-ALL CAPE KENNEDY	4625	1968-69	50.00-75.00
ACTION CARRY-ALL FIGHTING KNIGHTS	4635 & MO	1968-69-70-71/73	55.00-75.00
ACTION CARRY-ALL FIGHTING KNIGHTS	4685 & MO	1968-69-70-71-72-73	50.00-75.00
ACTION CARRY-ALL FORT APACHE	4685	1968-71	50.00-75.00
ACTION GAMES ASST, GAMES OF SKILL	G-140	1964/69/73	
ACTION LAND-A-SLIDE	5300	1970-71-72	
ACTION LAND COMBINATION SET	9003	1971	
ACTION MOWING MACHINE	244	*	
ADM. HALSY W/WW II SAILORS	3069	1955	
AIR FORCE MISSILE BASE	4166	1961	
AIRPLANE, DC-6 PULL	1481-2	*	
AIRPLANE, DC-6 PULL	1485-6	*	
AIRPORT & HANGAR SET	0796	1952	
AIRPORT HELICOPTER AND BUS SET	478	1961	
AIRPORT PRE-FAB	3829-30	1952	50.00-100.00
AIRPORT W/ACCESS. PRE-FAB	3831-2	1952	50.00-100.00

Safety and Testing of Marx Toys

Within the Quality Control and Reliability Laboratory at our factory finished Marx Toys are continually subjected to the following tests and machines 48 times a day:

Lifespan Treadmill, Weighted Item Merry-Go-Round over rough concrete, Vibrator, Destructor, Bender, Impact/Puncture, Drop and Incline Tester, Puller, and Re-Cycler.

Such machine tests are designed to exceed the guidelines as set out by the Bureau Of Product Safety, Food and Drug Administration. Technicians then accomplish tests that machines never thought of. Our final testing is accomplished with at-random local kids and their parents. If Marx toys do not pass any or all of the above tests, they are simply not shipped.

In our design, testing and manufacture we produce toys that are part of "growing up" . . . not a temporary placating diversion. All of our toys have "an intended use" and we cooperate with our distributive and consuming public to fulfill that intention.

No. 4733 KNIGHTS, VIKINGS, CASTLE SET
Including over 72 pieces, the Castle proper measures 22½" l, 13" deep and 13" to the top of the flag. Of rolled edge brightly lithographed steel, the set has 3 horses, two catapults, 27 Knights and 45 Vikings set up on a full color poly layout sheet for realism.
PACKED: 3, Wgt. 16 lbs. (Cube 2.36)
F.O.B. Glen Dale, W. Va.

No. 4814 INTERNATIONAL AIRPORT
Centering around a lithographed steel administration building, the hustle and bustle of a modern all purpose airport is characterized here. With commercial and private planes, ground support equipment, civilian cars and hangars, the whole scene takes place on a 27½" x 42" printed poly play layout sheet.
PACKED: 3, Wgt. 21 lbs. (Cube 2.84)
F.O.B. Glen Dale, W. Va.

19

Page from the *Marx Toys 1973 Promotional Catalog.*

ITEM DESCRIPTION	ITEM NO.(S)	YEARS	PRICE VALUE GUIDE
AIRPORT, CITY	2419-20	*	
AIRPORT, HAPPI-TIME INTERNATIONAL	4818	1961	
AIRPORT, INTERNATIONAL	4814	1973	
AIRPORT, INTERNATIONAL (FOR SUPER MARKETS)	4808	1961	
AIRPORT, INTERNATIONAL (WARDS)	4816	1961	
AIRPORT, INTERNATIONAL JETPORT	4824	1963	
AKRO BALL	G-15	1948	
ALAMO	3548	1972	
ALL STAR BASKETBALL GAME	G-288	1966	
ALLIGATOR	3055 & MO	1971/73	
AMBULANCE, ARMY	2561-2	*	
AMERICAN AIRLINES ASTRO JETPORT	4821-2	1961	150.00-250.00
AMERICAN AIRLINES INTERNATIONAL JETPORT	4811-12	1960	
AMERICAN PATROL SET (SEARS)	4165	1964	
AMERICAN PATROL SET (SEARS)	4168	1964	
ANTELOPE	57/5	1957	5.00-10.00
APOLLO ASTRONAUTS (6 SPACE EXPLORERS)	1979	1970	8.00-12.00 each
APOLLO FIGURES	1979	1969/73	
ARCADE (BLUE CHIP)	G-168	1970	
ARMED FORCES FIGURES SET, 38-PIECE	0712	1957	1.00-3.00 each
ARMED FORCES SET W/GUIDED MISSILES	4143	1957	
ARMED FORCES TRAINING CENTER	4139-40	1956	50.00-75.00
ARMED FORCES TRAINING CENTER	4141-2	1956	50.00-75.00
ARMED FORCES TRAINING CENTER	4149-50	1955	50.00-75.00
ARMED FORCES TRAINING CENTER	4151-2	1958	50.00-75.00
ARMED FORCES TRAINING CENTER	4155-6	1960	50.00-75.00
ARMED FORCES TRAINING CENTER (32 PIECES)	4102	1957	50.00-75.00
ARMED FORCES TRAINING CENTER W/NIKE BASE	4163-4	1957	
ARMORED MILITARY PATROL SET	2617	1950s	
ARMY & AIR FORCE TRAINING CENTER	4145	1954	50.00-75.00
ARMY & AIR FORCE TRAINING CENTER	4147-8	1954	50.00-75.00
ARMY & AIR FORCE TRAINING CENTER	4158-9	1954	100.00-125.00
ARMY BARRACK - PRE-FAB	3739-40	1954	
ARMY BARRACKS W/ACCESS.	3741-42	1954	
ARMY COMBAT SET	2658	1958	
ARMY COMBAT SET (CHG'D TO AMERICAN PATROL '64)	4155	1964	
ARMY COMBAT SET (SEARS)	4158	1963	150.00-175.00
ARMY COMBAT TRAINING CENTER	2654	1959	45.00-50.00
ARMY COMBAT TRAINING CENTER	4153	1958	40.00-50.00
ARMY COMBAT UNIT	0657	1951	
ARMY FIELD EQUIPMENT ASST.	0590	*	
ARMY JEEP	1516	1951	
ARMY JEEP	1540	1967	
ARMY JEEP W/SEARCHLIGHT TRAILER & SOLDIERS	1077A-8A	1956	
ARMY MOBILE RADIO JEEP	878	1958	
ARMY PHONE SET	270-1	1950	
ARMY SETS, ASSORTED	4786	1972	
ARMY TRAINING CENTER	4110	1950s	50.00-75.00
ARMY TRAINING CENTER	4119-20	1952	50.00-75.00
ARMY TRAINING CENTER	4121-2	1952	50.00-75.00
ARMY TRAINING CENTER	4123-4	1955	50.00-75.00
ARMY TRAINING CENTER	4129-30	1950s	50.00-75.00
ARMY TRAINING CENTER	4131-2	1959	50.00-75.00
ARMY TRAINING CENTER	4133-4	1957	50.00-75.00

ITEM DESCRIPTION	ITEM NO.(S)	YEARS	PRICE VALUE GUIDE
ARMY TRAINING CENTER	4144	1952	50.00-75.00
ARMY TRAINING CENTER	4146	1954	50.00-75.00
ARTIC EXPLORER SET	3702	1958	
ARTICULATED STONY SMITH (NO ACCESSORIES)	2051	1965	
ASH TRAY	99	1950s	
ASSAULT RAFT W/SOLDIERS	2715-16	1959	
ASSORTED BAGATELLE GAMES	G-144	1964/69/73	
ASST. GAMES	G-125	1970	
AUTO CENTER, WESTGATE W/CAR WASH	3486	1968	50.00-100.00
AUTO TRANSPORT	2436	1959	
AUTO TRANSPORT	2619-20	1958	
AUTO TRANSPORT	631-2	*	
AUTO TRANSPORT	719-20	1955	
AUTO TRANSPORT (3-NO STAND, 4 W/STAND)	843-4	*	
AUTO TRANSPORT (PL. CAB)	841	1953	
AUTO TRANSPORT (STEEL)	842	*	
AUTO TRANSPORT W/2 CARS	1019	1957/65	
AUTO TRANSPORT W/2 CARS	3643-4	1955	
AUTO TRANSPORT W/3 CARS	1020	1957	
AUTO TRANSPORT W/3 CARS	2622	*	
AUTO TRANSPORT W/4 CARS	3688	1964	
AUTO TRANSPORT W/6 CARS	2436-AS/1	*	
AUTO TRANSPORT W/8 CARS	1019/8	1962	
AUTO TRANSPORT W/CARS (951-2 CARS--952-4 CARS)	951-2	1955	
AUTO TRANSPORT, 2-CAR	739-40	*	
AUTO TRANSPORT, 2-CAR	782	*	
AUTO TRANSPORT, 2-CAR	792	*	
AUTO TRANSPORT, 4-CAR	743-4	*	
AUTO TRANSPORT, ALLSTATE	2436AS	1960	
AUTO TRANSPORT, LARGE W/4 CARS	3687-8	1960	
AUTO TRANSPORT, MECH, (2 TAXIS)	731-2	*	
AUTOMATIC SHOOTING TARGET GAME	G-190	1966	
B-52 STRATO FORTRESS JET MODEL KIT	M-121-2	1953	
B.O. LANTERN	4282HK	1973	
B.O. MICKEY LITTLE BIG WHEEL	4671HK	1973	
B.O. REMOTE STEERING TANK	6402HK	1973	
B/M BEAR "GROWLY"	59	1965	
B/M HOUND DOG "BARKING"	603A	1961	
B/M LOCOMOTIVE W/WHISTLE & BELL	65B	1969/72-73	
B/M PLUTO	78	1966	
B/M SKORBALL GAME	G-226	1972	
BABY ELEPHANT	57/3	1957	5.00-10.00 each
BABYLAND NURSERY SET	3379-80	1955	50.00-75.00
BAG GAME	G-82	1964	
BAGATELLE ASSORTMENT	G-124	1969	
BAGATELLE GAME ASSORTMENT	G-72	1969-70-71-72-73	
BAGATELLE GAME ASST.	G-72	1964	
BAGATELLE GAMES ASST.	G-72A/74/104	1967	
BALL GAME	GJ-90	*	
BARN SET	3930	1950	45.00-50.00
BARN W/SILO & ACCESS. PRE-FAB	3861-2	1952	45.00-75.00
BARN W/SILO PRE-FAB	3859-60	1952	45.00-75.00
BASEBALL GAME	G-73-74	1964	
BASKETBALL BAGATELLE	G-114	1964/72-73	

ITEM DESCRIPTION	ITEM NO.(S)	YEARS	PRICE VALUE GUIDE
BASKETBALL GAME	G-42	1964	
BAT & BALL, BIG SWAT	302	1972-73	
BATMAN ARCADE	G-266/266MO	1966	
BATMAN BAGATELLE	G-164	1966	
BEACH BUGGY JEEP	889-90	*	
BEACHHEAD ASSAULT SET	2651	1964	
BEACHHEAD LANDING SET	4638	1964	
BEACHHEAD LANDING SET (WARDS)	4639	1964	
BEAR	57/4	1957	5.00-10.00
BEEP BEENY HELMET	4300	1965	
BEGINNERS CYCLE	5036 & MO	1973	
BEGINNERS PLAN BEARING ROLLER SKATES	200-1	1954	
BEGINNERS ROLLER SKATES	201P	1950s	
BEGINNERS SKATES	100-101	1952	
BEN HUR CHARIOT SET	2759-60	1960	
BEST OF THE WEST	2047-D	1972	
BEST OF THE WEST DEMONSTRATOR	2068/D	1966	
BEST OF THE WEST DEMONSTRATOR	2069/D	1966	
BIG BRAVO	5395	1970	
BIG BRAVO HORSE W/GOLD ARMOR	5395	1971	
BIG INCH PIPE LINE	4445	1963	
BIG INCH PIPE LINE	4448	1961	
BIG SHOT ARCADE	G-218	1967	
BIG WHEEL	5070	1969-70-71-72	
BIG WHEEL DEMO (GRANT)	507D/1	1969	
BIG WHEEL REPLACEMENT	5072W	1970s	
BIG WHEEL REPLACEMENT	5080W	1973	
BIG WHEEL W/HAND BRAKE	5080	1973	
BIG WHEEL W/SADDLE BAG	5072	1971	
BILL BUCK (G.C. MURPHY)	1868M	1967	
BLACK KNIGHT SET	324	1968	
BLAME-IT FIGURES	2019	1964	20.00-30.00 each
BLISTER PACKS (0890C-2753-2741) ASST.	2773	1960	
BLISTER PACKS ASST.	0900	1954	
BLISTER PACKS ASST.	2777-8-9-80-81	*	
BLOW MOLDED 18" DOLL	74	1965	
BLOW MOLDED ASST. ANIMAL SET	87	1966	
BLOW MOLDED BIRD	75	1965	
BLOW MOLDED DUCK	63	1964	
BLOW MOLDED HOUND DOG	60	1965	
BLOW MOLDED LOCOMOTIVE	65	1965	
BLOW MOLDED PIG	72	1966	
BLOW MOLDED PLUTO DOG	78B	1969/72-73	
BLOW MOLDED TUG BOAT	66	1965	
BOAT #85 W/LITHO CRUISER DECK	86	*	
BOAT W/LITHO CARRIER DECK	124	1950s	
BOAT W/SAND SIFTER	124	1950s	
BOMBARD MISSILE SET	2749-50	1960	
BOOMERANG GAME	G-104	1964	
BOWLING SET (10 PINS)	G-189-190	*	
BOY CAMPERS SET FIGURES, 27-PIECE	0715	1957	2.00-3.00 each
BOY SCOUT CAMP	4103-4	1956	
BRAVE EAGLE RIDER & HORSE	2696-1	1956	
BRAVE ERIK VIKING	5430	1970-71	20.00-35.00

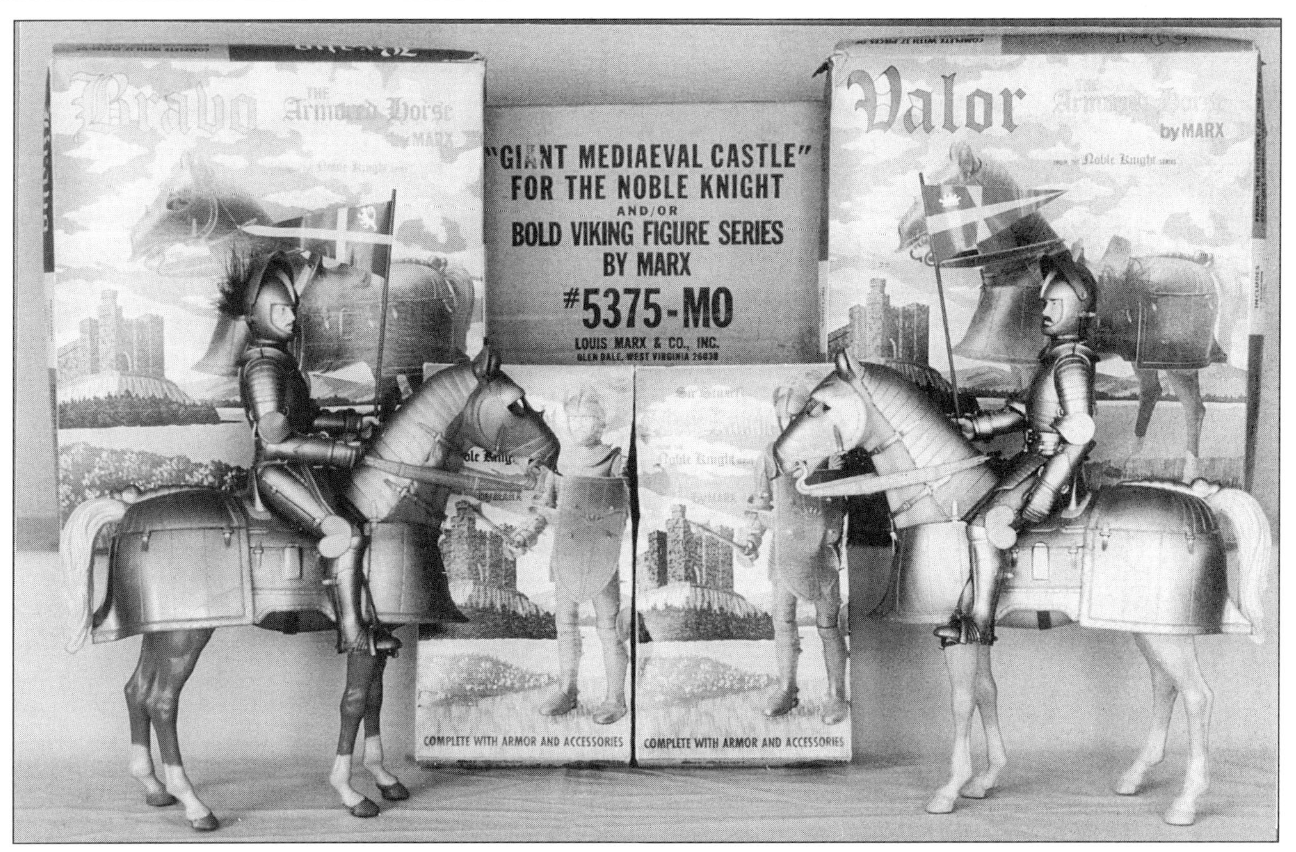

Noble Knight series Bravo, Valor, Silver Knight and Gold Knight.

ITEM DESCRIPTION	ITEM NO.(S)	YEARS	PRICE VALUE GUIDE
BRAVO HORSE W/GOLD ARMOR	5371	1968-69-70-71	20.00-25.00
BRIDGE, RAILROAD GIRDER	1304-5	1950s	
BUCKBOARD	4424	1970	10.00-15.00
BUCKBOARD	4420	1967	
BUCKBOARD & HORSE	4427 & MO	1967	
BUCKBOARD & THUNDERBOLT	4424 & MO	1967	15.00-25.00
BUCKBOARD MODEL KIT	M-109-10	1954	
BUCKBOARD W/2 HORSES & DRIVERS	1366P	1959	
BUCKBOARD W/HORSES	4424	1970-71-72-73	15.00-25.00
BUCKBOARD, HORSE & COWBOY SET (SUITCASE)	4428	1967	
BUCKET BALL GAME	6319HK	1973	
BUCKSIN, JOHNNY WEST HORSE W/ACCESS.	2036	1970	15.00-25.00
BUCKSKIN HORSE	2036	1970	
BUCKSKIN HORSE W/MOVING HEAD	2036	1973	25.00-45.00
BUCKSKIN, THE MOVING HEAD HORSE	2036	1970-71	
BUDDING BEAUTY VANITY	7114	1965	
BUDGET BANK	723	*	
BUDGET BANK W/LITHO TOP	728	*	
BUFFALO	2033	1967-68	20.00-25.00
BULLSEYE PINBALL BAGATELLE	G-154	1965/69/73	
BUS TERMINAL	2450	1950s	
BUS W/PASSENGERS	2139-40	*	
BUS, MECH. PLASTIC	1175	1960s	
BUSY PARKING LOT	2750	1960s	
CABIN CRUISER	139-40	1954	
CADETS IN BAG SET	3195	1956	2.00-5.00 each

ITEM DESCRIPTION	ITEM NO.(S)	YEARS	PRICE VALUE GUIDE
CALVARY FIGURE SET (30 PIECES)	54/2	1957	1.00-2.00 each
CALVARY FIGURE SET (33 PIECES)	54/1	1957	1.00-2.00 each
CALVARY SOLDIER SET	55/2	1956	1.00-2.00 each
CALVARY, 6 FIGURES	1984B	1973	8.00-10.00 each
CAMPUS CUTIES, FIRST SERIES	2018	1964	8.00-10.00 each
CAMPUS CUTIES, SECOND SERIES	2020	1964	20.00-25.00 each
CANADIAN MOUNTIE FIGURES, FOUR	0838	1954	3.00-5.00 each
CANNON & CAISSON SET	2748	1960	
CAPT. GALLANT FOREIGN LEGION	4729-30	1956	
CAPT. KIDD W/PIRATES	3127-8MO	1954	2.00-5.00 each
CAPT. MADDOX & COMANCHE SET	1883	1967	45.00-75.00
CAPT. MADDOX & COMANCHE SET	1883MO	1967	45.00-75.00
CAPT. MADDOX, HORSE, FT. EAGLE SET (CARRYCASE)	1876	1967	
CAPT. SPACE SOLAR ACADEMY	7026	1953	200.00-250.00
CAPT. SPACE SOLAR PORT	7018	1954	75.00-100.00
CAPTAIN GALLANT SET FIGURES, 22-PIECE	0711	1957	
CAPTAIN SPACE FIGURES	0908	1953	2.00-5.00 each
CAPTAIN TOM MADDOX	1865	1970-71-72-73	25.00-45.00
CAR, 1910 FORM MODEL KIT	M-143-4	1953	
CAR, ARMORED MILITARY SCOUT CAR	0630	*	
CAR, ARMY COMMAND	2496	1963	
CAR, CORVETTE, MINI. TAKE-APART	0355	1956	
CAR, DICK TRACY	3033	1967	
CAR, DICK TRACY (KRESGE)	3033/4	1967	
CAR, MINI. T.A.P.	0237-8	1953	
CAR, MODEL "T" FORD	1363-4	1959	
CAR, MODEL "T" FORD	1908	*	
CAR, OLD TIME MAXWELL	M-147-8	1954	
CAR, P. PULL CADILLAC	2719	*	
CAR, POLICE	1493-4	1950	
CAR, R.C.A. SERVICE	1431-2	1950s	
CAR, ROLLS ROYCE TOWN	1513-14	*	
CAR, SPEED BOY MYSTERY	647	*	
CAR, SPORTS, MINI. TAKE-APART	0354	1956	
CARBINE, AUTOMATIC SPARKLING	2284-85	1968	
CARBINE, SPACE AGE, SPARKLING ACTION	2294	1969/71-72-73	
CARPET SWEEPER	83	*	
CARPET SWEEPER W/NOISE	185	1960s	
CARRY-ALL DEMONSTRATOR	4688D/1	1970	
CARRY ALL JOHNNY APOLLO MOON LAUNCH	4630	1970-71-72-73	50.00-75.00
CARRYALL	849	*	
CARRYALL ACTION PLAYSET UNIVERSAL DISPLAY	4689D	1969	
CARS, ASST. FUTURISTIC CARS (4)	0327	1953	
CARS, PARKWAY SET	166	1953	
CARS, SPORT, ASST.	1510	1950s	
CARS, SPORT, SET OF MIN.	0897	1955	
CARS, SPORTS W/DIE CAST WHEELS, MINI.	165	1955	
CHAIR, B/M CLUB	5184	1969-70-71-72	
CHAIR, B/M LOVE SEAT	5188	1969-70-71-72-73	
CHAIR, B/M ROCKER	5186	1969-70-71-72-73	
CHAIR, HUSKI BUILT SINGLE	5189	1973	
CHAIR, KIDDI ROLLER ROCKER	5171 & MO	1971-72-73	
CHAIR, LITTLE MITE, BEGINNER'S	5162	1971-72-73	

LOUIS MARX & CO., INC.
200 FIFTH AVE. NEW YORK

ERIE DIVISION
F.O.B. Factory – Erie, Pa.

a. No. 1998 GIANT SIZE WORLD WAR II GERMAN COMBAT SOLDIERS

These Marx copyrighted new action figures measuring up to six inches tall – are accurate in historical detail and "big" in demand by kids everywhere. A brand new item by Marx, in the new popular category of super figure molding. They are a "must" to stock and promote. Of solid poly in characteristic gray color. Each has a solid molded – on base for active play or display. ACTUAL SIZE: Fantastic in design, expression & detail. All six completely different.

PACKED: Bulk
12 doz. weighing 18 lbs.

b. No. 2014 NUTTY MADS

The mad-caps of today captured in wildly nutty poses! "Roddy" the Hot Rod, "Rocky" the Champ, "Dippy" the Deep-Diver, "Waldo" the Weight Lifter, "Donald" the Demon, "Manny" the Reckless Mariner; 6 absolutely cra-a-azy characters all molded of solid poly, they are 6" high with sturdy molded-on bases and come in assorted nutty fluorescent colors. Eye-catching 10" x 24" window streamer in black and wonderfully bilious rose included in each carton to help your promotion!

PACKED: Bulk
1 gross assorted to a carton
Carton weight – 43 lbs.

Each completely different Nutty Mad sculptured in fantastic design, expression and details.

c. No. 2018 CAMPUS CUTIES

From "Smith, Skidmore and Southern Cal." they're all here – the CAMPUS CUTIES. Now duplicated by Marx in a new 6" figure series of solid poly-plastic in soft beige color. Each figurine is dressed in the latest fashions and named according to her activity. "Shopping Anyone?," "Stormy Weather," "Lodge Party," "Dinner For Two," "On The Beach," "Nitey-Nite," "Lazy Afternoon," "On The Town."

PACKED: Bulk
1 gross per shipping carton
Weight – 13 lbs.

a.

b.

c. **Flash! Second series Campus Cuties now ready. Write and ask us about them.**

12

Page from the *Marx Toys 1964 Promotional Catalog*.

ITEM DESCRIPTION	ITEM NO.(S)	YEARS	PRICE VALUE GUIDE
CHAIRS & TABLE, HUSKI BUILT	5190	1973	
CHAMPION DOG SERIES	2735-6	1961	
CHEROKEE & FIGHTING EAGLE ASST.	2092	1973	45.00-65.00
CHEROKEE & FLAME SET	2084	1966	45.00-65.00
CHEST, METAL LITHO TOY CHEST	3729-30	1956	25.00-50.00
CHICKEN COOP	3855	1953	35.00-50.00
CHICKEN COOP SET	3856	1954	35.00-75.00
CHIEF CHEROKEE & TEPEE SET	2073	1966	45.00-65.00
CHIEF CHEROKEE INDIAN	2063&MO	1965/68	40.00-70.00
CHING LING PANDA	3067	1973	
CHINGLING PANDA	3067	1972	
CHUGGING CHOO-CHOO	5873	1973	50.00-100.00
CHURCH PRE-FAB	3849-50	1952	50.00-100.00
CHURCH SET PRE-FAB	3851-2	1952	
CIRCUS SET, BIG TOP	4309-10	1952	200.00-300.00
CIRCUS SET, MAGIC MIDWAY	2678	1962	
CLIMB-A-ROO	5400	1970	
CLIMB-A-ROO	5400	1970-71	
CLIMB-A-ROO	5400	1971	
COAL BUCKET	215	*	
COAL PAIL	213	*	
COINS, BIG SPENDER	314	1972-73	3.00-5.00 each
COL. TEDDY ROOSEVELT W/SPAN. AM. ROUGH RIDERS	3065	1955	3.00-10.00 each
COLLAPSIBLE METAL TUNNEL	390-1-2	1950s	15.00-25.00
COMANCHE ARTICULATED HORSE	1861B	1970-71	25.00-40.00
COMANCHE HORSE	1861	1973	25.00-35.00
COMBAT GAME	G-88	1964	
COMBAT LANDING FORCE	2649	1964	
COMBAT SOLDIER SET	55/11	1956	1.00-2.00 each
COMET JET PASSENGER	M-123-4	1953	
COMM. PERRY W/1812 SAILORS	3061	1955	3.00-10.00 each
COMMANCHE HORSE, ARTICULATED	1861	1972-73	25.00-40.00
CONSTRUCTION CAMP	4439-40	1954	
CONSTRUCTION CAMP SET	4446	1957	
CONSTRUCTION CAMP W/FRICTION EQUIPMENT	4444	1955	10.00-20.00
CONSTRUCTION CAMP W/FRICTION VEHICLES	4441-2	1955	
CONSTRUCTION SET	5107	1968-69	
CONSTRUCTION SET	5108	1967	
CONSTRUCTION SET W/FIGURES (GRANT), 3 PC.	5105	1964	
CONSTRUCTION SET W/FIGURES, 3 PC.	5103	1962	
CONSTRUCTION SET, 3 PC.	5102	1962	
CONSTRUCTION SET, 3 PC.	5104	1963	
CONSTRUCTION SET, GRANT	5109 & D/1	1973	
CONSTRUCTION SET, SPEC. W.T. GRANT	5101	1962	
CONSTRUCTION SET, TURNPIKE	5106	1965	
CORRAL FENCE	2034	1967-68	5.00-10.00
CORVETTE & JAGUAR	2705-6	1962	
COVERED WAGON	4434	1970	
COVERED WAGON	1369-70	1959	
COVERED WAGON	4434	1970	15.00-25.00
COVERED WAGON SET	1383	1966	
COWBOY & INDIAN SET	2660	1958	
COWBOY & INDIAN SET	3949-50	1953	
COWBOY AND INDIAN SET (32 PIECES)	54/10	1957	1.00-2.00 each

Marx Construction Camp.

Marx 11" tall Daniel Boone, Wilderness Scout.

ITEM DESCRIPTION	ITEM NO.(S)	YEARS	PRICE VALUE GUIDE
COWBOY FIGURE SET (73 PIECES)	54/109	1958	1.00-2.00 each
COWBOY FIGURES (38 PIECES)	54/9	1957	1.00-2.00 each
COWBOY JEEP	1541	1967	
COWBOYS & ANIMALS	3161-2	1951	1.00-2.00 each
COWBOYS & HORSES	3163-4	1952	1.00-2.00 each
COWBOYS IN BAG SET	3193	1956	1.00-2.00 each
COWBOYS, 6 FIGURES	1983B	1973	
DANIEL BOONE FRONTIER WEAPONS	460	1964	
DANIEL BOONE W.S. SET	0631	1964	
DANIEL BOONE WILDERNESS KNIFE SET	305	1964	
DANIEL BOONE WILDERNESS OUTFIT	459	1964	
DANIEL BOONE WILDERNESS RIFLE	195	1964	
DANIEL BOONE WILDERNESS SCOUT	2060	1964-65	
DANIEL BOONE WILDERNESS SCOUT ($1.99 SIZE)	2640	1964	
DART GAME	G-13	1964	
DAVY CROCKET & FRONTIER FIGURES	0948	1955	
DEAL (BEAR, DUCK & PLUTO)	59/63/78	1967	
DESERT FOX	4178MO	1972	
DESIGN-ALL	100	1967	
DICK TRACY ARCADE	G-145	1967	
DICK TRACY BAGATELLE	G-193	1967	
DIESEL POWER SHOVEL	1782	1964/65/68/69	
DIESEL POWER SHOVEL	1782	1970	

ITEM DESCRIPTION	ITEM NO.(S)	YEARS	PRICE VALUE GUIDE
DIESEL POWER SHOVEL	1782	1972-73	
DINING ROOM UTENSILS	0178	1950s	5.00-800
DINNER-WARE ACCESSORIES	0176	1950s	5.00-800
DISC HARROW	243	*	
DISHWASHER W/21 DISHES	K-57-8	1954	25.00-50.00
DISNEY TELEVISION PLAYHOUSE	4349-50	1953	
DISNEY TELEVISION PLAYHOUSE	4352	1953	150.00-175.00
DISNEY TOOL CHEST	6330HK	1973	
DISNEYTHINGS	3361-62-68	1967	
DISNEYTHINGS	3366MO-69MO	1967	
DISPLAY	5105D/1	1970	
DOG ASSORTMENT	0384-6	1955	2.00-5.00 each
DOG, "FLACK" ENGLISH SETTER	2029B	1967-68	25.00-40.00
DOG, "FLICK" GERMAN SHEPHERD	2029A	1967-68	25.00-40.00
DOGS & CATS ASST.	3187-8MO	1953	2.00-5.00 each
DOLL CARRIAGE	127	1950s	
DOLL CASE TRAVELETTE SET	4661	1967	45.00-50.00
DOLL CASE TRAVELETTE SET (WARDS)	4662 & MO	1967	45.00-50.00
DOLL FURNITURE SET	4126	1956	15.00-35.00
DOLL HAT BOX W/ACCESS.	6706	1966	
DOLL HOUSE	4018B	1964-65/68	45.00-55.00
DOLL HOUSE	4029	1967	50.00-60.00
DOLL HOUSE	4029	1955	
DOLL HOUSE	4045MO	1960s	45.00-55.00
DOLL HOUSE	4072B	1964	45.00-75.00
DOLL HOUSE	5051-2	1950	50.00-100.00
DOLL HOUSE	5072	1969	50.00-75.00
DOLL HOUSE & PICKET FENCE SET	0276	1949/1950	50.00-75.00
DOLL HOUSE (NO ACCESS.)	4030	1964	45.00-55.00
DOLL HOUSE (SEARS)	4028	1966	45.00-55.00
DOLL HOUSE (SEARS)	4047	1964	45.00-55.00
DOLL HOUSE (SEARS)	4049	1950s	50.00-100.00
DOLL HOUSE (SEARS)	4086	1965	50.00-75.00
DOLL HOUSE (SEARS)	4087	1967	50.00-75.00
DOLL HOUSE (WARDS)	4063	1964	75.00-100.00
DOLL HOUSE ACCESSORY SET	0278-9	1957	15.00-25.00
DOLL HOUSE ACCESSORY SET	4034	1960s	15.00-25.00
DOLL HOUSE ACCESSORY SET	4036	1965	15.00-25.00
DOLL HOUSE ASSORTED FURNITURE	0391	1949	15.00-25.00
DOLL HOUSE ASSORTED FURNITURE SET	0319/B	1949	15.00-25.00
DOLL HOUSE ASSORTED FURNITURE W/CADILLAC	0395	1949	15.00-30.00
DOLL HOUSE ASSORTED ROOMS	4111	1955	15.00-35.00
DOLL HOUSE BUNK BEDS W/LADDER	4115	1956	5.00-6.00
DOLL HOUSE CARRYING CASE	4450	1968	35.00-50.00
DOLL HOUSE COLONIAL TYPE 2-STORY HOUSE W/ ACCESS	3801-2	1953	45.00-75.00
DOLL HOUSE COMPLETE W/ELECTRIC LIGHTS	4059-60	1960s	50.00-100.00
DOLL HOUSE EATON'S W/BREEZEWAY	R-4768	1963	50.00-75.00
DOLL HOUSE EXTENSION TABLE W/2 CHAIRS	4116	1956	8.00-15.00
DOLL HOUSE FOUR /SIX ROOMS ASST. FURNITURE	0818	1962/65/69	25.00-30.00
DOLL HOUSE FURNITURE SET	4033	1965	15.00-25.00
DOLL HOUSE FURNITURE SET	4118	1956	20.00-35.00
DOLL HOUSE FURNITURE SET (WARDS)	4032	1967	15.00-25.00
DOLL HOUSE MINI. APPLIANCES	0188-MO	1950	5.00-800
DOLL HOUSE MINI. TABLEWARE	0186-MO	1950	3.00-5.00
DOLL HOUSE PATIO & SWIMMING POOL SET	4010	1959	55.00-75.00

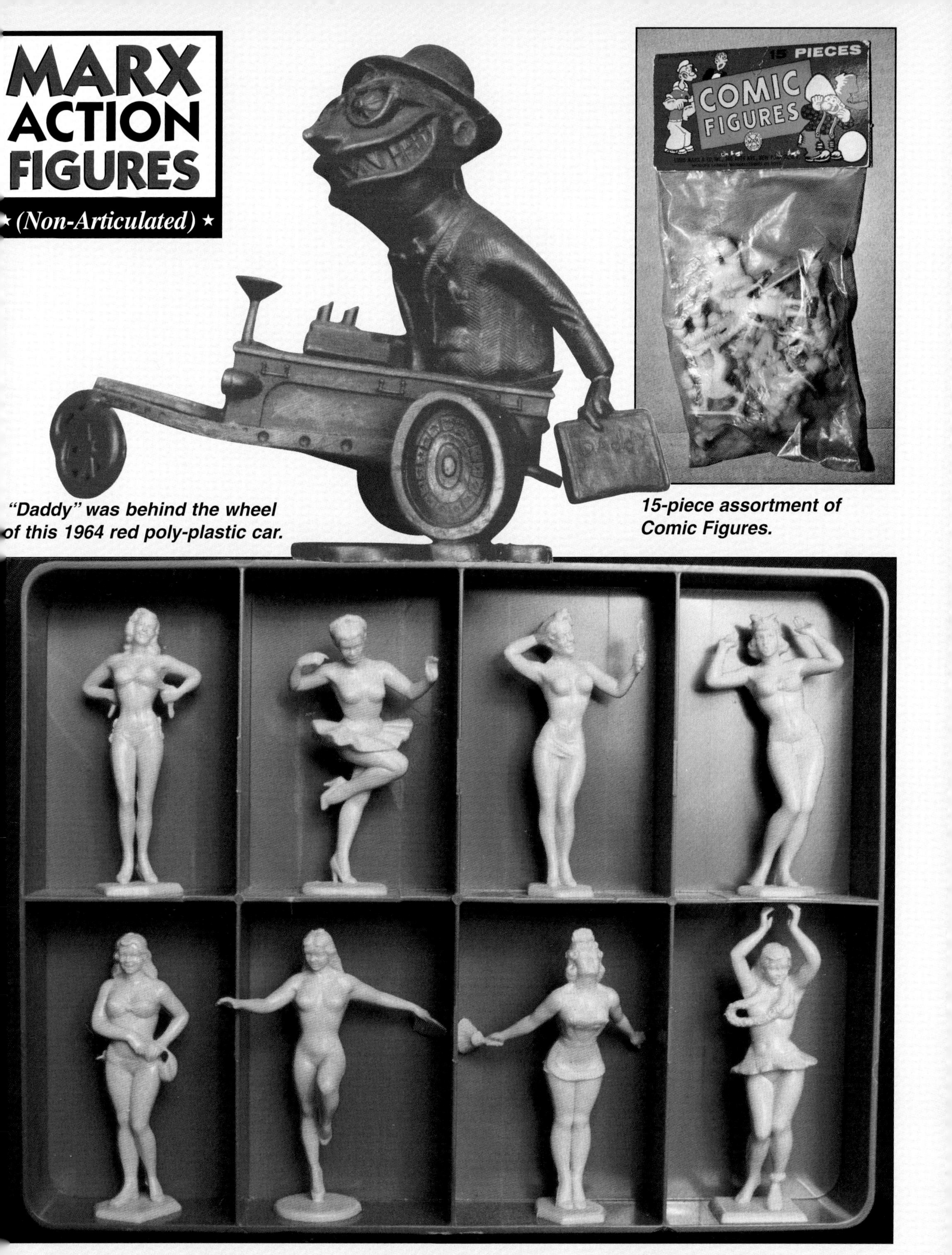

"Daddy" was behind the wheel of this 1964 red poly-plastic car.

15-piece assortment of Comic Figures.

Marx celebrated bathing beauties, buxom maids, and girls who knew how to shake up a lei.

Box set of hand-painted Marx Bavarian Figures.

Roman warriors battled it out with a vast array of weaponry.

Warriors of the World included cowboys, Indians, and Romans.

The Marx Animal Kingdom ranged from the mule deer to the rhinoceros.

AMERICAN HEROES

General Washington and Revolutionary War Soldiers
Revolutionary War 1775–1783

American Heroes of the Revolutionary war ready for battle.

The Warriors of the World included Revolutionary War figures.

End Zone Eddie in mustard (1960s).

Smokey Sam in flat green (1964).

Tinkerbell wasn't the only Disney character to cast her spell; also pictured are Peter Pan and Dopey.

Stony "Stonewall" Smith the Battling Soldier with equipment.

Josie West Movable Cowgirl from the Johnny West Series.

Viking Horse and Odin the Viking Chieftain.

Best of the West figures Johnny West, Jane West, and Sam Cobra.

The Fighting Eagle figure was also packaged singly.

Fort Apache Fighters Zeb Zachary & Captain Maddox are paired with Geronimo & Fighting Eagle in this set.

Daniel Boone Wilderness Scout with full woodsman's gear.

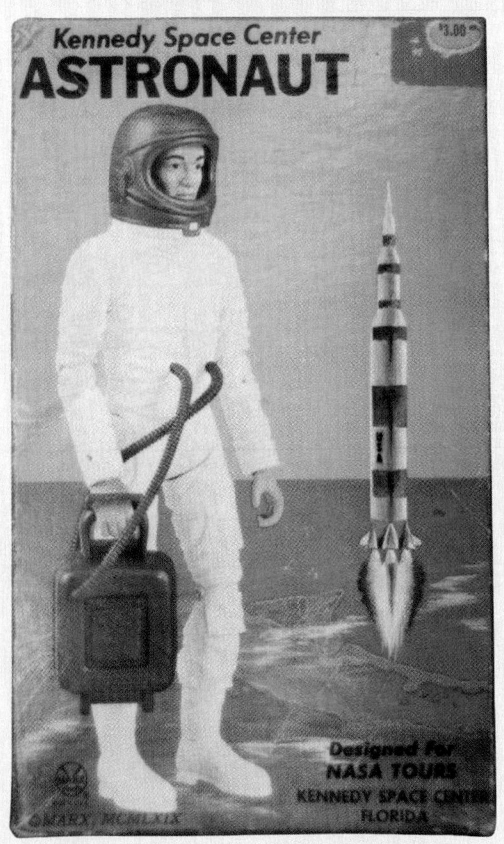

This Kennedy Space Center astronaut is ready for blastoff.

Fort Appache Fighters Captain Maddox and Best of the West figure Geronimo.

ITEM DESCRIPTION	ITEM NO.(S)	YEARS	PRICE VALUE GUIDE
DOLL HOUSE PATIO FURNITURE SET	0360	1949	12.00-15.00
DOLL HOUSE PLAYGROUND EQUIPMENT SET	0370	1954	12.00-15.00
DOLL HOUSE ROCKING CHAIR	4113	1956	5.00-6.00
DOLL HOUSE SINGLE BED	4112	1956	5.00-6.00
DOLL HOUSE VANITY W/BENCH	4114	1956	5.00-6.00
DOLL HOUSE W/BREEZEWAY & AWNINGS	4027	1952	50.00-100.00
DOLL HOUSE W/BREEZEWAY & FURNITURE	4025-6	1952	50.00-75.00
DOLL HOUSE W/BREEZEWAY & FURNITURE	4089-90	1950	50.00-100.00
DOLL HOUSE W/CARPORT & PLAYGROUND	4071-2	1953	50.00-100.00
DOLL HOUSE W/FURNITURE	4079-80	1949/70-71	50.00-75.00
DOLL HOUSE W/FURNITURE & AWNINGS	4083-4-5	1960s	50.00-75.00
DOLL HOUSE W/FURNITURE & ELECTRIC LIGHT	4056	1950s	50.00-100.00
DOLL HOUSE W/FURNITURE & SEDAN	4050	1953	50.00-100.00
DOLL HOUSE W/FURNITURE & SEDAN (WARDS)	4050MW	1953	50.00-100.00
DOLL HOUSE W/LIGHTS & DOORBELL	4028L	1955	50.00-100.00
DOLL HOUSE W/POOL & ACCESS.	4071	1966	50.00-100.00
DOLL HOUSE W/TALKING UNIT (NOT PROD.)	4088	1966	
DOLL HOUSE W/UTILITY ROOM & BREEZEWAY	4095	1956	50.00-100.00
DOLL HOUSE, "EARLY AMERICAN" HOUSE W/ACCESS.	4012	1959	55.00-75.00
DOLL HOUSE, "L" SHAPED RANCH HOUSE W/ACCESS.	3791-2	1953	45.00-75.00
DOLL HOUSE, "L" SHAPED RANCH W/FURNITURE	4769-70	1953	50.00-100.00
DOLL HOUSE, "L" SHAPED RANCH W/FURNITURE	4773-4	1957	50.00-100.00
DOLL HOUSE, "L" SHAPED RANCH W/FURNITURE & CAR	4772	1953	50.00-100.00
DOLL HOUSE, "MARX-A-MANSION" DREAM HOUSE	6999-7000	1961	150.00-200.00
DOLL HOUSE, 2-LEVEL IMAGINATION DOLL HOUSE	2007	1971	75.00-100.00
DOLL HOUSE, ASSORTED ROOMS	4109	1955	15.00-35.00
DOLL HOUSE, ASST. doll house PEOPLE	0891	1952	15.00-25.00
DOLL HOUSE, BATHROOM FURNITURE	0340B/C	1949	15.00-20.00
DOLL HOUSE, BEDROOM FURNITURE	0330B/C	1949	15.00-20.00
DOLL HOUSE, BLONDIE DOLL HOUSE	4660	1969	
DOLL HOUSE, CARRYALL	3726	1972	
DOLL HOUSE, CARRYALL, 2 STORY, 6 ROOMS	3726	1971	45.00-75.00
DOLL HOUSE, COLONIAL	4019-20	1950	50.00-75.00
DOLL HOUSE, COLONIAL	4039-40	1956	50.00-60.00
DOLL HOUSE, COLONIAL	4051	1964-65	45.00-55.00
DOLL HOUSE, COLONIAL	4052	1952	50.00-75.00
DOLL HOUSE, COLONIAL	4054	1967	45.00-55.00
DOLL HOUSE, COLONIAL	4055	1968-69-70-71-72-73	50.00-75.00
DOLL HOUSE, COLONIAL	4071-2	1962	50.00-75.00
DOLL HOUSE, COLONIAL	4073	1962	50.00-75.00
DOLL HOUSE, COLONIAL	4076	1961	45.00-75.00
DOLL HOUSE, COLONIAL	4796	1963	50.00-75.00
DOLL HOUSE, COLONIAL (SEARS)	4038	1958	50.00-60.00
DOLL HOUSE, COLONIAL (SEARS)	4080	1965	50.00-75.00
DOLL HOUSE, COLONIAL (SEARS)	4094	1963	50.00-75.00
DOLL HOUSE, COLONIAL (SPEC.FOR MUTUAL)	4091	1963	50.00-75.00
DOLL HOUSE, COLONIAL (WARDS)	4053MW	1968	45.00-55.00
DOLL HOUSE, COLONIAL MANSION	6997-8	1962	150.00-200.00
DOLL HOUSE, COLONIAL MANSION	7005-6	1962	125.00-150.00
DOLL HOUSE, COLONIAL METAL W/AWNINGS & FURN.	4021-2 & D	1951/68-69-70/72-73	45.00-75.00
DOLL HOUSE, COLONIAL TYPE TWO-STORY HOUSE	3799-3800	1953	45.00-75.00
DOLL HOUSE, COLONIAL W/AWNINGS (SEARS)	4053	1964	50.00-75.00
DOLL HOUSE, COLONIAL W/BAY WINDOW	4064	1961	50.00-75.00
DOLL HOUSE, COLONIAL W/BAY WINDOW	4074	1961	50.00-75.00
DOLL HOUSE, COLONIAL W/BREEZEWAY	4092	1954	50.00-100.00
DOLL HOUSE, COLONIAL W/BREEZEWAY & AWNINGS	4045	1957	50.00-100.00

ITEM DESCRIPTION	ITEM NO.(S)	YEARS	PRICE VALUE GUIDE
DOLL HOUSE, COLONIAL W/BREEZEWAY & FURNITURE	4034-4	1957	50.00-100.00
DOLL HOUSE, COLONIAL W/BREEZEWAY & FURNITURE	4041-2	1956	50.00-100.00
DOLL HOUSE, COLONIAL W/BREEZEWAY & PATIO FURN.	4045 & D	1969	50.00-100.00
DOLL HOUSE, COLONIAL W/BREEZEWAY & PLAY-GROUND	4093	1954	50.00-100.00
DOLL HOUSE, COLONIAL W/BREEZEWAY & POOL	4055	1959	50.00-100.00
DOLL HOUSE, COLONIAL W/BREEZEWAY & SHELTER	4771	1962	50.00-75.00
DOLL HOUSE, COLONIAL W/CAR PORT	4069	1961	45.00-55.00
DOLL HOUSE, COLONIAL W/CARPORT	4077	1965	50.00-75.00
DOLL HOUSE, COLONIAL W/CARPORT	4079 & MO	1968-69/72-73	50.00-75.00
DOLL HOUSE, COLONIAL W/CARPORT & FURN. (WARDS)	4023	1954	50.00-100.00
DOLL HOUSE, COLONIAL W/COLUMNS (SEARS)	4076	1967	50.00-75.00
DOLL HOUSE, COLONIAL W/FAMILY ROOM	4046	1960	45.00-55.00
DOLL HOUSE, COLONIAL W/FAMILY ROOM EXTENSION	4067	1961	45.00-55.00
DOLL HOUSE, COLONIAL W/FURNITURE	4015-6	1958	45.00-55.00
DOLL HOUSE, COLONIAL W/FURNITURE	4018 & D	1957	45.00-55.00
DOLL HOUSE, COLONIAL W/FURNITURE	4036	1956	50.00-100.00
DOLL HOUSE, COLONIAL W/FURNITURE	4060	1959	50.00-75.00
DOLL HOUSE, COLONIAL W/FURNITURE	4097	1957	50.00-100.00
DOLL HOUSE, COLONIAL W/FURNITURE & PICTURE WINDOW	4054	1957	50.00-100.00
DOLL HOUSE, COLONIAL W/FURNITURE (SEARS)	4023	1957	50.00-100.00
DOLL HOUSE, COLONIAL W/PLASTIC AWNINGS (WARDS)	4051MO	1963	50.00-75.00
DOLL HOUSE, COLONIAL W/POOL	4056	1958	50.00-100.00
DOLL HOUSE, COLONIAL W/POOL	4057	1968	50.00-75.00
DOLL HOUSE, COLONIAL W/TWIN DORMERS	4053	1958	50.00-75.00
DOLL HOUSE, COLONIAL W/UTILITY ROOM & BREEZEWAY	4062	1960s	50.00-75.00
DOLL HOUSE, COLONIAL W/WING & ROOF EXTENSION	4090	1969-70-71	75.00-100.00
DOLL HOUSE, COLONIAL, 2 STORY	4061	1971	45.00-75.00
DOLL HOUSE, COLONIAL, W/FURN. (FOR SUPER MARKETS)	4078	1961	50.00-75.00
DOLL HOUSE, CONTEMPORARY "LIFT OFF ROOF"	5018	1968	75.00-125.00
DOLL HOUSE, CONTEMPORARY "LIFT OFF ROOF"	5025	1965/69	75.00-125.00
DOLL HOUSE, CONTEMPORARY W/LIFT OFF ROOF	5025	1970	75.00-100.00
DOLL HOUSE, CORR. CARRY CASE DOLL HOUSE	4650	1968-69-70-71-72	50.00-75.00
DOLL HOUSE, COUNTRY SPLIT LEVEL	6990	1963	75.00-100.00
DOLL HOUSE, DINING ROOM FURNITURE	0310B/C	1949	15.00-20.00
DOLL HOUSE, DISNEY	4006	1972-73	45.00-75.00
DOLL HOUSE, DISNEY W/FURNITURE & FIGURES	4024	1957	75.00-100.00
DOLL HOUSE, DOLL COTTAGE W/FURNITURE	3941-2	1950s	50.00-75.00
DOLL HOUSE, doll house FAMILY FIGURES ASST.	0890	1954	15.00-25.00
DOLL HOUSE, doll house FAMILY FIGURES ASST.	0893-94	1951	15.00-25.00
DOLL HOUSE, DOUBLE WING	4775-6	1959	50.00-100.00
DOLL HOUSE, EXTRA LARGE COMPLETE	5054-6	1950	75.00-125.00
DOLL HOUSE, EXTRA LARGE COMPLETE (WARDS)	5053	1950	75.00-125.00
DOLL HOUSE, FANTASY	4002	1971-72-73	35.00-50.00
DOLL HOUSE, HAPPI-TIME W/LIGHTS & DOORBELL	4028	1955	50.00-100.00
DOLL HOUSE, IMAGINATION DOLL HOUSE	2010	1969	100-00-150.00
DOLL HOUSE, KITCHEN FURNITURE	0320B/C	1949	15.00-20.00
DOLL HOUSE, LARGE	5058-9-60	1950	100.00-125.00
DOLL HOUSE, LARGE (NO FURNITURE)	5039-40	1950	75.00-100.00
DOLL HOUSE, LARGE ACCESSORY SET	5034	1950s	25.00-35.00
DOLL HOUSE, LARGE BATHROOM FURNITURE	0840	1954	15.00-20.00
DOLL HOUSE, LARGE BEDROOM FURNITURE	0830	1954	15.00-20.00

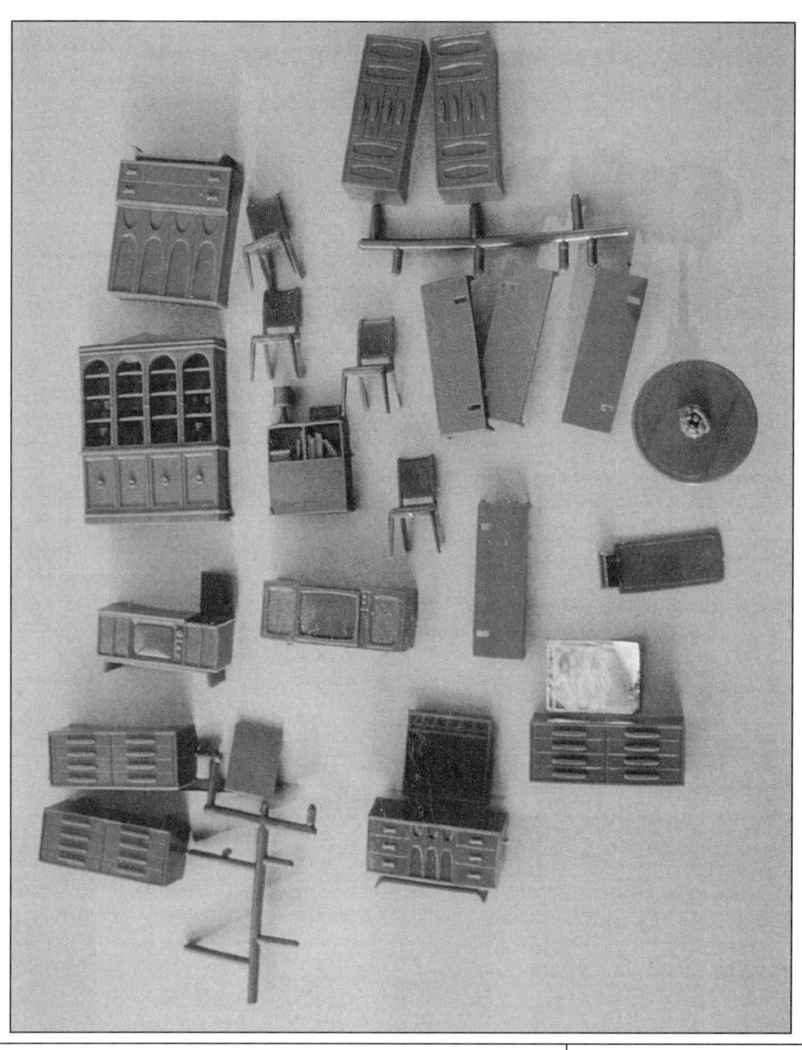

Assorted brown-colored furniture.

ITEM DESCRIPTION	ITEM NO.(S)	YEARS	PRICE VALUE GUIDE
DOLL HOUSE, LARGE COLONIAL	5086	1958	100.00-125.00
DOLL HOUSE, LARGE COLONIAL MANSION	6991-2	1963	125.00-150.00
DOLL HOUSE, LARGE COLONIAL MANSION W/FURNITURE	6994	1963	125.00-150.00
DOLL HOUSE, LARGE COLONIAL W/AWNINGS & ACCESS.	6085	1955	75.00-125.00
DOLL HOUSE, LARGE COLONIAL W/FURNITURE	5083-4	1957	100.00-125.00
DOLL HOUSE, LARGE COLONIAL W/FURNITURE	6083-R	1955	75.00-125.00
DOLL HOUSE, LARGE COLONIAL W/FURNITURE	6089-90	1957	75.00-125.00
DOLL HOUSE, LARGE DINING ROOM FURNITURE	0810	1951	15.00-20.00
DOLL HOUSE, LARGE DOUBLE WING	4798	1963	75.00-100.00
DOLL HOUSE, LARGE DREAM	6996	1961	150.00-175.00
DOLL HOUSE, LARGE KITCHEN FURNITURE	0820	1954	75.00-125.00
DOLL HOUSE, LARGE LIVING ROOM FURNITURE	0800	1950	15.00-20.00
DOLL HOUSE, LARGE NURSERY FURNITURE	0850	1954	15.00-20.00
DOLL HOUSE, LARGE PATIO FURNITURE	0860	1954	15.00-20.00
DOLL HOUSE, LARGE W/FURNITURE	5049-50	1950	10.00-15.00
DOLL HOUSE, LARGE W/FURNITURE	5070	1954	75.00-100.00
DOLL HOUSE, LIVING ROOM FURNITURE	0300B/C	1949	100.00-125.00
DOLL HOUSE, LONG VIEW	4065 & MO	1972	15.00-20.00
DOLL HOUSE, NEW COLON. MANSION W/VOICE (NOT.PROD)	6995	1962	50.00-75.00
DOLL HOUSE, NURSERY FURNITURE	0350B/C	1949	N/A

ITEM DESCRIPTION	ITEM NO.(S)	YEARS	PRICE VALUE GUIDE
DOLL HOUSE, PRE-FAB "L" SHAPED RANCH	3789-90	1954	15.00-20.00
DOLL HOUSE, RANCH	4739-40	1954	45.00-75.00
DOLL HOUSE, RANCH	4759-60	1953	50.00-75.00
DOLL HOUSE, RANCH STYLE W/FURNITURE	4737-8 & D	1957/68-69-70-71-72-73	50.00-100.00
DOLL HOUSE, RANCH W/FURNITURE	4742	1954	45.00-75.00
DOLL HOUSE, RANCH W/PLAYGROUND EQUIPMENT	4739/0275	1954	50.00-100.00
DOLL HOUSE, SEARS	4017	1964	50.00-100.00
DOLL HOUSE, SEARS	4058	1966	45.00-55.00
DOLL HOUSE, SEARS	4872	1964	50.00-75.00
DOLL HOUSE, SIX ROOMS ASST FURNITURE	0819	1956	50.00-75.00
DOLL HOUSE, SO. COLONIAL (SEARS)	4048	1959	25.00-30.00
DOLL HOUSE, SO. COLONIAL MANSION	4057-8	1959	50.00-100.00
DOLL HOUSE, SPLIT LEVEL	4861-2	1958/68-69-70-71-72-73	50.00-100.00
DOLL HOUSE, SPLIT LEVEL	4868	1961	75.00-100.00
DOLL HOUSE, SPLIT LEVEL W/FURNISHINGS & POOL	4865-6	1960/65	75.00-100.00
DOLL HOUSE, SPLIT LEVEL W/POOL	4863-4	1958	75.00-100.00
DOLL HOUSE, TWO CAR GARAGE	4815-6	1954	75.00-100.00
DOLL HOUSE, ULTRA CONTEMPORARY DOLL HOUSE	2000&MO	1968-69	75.00-100.00
DOLL HOUSE, UTILITY ROOM ACCESSORIES	0315	1949	100.00-150.00
DOLL HOUSE, UTILITY ROOM FURNITURE	0815	1950s	10.00-15.00
DOLL HOUSE, WARDS	6976 & MO	1969	10.00-15.00
DOLL HOUSE, WARD'S	4059	1969	50.00-75.00
DOLL HOUSE< LARGE ESTATE, 2 STORY, 7 ROOMS	6981	1950s/1960s	50.00-75.00
DOLLY ROOMETTE, FURN. PLAYHOUSE BEDROOM	4066	1957	50.00-75.00
DOUBLE FACE, 2 -IN- 1 TARGET GAME	G-44-45	*	
DOUBLE RUNNER ICE SKATES	702-3	*	N/A
DR. KILDARE PLAYSET (NOT PROD)	F4681-2	1960s	
DRAWING SET, "DESIGN ALL"	6350	1968	
DUNE BUGGY, ALL AMERICAN	4476	1972	20.00-45.00
DUSTY SLADE COWBOY (BAD GUY)	1702B	1967	
E-Z WEAVER (LITHO. BOX)	4189	1965	
E-Z WEAVER LOOM	4190 & MO	1963	
EARTH GRADER	247	*	
EASTER BASKET	219	*	
ELEC. CONST. TRAIN W/CLAM BUCKET	2727	*	
ELECTRO SHOT	G-272	1967	
ELEPHANT	59	1957	5.00-10.00
ENCHANTED VILLAGE	3249-50	1952	
EQUIPMENT SET	5916MO	1971	
ERIC & HORSE	5432	1970	25.00-45.00
EXPLODING MACHINE GUN NEST	2737-8	1961	
F-86 SABRE JET FIGHTER PLANE	M-101-2	1953	
F-90 PENETRATION JET FIGHTER KIT	M-105-6	1953	
FACTORY PRE-FAB	3810	1952	
FACTORY SET W/ACCESS. PRE-FAB	3811-12	1952	
FAMOUS LEADERS OF U.S. ARMED FORCES	0950	1954	5.00-15.00 each
FANTASY FUN FARM W/COW	3727	1972-73	25.00-50.00
FARM ACCESSORY SET	0912	1951	10.00-15.00
FARM ACCESSORY SET (3 PIECES)	248	*	3.00-5.00 each
FARM ACCESSORY SET (4 PIECES)	249	*	3.00-5.00 each
FARM ANIMAL SET	3190MO	1952	1.00-3.00 each
FARM ANIMAL SET (47 PIECES)	54/7	1957	1.00-3.00 each
FARM ANIMALS	55/7	1956	1.00-3.00 each
FARM ANIMALS (53 PIECES)	54/107	1958	1.00-3.00 each
FARM SET	3923-4	1953	35.00-50.00

No. 3727 FANTASY FUN FARM
The all steel fully lithographed fun barn measures 11¾" l, 9¼" w and 10⅝" h. The rolled-edge steel building includes a plastic carry-all handle. Features a walking cow, a walking ramp, equipment and family. Ages 3 to 6.
PACKED: 3, Wgt. 21½ lbs. (Cube 3.00)
F.O.B. Glen Dale, W. Va.

No. 3931 FARM SET
An economy yet complete farm set featuring a 20" all steel barn. Has 14 farm animals, 5 sections of fence, 4 rows of crops and a plastic tractor with 7 attachments. Additional accessories include indoor freight traverse rod in the barn, farm tools, and feed boxes. Ages 4 to 7.
PACKED: 6, Wgt. 30 lbs. (Cube 4.06)
F.O.B. Glen Dale, W. Va.

No. 4756 U.S.-GERMAN ARMY BATTLEGROUND SET
Playset includes an assortment of German figures in characteristic poses plus new German field pieces, rolling tank, jeep and half-track, pontoon bridge, Howitzer, fences, wire entanglements and all scale size equipment needed for 2 opposing platoons. Ages 4 to 10.
PACKED: 6, Wgt. 28 lbs. (Cube 6.36)
F.O.B. Glen Dale, W. Va.

No. 3814 STAGECOACH SET WITH COWBOYS AND INDIANS
As the 26" long Stagecoach rig rolls along, it is attacked by 6 Indians, each measuring 6" tall. Defending the Stage are 6 Cowboys of like size. Stagecoach proper is of high impact plastic, measures 7½" x 11". Complete with 4 horses, reins and 2 drivers. Ages 4 to 10.
PACKED: 3, Wgt. 16 lbs. (Cube 3.25)
F.O.B. Glen Dale, W. Va.

17

ıge from the *Marx Toys 1973 Promotional Catalog.*

ITEM DESCRIPTION	ITEM NO.(S)	YEARS	PRICE VALUE GUIDE
'ARM SET	3931 & D	1965/68-69-70-71-72-73	35.00-50.00
'ARM SET	3931-2	1951	35.00-50.00
'ARM SET (SEARS)	3932	1967	35.00-50.00
'ARM SET (SEARS) VINYL CASE	4631 & MO	1967	35.00-50.00
ARM SET, ALDEN'S	3959	1961	35.00-50.00
ARM SET, DELUXE IRRIGATED	3975	1962	50.00-75.00
ARM SET, HAPPI-TIME	3940	1953	35.00-50.00
ARM SET, HAPPI-TIME	3951	1959	35.00-50.00
ARM SET, HAPPI-TIME	3954	1960	35.00-50.00
ARM SET, HAPPI-TIME	3970	1961	35.00-50.00
ARM SET, HAPPI-TIME	3972	1961	35.00-50.00
ARM SET, HAPPI-TIME W/CHICKEN COOP	3943	1957	45.00-75.00
ARM SET, HAPPI-TIME W/NEW CHICKEN HOUSE	3944	1955	45.00-75.00
ARM SET, HAPPI-TIME W/TWIN SILOS	3948	1958	35.00-50.00
ARM SET, LARGE STOCK	3949	1960s	
ARM SET, LASSIE	3927-8	1957	45.00-75.00
ARM SET, LAZY DAY	3940	1958	35.00-50.00

Modern Farm Set with animals and equipment.

ITEM DESCRIPTION	ITEM NO.(S)	YEARS	PRICE VALUE GUIDE
FARM SET, LAZY DAY (WARDS)	3925	1952	35.00-50.00
FARM SET, MODERN	3737-8	1953	35.00-50.00
FARM SET, MODERN	3930	1958	35.00-50.00
FARM SET, MODERN	3933-4	1960s	35.00-50.00
FARM SET, MODERN	3935-6	1964	35.00-50.00
FARM SET, MODERN	3939	1957	35.00-50.00
FARM SET, MODERN	3941-2	1957	35.00-50.00
FARM SET, MODERN	3945-6	1960	35.00-50.00
FARM SET, MODERN (SEARS)	3943	1963	35.00-50.00
FARM SET, MODERN (SEARS)	3950	1963	35.00-50.00
FARM SET, MODERN (WARDS)	3926	1952	35.00-50.00
FARM SET, MOTORIZED MODERN	3957-8	1961	50.00-75.00
FARM SET, PENNY'S	3934	1967	35.00-50.00
FARM SET, PENNY'S	3971	1967	35.00-50.00
FARM SET, SEARS	3948	1968	35.00-50.00
FARM SET, SEARS	3952	1966	35.00-50.00
FARM SET, SEARS, BARN W/CURVED ROOF	3955	1965	35.00-50.00
FARM SET, SEARS, NEW BARN W/CURVED ROOF	3944	1965	35.00-50.00
FARM SET, WARD'S	3953 & MO	1969	35.00-50.00
FARM TRACTOR ACCESS. SET	0976	1963	
FARM TRACTOR ACCESSORIES	0249	*	
FARM TRACTOR, MINI. TAKE-APART	0353	1956	
FARM TRUCK ASST.	0977	1963	
FARM W/GARDEN	3976 & D	1972	45.00-50.00
FIGHTING EAGLE & COMANCHE SET	1885	1967	45.00-75.00
FIGHTING EAGLE INDIAN	1864	1968	25.00-35.00

Page from the *Marx Toys 1975 Promotional Catalog.*

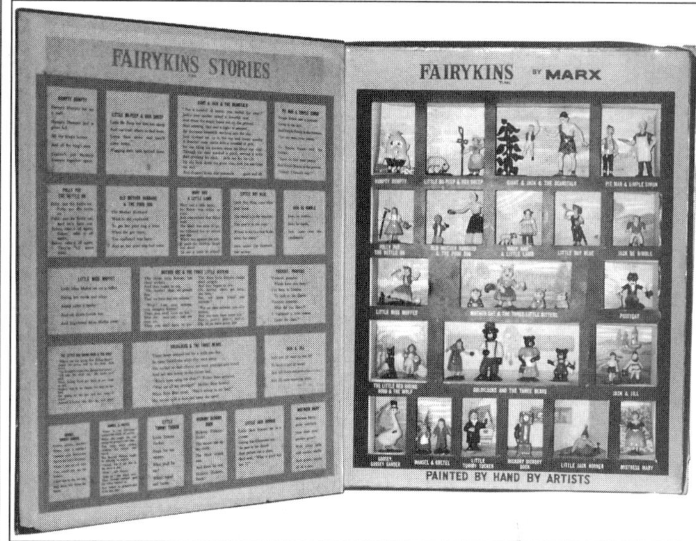

Hand-painted Fairykins in box.

ITEM DESCRIPTION	ITEM NO.(S)	YEARS	PRICE VALUE GUIDE
FIGHTING EAGLE/CHIEF CHEROKEE	2092	1970	25.00-50.00
FIGHTING GERONIMO	1863	1970-71-72-73	25.00-45.00
FIGHTING INDIAN'S TEEPEE	1867	1968	10.00-15.00
FIGURE, ADLAI STEPHENSON	0919	1955	
FIGURE, ENGLISH LIFEGUARD	0975	1954	5.00-10.00
FIGURE, MAMIE EISHENHOWER	0928	1954	
FIGURE, PRESIDENT EISENHOWER	0931	1954	
FIGURE, PRESIDENT EISENHOWER & MAMIE	0933	1954	
FIGURE, PRESIDENT EISENHOWER IN 3 POSES	0926	1954	
FIGURE, WINSTON CHURCHILL	0920	1954	
FIGURES	479	1953	
FIGURES (COWBOYS&HORSES (100 PC. SET)	1704	1960s	
FIGURES ASST.	0987	1952	1.00-3.00 each
FIGURES ASST.	3177	1950s	1.00-3.00 each
FIGURES CATALOG	1955/3	1955	8.00-10.00
FIGURES W/DEMO. ASST.	0627-8-9	1955	
FIGURES, ANIMAL & FARM	2819-20	1950s	1.00-3.00 each
FIGURES, ARMY BAND	3131-2	1950s	4.00-6.00 each
FIGURES, ARMY BAND ASST.	0996	1952	4.00-6.00 each
FIGURES, ASSORTED AMERICAN HEROES SET	3077	1955	20.00-40.00 set
FIGURES, ASSORTED ON CARDS	3156/1/2/3	1957	1.00-3.00 each
FIGURES, ASST.	0963-4	1956	1.00-3.00 each
FIGURES, ASST. BAGGED W/RACK	0570	1956	1.00-3.00 each
FIGURES, BAGGED ASST.	0700	1956	1.00-3.00 each

ITEM DESCRIPTION	ITEM NO.(S)	YEARS	PRICE VALUE GUIDE
FIGURES, BIRD SERIES	2707-8	1961	1.00-3.00 each
FIGURES, BIRDS ASST.	0726	1950s	1.00-3.00 each
FIGURES, BIRDS ASST.	0807	1950s	1.00-3.00 each
FIGURES, CALVARY FIGURES (101 PC.)	1706	1960s	1.00-2.00 each
FIGURES, CAVEMEN ASST.	0840	1950s	1.00-2.00 each
FIGURES, CHAMPION DOG SERIES	2735-6	1950s	3.00-5.00 each
FIGURES, CHAMPION SHOW DOGS, ASST.	0805	1950s	2.00-5.00 each
FIGURES, CHURCH	2829-30	1950s	1.00-2.00 each
FIGURES, CIRCUS	3134-MO	1954	5.00-10.00 each
FIGURES, CIRCUS & ANIMAL	0767	1956	3.00-5.00 each
FIGURES, CIRCUS ANIMALS, SET OF SIX	0755	1955	5.00-10.00 each
FIGURES, CIRCUS PEOPLE, SET OF SIX	0754	1955	5.00-15.00 each
FIGURES, COMBAT SOLDIERS ASST.	0994	1952	2.00-5.00 each
FIGURES, COMIC ASST.	0812	1953	
FIGURES, COMIC FIGURES	3111-12MO	1950s	5.00-10.00 each
FIGURES, COMIC SCULPTURED,1 5 PIECES	0761	1956	5.00-10.00 each
FIGURES, COMIC, 15-PIECES	0704	1957	5.00-10.00 each
FIGURES, CONFEDERATE SOLDIERS	0983	1953	2.00-5.00 each
FIGURES, COWBOYS & INDIANS	0763	1956	1.00-2.00 each
FIGURES, COWBOYS & INDIANS (102 PC.)	1709	1960s	1.00 each
FIGURES, COWBOYS, RIDING AND STANDING ASST.	0870	1950s	1.00-2.00 each
FIGURES, COWBOYS, SET OF SIX	0752	1955	2.00-3.00 each
FIGURES, DISNEY	3116-7-8MO	1954	
FIGURES, DISNEY ASST.	0827	1954	
FIGURES, DISNEY FAIRYTALE ASST.	0829	1953	5.00-20.00 each
FIGURES, DISNEY MINI. ASST.	0729	1955	
FIGURES, DISNEY SCULPTURED, 15 PIECES	0760	1956	
FIGURES, DISNEY, 15-PIECES	0703	1956	5.00-10.00 each
FIGURES, DISNEY, ASST.	1978B	1970/73	3.00-5.00 each
FIGURES, DOGS ASST.	0805	1953	
FIGURES, DOGS, SET OF SIX	0756	1955	1.00-2.00 each
FIGURES, DOLL HOUSE	2702	1961	3.00-5.00 each
FIGURES, DOLL HOUSE FAMILY	0999	1960	3.00-5.00 each
FIGURES, ENGLISH ROYALTY	0918	1954	5.00-10.00 each
FIGURES, FAMOUS COMIC, ASST.	0812	1954	5.00-20.00 each
FIGURES, FARM & ANIMALS (67 PC. SET)	1705	1960s	1.00-2.00 each
FIGURES, FARM ANIMALS ASST.	0862-4	1952	1.00-2.00 each
FIGURES, FARM WORKERS ASST.	0884	1952	2.00-3.00 each
FIGURES, FISH SERIES, ASST.	0727	1956	4.00-8.00 each
FIGURES, FLEXIBLE PLASTIC ANIMAL ASST.	0924	1950s	2.00-3.00 each
FIGURES, FLEXIBLE PLASTIC ANIMALS ASST.	0944	1955	2.00-3.00 each
FIGURES, FLEXIBLE PLASTIC SCULPTURED ASST.	0923	1950s	2.00-3.00 each
FIGURES, FOREIGN LEGION (102 PC.)	1711	1960s	4.00-6.00 each
FIGURES, FOREIGN LEGION (16 PIECES)	55/4	1956	5.00-8.00 each
FIGURES, FREIGHT STATION WORKERS ASST.	0882	1952	3.00-4.00 each
FIGURES, FRONTIERSMEN ASST.	0832	1952	3.00-5.00 each
FIGURES, HOUSE & HOME	2839-40	1950s	2.00-3.00 each
FIGURES, HOWDY DOODY	0811	1955	25.00-45.00 each
FIGURES, HUNT PEOPLE ASST.	0844	1950s	5.00-10.00 each
FIGURES, INAUGURATION	0942	1954	25.00-50.00
FIGURES, INDIANS & COWBOYS ASST.	1991	1972	1.00-2.00 each
FIGURES, INDIANS (102 PC.)	1708	1960s	1.00-2.00 each
FIGURES, INDIANS (NEW) ASST.	0835	1953	2.00-3.00 each
FIGURES, INDIANS ASST.	0834	1952	2.00-3.00 each
FIGURES, INDIANS, SET OF SIX	0753	1955	2.00-3.00 each

Snow White, from the 1950s/1960s. (M. L. Smith collection, photo by J. S. Smith)

1960s TV Tinykins cartoon characters featured Yakky Duck, Gator, Boo Boo Bear, Yogi Bear, Yogi's Girlfriend, Park Ranger, Fox, Wolf, and many others. (M.L. Smith collection, photo by J. S. Smith))

No. 1978B Disney Characters from the 1970s, featuring Mickey Mouse and Pinnochio. (M. L. Smith collection, photo by J. S. Smith)

1960s TV Tinykins. Cartoon characters included Boo Boo Bear, Quick Draw McGraw, and Mouse. (M. L. Smith collection, photo by J. S. Smith)

No. 1978B Disney Character, Mickey Mouse, from the 1970s. (M. L. Smith collection, photo by J. S. Smith)

No. 1998, six-inch German soldier from the 1960s. (Gaylord A. Whipkey collection, photo by M. L. Smith)

1960s TV Tinykins. Assorted cartoon characters. (M. L. Smith collection, photo by J. S. Smith)

No. 1984, six-inch Calvary soldier from the 1960s. (Gaylord A. Whipkey collection, photo by M. L. Smith)

Cowboy and Indian figures with horses.

Fairy Tale figures, Simple Simon, Pie Man, Mother Hubbard and her dog.

Marx Disneykins 34 hand-painted characters.

Famous Americans, Crockett, Sitting Bull, Boone, Buffalo Bill.

ITEM DESCRIPTION	ITEM NO.(S)	YEARS	PRICE VALUE GUIDE
FIGURES, KENTUCKY FOX HUNT ANIMALS	0842	1950s	5.00-10.00 each
FIGURES, KNIGHT & MERRYMEN (60 PC.)	1713	1960s	2.00-3.00 each
FIGURES, KNIGHTS 10 ASST.	0846	1953	2.00-3.00 each
FIGURES, LARGE SIZE ACTION MARINES	1993MO	1958	8.00-12.00 each
FIGURES, LARGE SIZE CALVARYMEN	1984	1964	8.00-12.00 each
FIGURES, LARGE SIZE CAVEMEN	1980	1964	8.00-12.00 each
FIGURES, LARGE SIZE COWBOYS	1983	1964	8.00-12.00 each
FIGURES, LARGE SIZE FRONTIERSMEN	1986	1964	8.00-12.00 each
FIGURES, LARGE SIZE GERMAN SOLDIERS	1998	1964	8.00-12.00 each
FIGURES, LARGE SIZE INDIANS	1982	1964	8.00-12.00 each
FIGURES, LARGE SIZE JAPANESE	1996	1964	8.00-12.00 each
FIGURES, LARGE SIZE KNIGHTS	1985	1964	8.00-12.00 each
FIGURES, LARGE SIZE MARINES	1994	1964	8.00-12.00 each
FIGURES, LARGE SIZE RUSSIANS	1992	1964	8.00-12.00 each
FIGURES, LARGE SIZE VIKINGS	1981	1964	8.00-12.00 each
FIGURES, MARCHING AMERICAN SOLDIERS	0981	1953	2.00-3.00 each
FIGURES, MARINES (6 PC.)	1994B	1973	5.00-10.00 each
FIGURES, MARVEL COMIC	1997	1970	
FIGURES, MEDICAL SOLDIERS ASST.	0992	1952	2.00-5.00 each
FIGURES, MONKEYS ASST.	0856	1950s	1.00-3.00 each
FIGURES, PARADE & COMBAT SOLDIERS	0980	1951	1.00-3.00 each
FIGURES, PARADE & COMBAT SOLDIERS	3114-MO	1954	1.00-3.00 each
FIGURES, PEOPLE ASST.	0895	1950	2.00-3.00 each
FIGURES, PEOPLE, SITTING & STANDING	0892	1950s	2.00-3.00 each
FIGURES, PETER PAN	0824	1953	
FIGURES, PETER PAN, PAINTED	0839	1950s	
FIGURES, PETER PAN, W/DEMO.	0822	1953	
FIGURES, PIRATES ASST.	0828	1953	5.00-10.00 each
FIGURES, PIRATES IN BAG SET	3191	1956	3.00-5.00 each
FIGURES, POLITICAL CARICATURES	2023	1965	
FIGURES, PRESIDENT KENNEDY & JACKIE	0910	1962	10.00-20.00
FIGURES, PRESIDENT SERIES (33)	0934	1954	3.00-8.00 each
FIGURES, PRESIDENTS (33)	0939MO	1954	2.00-5.00 each
FIGURES, PRESIDENTS, MINI.	0734	1955	2.00-5.00 each
FIGURES, PRINCE VALIANT	0837	1954	5.00-25.00 each
FIGURES, RAILROAD	3182MO	1953	3.00-5.00 each
FIGURES, RAILROAD	2808	1953	1.00-3.00 each
FIGURES, RAILROAD, 10 ASST.	0782	1956	1.00-3.00 each
FIGURES, RANCH CHILDREN ASST.	0865	1950s	2.00-3.00 each
FIGURES, RELIGIOUS CHRIST & APOSTLES	0915-6	1955	5.00-10.00 each
FIGURES, RELIGIOUS STATUETTES SET	3016	1955	5.00-10.00 each
FIGURES, REVOLUTIONARY SOLDIERS	0984	1953	5.00-8.00 each
FIGURES, RIN TIN TIN CALVARY SET, 26 PIECES	0709	1957	
FIGURES, RIN TIN TIN SET, 22 PIECES	5160	1960	
FIGURES, ROBIN HOOD	0852	1950s	5.00-25.00 each
FIGURES, ROBIN HOOD SERIES, 22 PIECES	0713	1957	
FIGURES, RODEO ANIMALS ASST.	0874	1955	2.00-5.00 each
FIGURES, RODEO COWBOYS ASST.	0868	1954	2.00-5.00 each
FIGURES, ROMAN SOLIDERS	0841	1957	3.00-8.00 each
FIGURES, ROY ROGERS , 6 ASST.	0866	1954	5.00-15.00 each
FIGURES, SAILORS ASST.	0998	1952	2.00-5.00 each
FIGURES, SAILORS, WAR OF 1812	0958	1955	2.00-5.00 each
FIGURES, SCOUT ASST.	0833	1952	
FIGURES, SCULPTURED ASST.	0943	1954	

ITEM DESCRIPTION	ITEM NO.(S)	YEARS	PRICE VALUE GUIDE
FIGURES, SCULPTURED FIGURE SETS, ASST.	0720-1-2-3-4	1957	
FIGURES, SERVICE STATION & CAR SET	0898-9	1951	
FIGURES, SERVICE STATION ATTENDANTS	0896	1952	3.00-5.00 each
FIGURES, SOLDIERS BAGGED	0764	1956	
FIGURES, SOLDIERS, MEXICAN WAR	0969	1955	2.00-5.00 each
FIGURES, SOLDIERS, SET OF SIX	0751	1955	
FIGURES, SOLDIERS, SPANISH AMERICAN WAR	0970	1954	2.00-5.00 each
FIGURES, SOLDIERS, WAR OF 1812	0962	1955	2.00-5.00 each
FIGURES, SOLDIERS, WAR OF 1812	0968	1950s	
FIGURES, SPACE	0748MO	1950s	3.00-8.00 each
FIGURES, SPACE	0854	1950s	3.00-8.00 each
FIGURES, SPORT ASST.	0900	1953	3.00-10.00 each
FIGURES, SPORT, BAGGED	0766	1956	3.00-10.00 each
FIGURES, STAR U.S. GENERALS (SET OF 5)	3050	1954	5.00-15.00 each
FIGURES, TEX FRONTIER SET, 34 PIECES	0710	1957	
FIGURES, TEXAN FRONTIER (104 PC.)	1710	1960s	2.00-3.00 each
FIGURES, TRAINING SOLDIERS ASST.	0990	1952	2.00-5.00 each
FIGURES, UNION SOLDIERS	0982	1953	2.00-5.00 each
FIGURES, VIKING	0839	1950s	1.00-3.00 each
FIGURES, WEST POINT CADETS ASST.	0991	1953	3.00-5.00 each
FIGURES, WESTERN ANIMALS ASST.	0878	1952	1.00-3.00 each
FIGURES, WESTERN ANIMALS ASST.	0879	1950s	2.00-3.00 each
FIGURES, WESTERN COWBOYS ASST.	0880	1952	2.00-3.00 each
FIGURES, WESTERN HORSES	0876	1955	2.00-3.00 each
FIGURES, WESTERN TOWN (COWBOYS) ASST.	0872	1953	2.00-3.00 each
FIGURES, WILD ANIMAL SET	0765	1956	3.00-5.00 each
FIGURES, WILD ANIMALS ASST.	0858-9	1952	3.00-5.00 each
FIGURES, WILD LIFT, 31 PIECES	54/106	1958	15.00-20.00
FIGURES, WILD WEST FRONTIER	0762	1956	
FIGURES, WILDLIFE SET (34 PC.)	1714	1960s	
FIGURES, WORKMEN SET	3151-2	1950s	2.00-5.00 each
FIGURES, WWI ASST.	0989	1953	2.00-5.00 each

Marx Fairykins.

Football player sports figures.

ITEM DESCRIPTION	ITEM NO.(S)	YEARS	PRICE VALUE GUIDE
FIGURES, ZOO SET	3359-60	1954	3.00-5.00 each
FIRE ENGINE, MINI. TAKE-APART	0352	1956	
FIRE FIGHTERS UNIT	5110	1965	
FIRE HOUSE	3400	1950s	50.00-100.00
FIRE HOUSE	3779-80	1953	75.00-150.00
FIRE HOUSE W/ACCESS.	3781-2	1953	75.00-150.00
FIRE HOUSE W/FIGURES & ACCESS.	4819-20	1954	
FIRE PATROL	9000	*	
FIRE TRUCK SET	3242	1960	
FIXALL AIRPLANE	2579-80	*	
FIXALL ATOMIC ROADSTER	2599-2600	1954	
FIXALL CHRYSLER CONVERTIBLE	2581-2	1953	75.00-100.00
FIXALL CITIES SERVICE WRECKER	2569-70	1952	
FIXALL FARM TRACTOR	2588	1954	
FIXALL FARM TRACTOR	2589-90	1953	75.00-100.00
FIXALL FARM TRACTOR W/MOTOR	2609-10	1955	
FIXALL HARD TOP PONTIAC SEDAN	2137-8	1960s	
FIXALL HOT ROD	2597-8	1954	
FIXALL JEEP	2573-4	1954	
FIXALL JEEP W/LIGHTS & HORN	2595-6	1954	
FIXALL LOCOMOTIVE	2585-6	1954	
FIXALL MERCURY STATION WAGON	2591-2	1954	
FIXALL MOTORCYCLE W/LIGHT	2583-4	1953	
FIXALL PIRATE SHIP	2567-8	*	
FIXALL PONTIAC & WRECKER	2577	1953	
FIXALL SERVICE WRECKER	2593-4	1954	
FIXALL SERVICE WRECKER W/TRUCK	2593/1426	1954	
FIXALL SPORTS CAR (JAQUAR)	2571-2	1953	75.00-100.00
FIXALL STAGECOACH	2565-6	*	
FIXALL T.V. TRUCK	2531-2	1954	
FIXALL TAXI	2141-2	1953	
FIXALL WRECKER	2598	1958	
FIXALL WRECKER & HOT ROD	2578	1953	
FIXALL WRECKER W/FIXALL CONVERTIBLE	2599	1955	
FLAME & CORRAL FENCE SET	2083	1966	20.00-30.00
FLAME (BROWN W/BLACK TRIM)	2081B	1966	15.00-25.00
FLAME (PALOMINO W/WHITE TRIM)	2081A	1966	15.00-25.00
FLAME, THE PRANCING HORSE	2081	1966/68	25.00-40.00
FLASH GORDON SPACE PHONE	273-4	1952	
FLAT COMBAT ASST. & PARADE SOLDIERS	0780	1951	
FLATBED TRAILER W/BULLDOZER	0648-9	1951	
FLATIRON	87-88	1950s	
FLYING DIP ROLLER COASTER	5290	1971	
FLYING SAUCER SET	2711-12	1959	
FOOT LOCKER	2042&MO	1965	
FOOT LOCKER (NO ACCESSORIES)	2041	1966	
FORT APACHE-JOHNNY WEST DEMO (JAY SHEA)	2049/D	1968-69	
FORT APACHE FIGHTER DEMONSTRATOR	1869/D	1967	
FORT APACHE FIGHTERS & JOHNNY WEST DEMONSTRATOR	1871/D	1967	
FORT APACHE FIGURES	1877	1973	
FORT APACHE FORT	1875	1967	
FORT APACHE FORT	1875MO	1967	
FORT APACHE FORT	1875SMO	1967	
FORT APACHE STOCKADE	3606-7	1951	

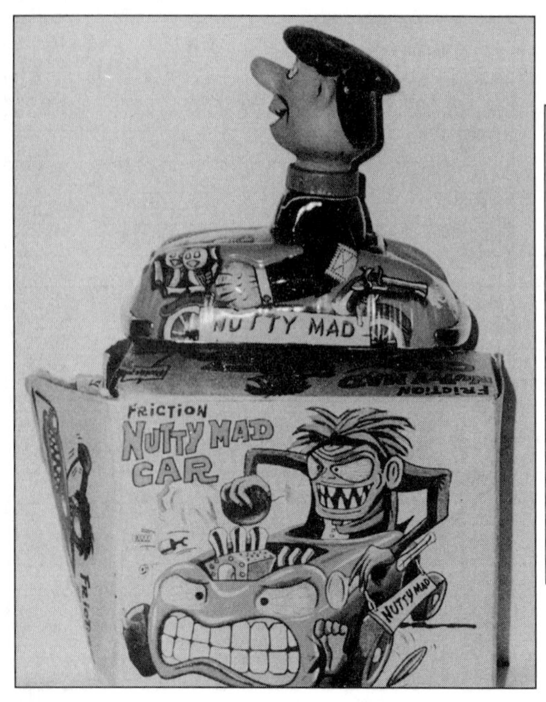

Marx Nutty Mad friction car with vinyl driver.

Official Gunsmoke Dodge City.

ITEM DESCRIPTION	ITEM NO.(S)	YEARS	PRICE VALUE GUIDE
FORT APACHE STOCKADE	3609-10	1951	50.00-100.00
FORT APACHE STOCKADE	3647	1957	150.00-175.00
FORT APACHE STOCKADE	3649	1958	
FORT APACHE STOCKADE	3660	1957	85.00-125.00
FORT APACHE STOCKADE (SEARS)	3614	1954	
FORT APACHE STOCKADE W/FAMOUS AMERICANS	3615-6	1955	75.00-100.00
FORT APACHE STOCKADE W/SHELL SHOOTING CANNON	3612	1953	50.00-100.00
FORT APACHE WAGON SET	1394	1965	
FORT DEARBORN	3688MO	1972	
FORT DEARBORN STOCKADE	3504	1953	
FORT DEARBORN STOCKADE	3509-10	1952	150.00-200.00
FORT DEARBORN STOCKADE W/SHELL SHOOTING CANNON	3514	1953	75.00-125.00
FORT W/30 SOLDIERS	2114	1960s	
FORT W/PAINTED SOLDIERS	2111	1960s	
FOUR ASST. PLANE KITS	M-116-7	1953	
FREIGHT DEPOT SET	835	*	
FREIGHT STATION	5414-16	1951	45.00-75.00
FREIGHT STATION	5459-60	1950s	50.00-75.00
FREIGHT TERMINAL	5425-6	1956	45.00-75.00
FREIGHT TRUCK RAIL TERMINAL	5424	1953	45.00-75.00
FREIGHT TRUCKING TERMINAL	5420	1950	45.00-75.00
FRICTION BOATS ASST.	1124	1950s	10.00-20.00
FRICTION DISNEY TOYS ASST.	13-14-15-16	1954	15.00-25.00
FRICTION NAVY PLANES ASST.	1123	1950s	10.00-20.00
FRICTION OLD TIME CARS ASST.	1122	1950s	15.00-25.00
FRICTION SPORTS CARS ASST.	1121	1950s	10.00-20.00
FRICTION VEHICLES, "POCKETOY"	1131-2	1954	10.00-20.00
FRICTION VEHICLES, SILVERED	1147	1950s	10.00-20.00
FRONT WHEEL ASSEMBLY	5070W	1971	
FRONTIERSMEN & INDIAN SET	3171-2	1952	
FRYING PAN	306	*	

ITEM DESCRIPTION	ITEM NO.(S)	YEARS	PRICE VALUE GUIDE
FURY WHEEL	5323	1972	
FURY WHEEL & LAUNCHER	5332	1973	
FURY WHEEL ASST.	5324	1972	
G.I. WEAPONS SET (BLUE CHIP STAMPS)	422	1968	
GALLANT MEN COMBAT SOLDIERS W/TANK	2733-4	1963	
GARAGE, HONEYMOON	894-5	1950s	
GARAGE, MINIATURE	270	1950s	25.00-50.00
GARAGE, TWO-CAR W/CARS	3805-6	1954	50.00-75.00
GARDEN SET (3 PIECES)	476-7	1958	10.00-15.00
GARDEN SET (4 PIECES)	376-7	1949	10.00-15.00
GARDEN SET, LARGE 3-PIECE	290	1958	
GARDEN SET, MEDIUM 3-PIECE	291	1958	
GEN. CUSTER W/CAVALRY SOLDIERS	3072	1955	
GEN. EISENHOWER W/ WW II SOLDIERS	3067	1955	
GEN. GRANT W/CIVIL WAR SOLDIERS	3063	1955	
GEN. LEE W/CONFEDERATE SOLDIERS	3064	1955	
GEN. MACARTHUR W/AM. SOLDIERS OF KOREAN WAR	3071	1955	
GEN. PATTON W/WW II COMBAT SOLDIERS	3068	1955	
GEN. PERSHING W/ WW I SOLDIERS	3066	1955	
GEN. VANDEGRIFT W/WW II MARINES	3070	1955	
GEN. WASHINGTON W/REV. SOLDIERS	3060	1955	
GEN. Z. TAYLOR W/MEXICAN WAR SOLDIERS	3062	1955	
GENERAL CUSTER	1866	1970-71-72-73	25.00-45.00
GENERAL STORE PRE-FAB	3829-40	1952	50.00-100.00
GENERAL STORE SET PRE-FAB	3841-2	1952	50.00-100.00
GERONIMO & PINTO THUNDERBOLT	2087MO	1972	45.00-60.00
GERONIMO, FLAME, & TEPEE SET	1884MO	1967	45.00-75.00
GERONIMO, TEPEE, AND THUNDERBOLT SET	1873	1967	50.00-75.00
GIRAFFE	58/2	1957	5.00-10.00
GIRL FROM U.N.C.L.E.	2097	1966	15.00-25.00
GIRL,PONY,DOG, & FENCE SET (CARRY CASE)	1068	1967	
GO-GO CAR	4820	1968-69	
GO-GO CYCLE	4816	1973	
GO-GO 'DE-BURRO	5004	1968	
GO-GO KART	3100 & MO	1972	
GO-GO SCOOTER	4816	1967-68	
GOLD KNIGHT & HORSE	5396MO	1970	25.00-50.00
GORILLA	58/1	1957	5.00-10.00
GRANDCHILD'S CLOCK	5330	1967-68-69/72	
GRANT FIGURE DEMO (J.WEST; FT.APACHE;KNIGHTS)	556D/1&557D	1968	
GRUNTSIE THE LOVEABLE PIG	72B	1972-73	
GUIDED MISSILE LAUNCHER SET W/FIGS.	2713-14	1959	
GUIDED MISSILE UNIT	2743-4	1959	
GUN, 105MM HOWITZER	J702	1964	
GUN, APOLLO	2236B,B/2,W	1970/73	
GUN, APOLLO LUNAR LANDING W/SPARKS	2231	1969	
GUN, APOLLO MACHINE	2236-7	1969-70-71	
GUN, APOLLO MACHINE	2237/1	1970	
GUN, BIG BOOMER	2326	1964	
GUN, BLITZ	2316	1964	
GUN, BUBBLE (HAND CRANK)	1106	1964	
GUN, DEFENSE TOMMY	2236B	1972-73	
GUN, DESERT PATROL	241	1968	
GUN, FINGER PULL TOMMY	2252	1967-68	
GUN, HOWITZER, SHOOTING, W/SOLDIERS	2719-20	1959	
GUN, INFANTRY SCOUT CAP	258B	1964	

ITEM DESCRIPTION	ITEM NO.(S)	YEARS	PRICE VALUE GUIDE
GUN, LONG RIFLE TOMMY	2258B	1972	
GUN, PEACEMAKER	0160B	1972	
GUN, PULL BACK BURP	2220&BW	1972-73	
GUN, TOMMY	2221	1968	
GUN, TOMMY	2225&AW	1968	
GUN, TOMMY BURP GUN W/SPARKS	2232	1967/79/73	
GUN, TOMMY W/SPARKS	2231/1	1970	
GUNSMOKE WESTERN TOWN (OFFICIAL)	4268	1960	375.00-450.00
HAIR DRYER	1402	1965	
HAIR DRYER W/HASSOCK	1403	1965	
HANDYMAN TOOL BOX W/TOOLS	329-30	*	
HANGING WALL VANITY, LITTLE HOSTESS	7108	1966/68-69-70	
HAPPI-TIME DAIRY FARM SET	3974	1961	35.00-50.00
HAY RAKE	241	1950s	
HELMET	230	1950	
HIFILOPHONE	3272	1967	
HIGH LIFT LOADER W/SCOOP	1756	1964/65	
HIPPOPOTAMUS	58/3	1957	5.00-10.00
HOCKEY BAGATELLE	G-78	1967	
HOCKEY BAGATELLE	G-90	1967	
HOE, MINIATURE	374	1950s	5.00-8.00
HOOK CRANE DERRICK CAR	3550	*	
HORSE & RIDER SERIES	0775-6	1956	
HORSE & WAGON, A & P	2684	1961	
HORSE AND SADDLE SET (24 PIECES)	54/8	1957	15.00-20.00
HORSE AND SADDLE SET (27 PIECES)	54/108	1958	15.00-20.00
HORSE, BIG BRAVO W/GOLD ARMOR	5395	1970s	20.00-30.00
HORSE, BIG VALOR	5391	1970	
HORSE, BIG VALOR W/SILVER ACCESS.	5391	1971	20.00-35.00
HORSE, BRAVO W/GOLD ARMOR	5371	20.00-30.00	
HORSES W/SADDLES & BRIDLES	55/8	1956	15.00-20.00
HOT ROD, "BIG RED"	5238	1965	
HOT ROD, MIN. T.A.P.	0247-8	1953	
HOUSE, RANCH TYPE SET, PRE FAB	3871-2	1952	45.00-75.00
HOUSE, RANCH TYPE, PRE-FAB	3869-70	1952	45.00-75.00
HUTCH BUFFET AND TEA SET	7104	1967-68	
HYD. TRACTOR W/FARM ACCESS.	4562	*	
INDIAN FIGURE SET (34 PIECES)	54/3	1957	3.00-5.00 each
INDIAN FIGURE SET (69 PIECES)	54/103	1958	3.00-5.00 each
INDIAN PRINCESS	2097	1973	25.00-50.00
INDIAN RIDER & HORSE	2698	1956	3.00-5.00 each
INDIAN RIDER ON HORSE	2797-8	1957	3.00-5.00 each
INDIAN SET	55/10	1956	1.00-3.00 each
INDIAN SET	55/16	1956	1.00-3.00 each
INDIAN W/SITTING BULL	3135-MO	1955	
INDIAN WARFARE SET	4778	1957	
INDIANS IN BAG SET	3192	1956	1.00-3.00 each
INDIANS SET	3170MO	1952	1.00-3.00 each
INDIANS, 6 FIGURES	1982B	1973	2.00-5.00 each
IRONING BOARD W/STAND	285	1950s	
J. WEST COWGIRL	1067B	1970s	15.00-25.00
J. WEST DISPLAY	2050D	1973	
J. WEST GIRLS	1067 & AMO	1970	15.00-25.00
J. WEST SET	2037&MO	1971	15.00-25.00
JAMES WEST	2082	1966	15.00-35.00
JAMIE WEST	1062A	1970-71-72-73	15.00-25.00

ITEM DESCRIPTION	ITEM NO.(S)	YEARS	PRICE VALUE GUIDE
JAMIE WEST BOYS	1062 & AMO	1968/70	15.00-25.00
JAMIE WEST COWBOY	1062A	1967	15.00-25.00
JAMMIE WEST, HORSE & BUCKBOARD	4426	1972-73	35.00-50.00
JANE APOLLO ASTRONAUT	1723	1968-69	20.00-35.00
JANE WEST & FLAME SET (WARDS)	2086MO	1967/72	45.00-65.00
JANE WEST COWGIRL	2067&MO	1966/68/70-71	15.00-35.00
JANE WEST SET (JANE, FLAME, SHEPHERD & FENCE)	2093	1967	50.00-75.00
JANE WEST, THUNDERBOLT & BUCKBOARD	4426MO	1967	50.00-75.00
JANE WEST, THUNDERBOLT & COLT W/FENCE SET	2077	1967	50.00-75.00
JANICE WEST	1067A	1970-71-72-73	15.00-25.00
JANICE WEST COWGIRL	1067B	1967	15.00-25.00
JAY WEST	1062B	1967, 70-73	15.00-25.00
JEEP	1416	1952	
JEEP	2322	1951	
JEEP & HORSE TRAILER	4542	1966	
JEEP PICKUP TRUCK W/LIGHTS	1073-4	1960s	
JEEP SET, JAMES WEST	4551	1966	
JEEP W/DISNEY FIGURES	1435-6	1950	
JEEP W/ELEC. HORN	979	*	
JEEP W/ELEC. HORN & TRAILER	978/246	*	
JEEP W/HEADLIGHTS	1067-8	1950s	
JEEP W/HEADLIGHTS & TRAILER	1067/246	1952	
JEEP W/HEADLIGHTS & TRAILER	1068/246	1950	
JEEP W/HEADLIGHTS & TRAILER	1069/246	1955	
JEEP W/HORN & HEADLIGHTS	1167-8	1960s	
JEEP W/HORN & HEADLIGHTS & TRAILER	1167/246-8/246	1960s	
JEEP W/LIGHT & TRAILER	4555MO	1972	
JEEP W/RADAR TRAILER (880 IS A.F.)	879-80	1958	
JEEP W/TRAILER	1567-8	1958	
JEEP W/TRAILER	1579	1959	
JEEP W/TRAILER	868/246	*	
JEEP WRECKER TRUCK W/LIGHTS	1073-4	1960s	
JEEP, A. F. MOBILE RADIO	877	1958	
JEEP, ARMY W/LIGHT & TRAILER	4556MO	1972	
JEEP, MECH. PLASTIC	1441-2	*	
JEEP, MILITARY	4540	1966	
JEEP, MILITARY & STONY	4546	1966	
JEEP, MILITARY W/S.L. TRAILER	4544 & MO	1966	
JEEP, MINI. TAKE-APART	0351	1956	
JEEP, RAT PATROL W/2 SOLDIERS	1545	1967	
JEEPSTER, MECH. PLASTIC	2343-4	1949	
JESSE JAMES	2080	1966	20.00-35.00
JET PLANES ASST.	0797-8	1953	
JET PORT (WARDS)	4806	1962	
JET PORT AIR TERMINAL	4809-10	1960	50.00-75.00
JOG-0 MONKEY ON STICK	05-011	1930s	
JOHNNY APOLLO ASTRONAUT	1724	1968-70	25.00-50.00
JOHNNY APOLLO ASTRONAUT DISPLAY	1724D	1969-70	
JOHNNY KOLT COWBOY (GOOD GUY)	1702A	1967	15.00-35.00
JOHNNY RINGO WESTERN FRONTIER SET	4784	1960	100.00 & up
JOHNNY WEST & COMANCHE SET	2075	1967	45.00-75.00
JOHNNY WEST & MUSTANG SET	2076	1966	45.00-75.00
JOHNNY WEST & THUNDERBOLT	2065&MO	1965/72-73	45.00-75.00
JOHNNY WEST BUCKO	5520	1970	
JOHNNY WEST BUCKO	5730	1970	
JOHNNY WEST CAMPER	3094	1973	

ITEM DESCRIPTION	ITEM NO.(S)	YEARS	PRICE VALUE GUIDE
JOHNNY WEST CAMPER JEEP	4560	1973	
JOHNNY WEST COVERED WAGON	4434	1970-71-72-73	
JOHNNY WEST COWBOY	2062&MO	1965/68/70-71-72-73	25.00-50.00
JOHNNY WEST DISPLAY	558D/DR/D/1/DR1	1972	
JOHNNY WEST HORSE ASSORTMENT	1878	1973	15.00-30.00
JOHNNY WEST JEEP	4541	1966	
JOHNNY WEST JEEP SET (JEEP/HORSE TRLR & HORSE)	4543	1966	
JOHNNY WEST MINI DISPLAY DEMO.	2054D	1972-73	
JOHNNY WEST RANCH SET(JEEP,HORSE,TRLR,J.W.,HORSE)	4550	1966	
JOHNNY WEST SERIES DEMONSTRATOR	2064/D	1965	
JOHNNY WEST SPECIAL DEAL	571/D	1973	
JOHNNY WEST TERRAIN RANCH SET	4194	1967	
JOHNNY WEST, COMANCHE & BUFFALO SET	2079	1967	
JOHNNY WEST, JANE, THUNDERBOLT & FLAME SET	2095MO	1967	
JONNY TREMAIN RIDER ON HORSE	2791-2	1957	
JOSIE WEST	1067B	1970-71-72-73	15.00-25.00
JOSIE WEST COWGIRL	1067A	1967	15.00-25.00
JR. RIFLE W/CLICK	209-10	*	
JUNGLE ANIMALS	57	1957	
JUNGLE ARCADE	G-167-8	1964	5.00-10.00 each
JUNGLE SERIES	58	1957	
JUNGLE SET	3378	1957	2.00-5.00 each
JUNGLE SET	3703-4	1958	
JUNGLE SET	3713-4	1960	
JUNGLE SET	3716	1960	
JUNGLE SHOOTING RANGE	G-165	1967/69-70/73	25.00-40.00
KANGAROO	57/6	1957	
KENTUCKY FOX HUNT	3670	1952	5.00-10.00
KEYHOUSE FARM	5025HK	1973	
KIDDIE KAR	123	*	20.00-25.00
KIDDIE SPELLER SET	3744	1954	
KINDERGARTEN WAGON	3061	1972	
KITCHEN APPLIANCE SET	K-67-8	1953	
KITCHEN APPLIANCE SET (LITHO), 3 PC.	47	1964	25.00-50.00
KITCHEN APPLIANCES	0180	1950s	50.00-75.00
KITCHEN APPLIANCES	K-59	1954	
KITCHEN CABINET SET	356	1950s	5.00-800
KITCHEN SET, 3 PIECE	K-46-7	1950s	25.00-50.00
KITCHEN SET, 3 PIECE	K-87	1950s	25.00-50.00
KITCHEN UNIT	K-63-4	1953	25.00-50.00
KITCHEN UNIT (SEARS)	K-66	1950s	25.00-50.00
KITCHEN UTENSIL SET	2757-8	1960	25.00-50.00
KITCHEN UTENSILS	0182	1950s	3.00-5.00
KNIGHT & HORSE SET	5377-78	1969	3.00-5.00
KNIGHT & VIKING CASTLE	4733 & D	1972-73	
KNIGHT & VIKING COMBINATION SET	9002	1971	100.00 & up
KNIGHTS - HORSES	5361/64/66/71	1968	
KNIGHTS & HORSES	3147-8-MO	1953	
KNIGHTS & VIKING SET	4743MO	1972	2.00-3.00 each
KNIGHTS & VIKINGS CASTLE SET	4715	1965	90.00-125.00
KNIGHTS & VIKINGS SET	4735	1965	
KNIGHTS & VIKINGS SET W/MOAT & BASE	4707	1965	
KNIGHTS AND HORSES	55/15	1958	75.00-100.00
KNIGHTS HORSES TWO ASST.	0848	1953	2.00-3.00 each
KNIGHTS, 6 FIGURES	1985B	1973	2.00-4.00 each

ITEM DESCRIPTION	ITEM NO.(S)	YEARS	PRICE VALUE GUIDE
KOOKIE KOMBO	5120	1965	
KRAZY KAR	5820-21	1968-69-70-71-72-73	
KRAZY KAR JR.	5810	1969-70-71-72	
KRAZY KAR SENIOR	5830	1969	
LADDEROO	6210	1970-71	
LADY AND THE TRAMP	0817	1955	
LARGE COWBOYS	56/1	1957	
LARGE EASTER BASKET	353	*	8.00-12.00
LARGE GONDOLA (OLD)	4925	*	
LARGE INDIANS	56/2	1957	
LARGE JEEP	1577-8	1959	8.00-12.00
LARGE PAIL W/SHOVEL	0500	1950	
LARGE PREHISTORIC MONSTERS	892	1973	
LARGE SHOVEL	351	*	
LARGE SINK	K-64	1950s	
LARGE SKILL BALL GAME (SKI-SHOT)	G-79	*	25.00-50.00
LARGE SOLDIERS	56/3	1957	
LARGE STOVE W/UTENSILS	K-51-2	1950s	8.00-12.00
LARGE STUBBY BUS	541	*	25.00-50.00
LARGE STUBBY VAN	542	*	
LASSIE FARM FIGURES, 21-PIECE	0706	1957	
LAUNDRY SET	2551-2	1950s	
LAUNDRY SET, DELUXE WASH DAY	2161-2	1950s	5.00-10.00
LAUNDRY SET, WASH DAY	2151-2	1950s	5.00-10.00
LAWN MOWER	361	1958	5.00-10.00

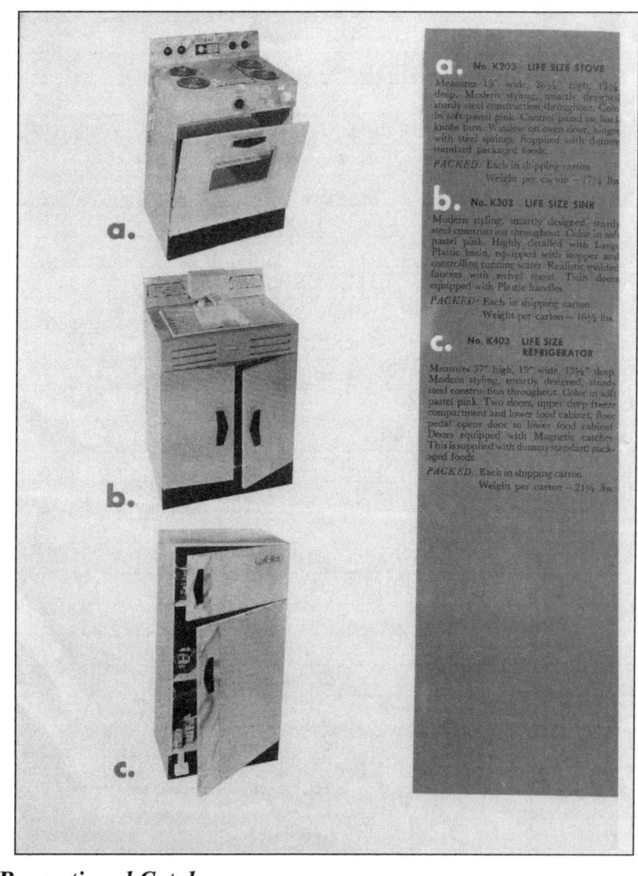

Pages from the *Marx Toys 1964 Promotional Catalog.*

ITEM DESCRIPTION	ITEM NO.(S)	YEARS	PRICE VALUE GUIDE
LAWN MOWER	371	1958	
LAWN MOWER	379-80-91	1956	
LAWN MOWER	683	1950s	
LAWN MOWER	787-8	1960s	
LAWN MOWER	79-80	1951	
LAWN MOWER W/RUBBER TIRES	279-80	1960s	
LAWN SET ON CARD	390	1958	
LEARNERS SKATES	400-1	1951	
LIFE SIZE CABINET	K-462	1971	
LIFE SIZE KITCHEN CABINET	K-449-50	1960s	25.00-50.00
LIFE SIZE KITCHEN CABINET	K-451	1960s	25.00-50.00
LIFE SIZE RANGE	K-199-200	1960	25.00-50.00
LIFE SIZE REFRIGERATOR	K-399-400	1960s	25.00-50.00
LIFE SIZE REFRIGERATOR	K-401	1960s	25.00-50.00
LIFE SIZE REFRIGERATOR	K-403-4	1960s	25.00-50.00
LIFE SIZE REFRIGERATOR	K-405	1960s	25.00-50.00
LIFE SIZE REFRIGERATOR	K-412	1970	25.00-50.00
LIFE SIZE SINK	K-299-300	1960s	25.00-50.00
LIFE SIZE SINK	K-301	1960s	25.00-50.00
LIFE SIZE SINK	K-303-4-5	1960s	25.00-50.00
LIFE SIZE SINK	K-312	1970	25.00-50.00
LIFE SIZE STOVE	K-201	1960	25.00-50.00
LIFE SIZE STOVE	K-203-205	1960s	25.00-50.00
LIFE SIZE STOVE	K-212	1970	25.00-50.00
LIFE SIZE UTILITY CABINET	K-455-6	1960s	25.00-50.00
LIFE SIZE WOOD GRAIN HUTCH CABINET	K-464	1971	25.00-50.00
LIFE SIZE WOOD GRAIN REFRIGERATOR	K-414	1971	25.00-50.00
LIFE SIZE WOOD GRAIN SINK	K-314	1971	25.00-50.00
LIFE SIZE WOOD GRAIN STOVE	K-214	1971	25.00-50.00
LIGHTED GAS PUMP	464	*	25.00-50.00
LIGHTED VANITY (SEARS)	7158 & MO	1968	
LION	57/1	1957	15.00-25.00
LITHO SKATE	190-201	1950s	5.00-10.00
LITHO STATION WAGON	632	*	
LITHO TRAIN (UNION PACIFIC)	225	1950s	
LITTLE HOMEMAKER KITCHEN & BATH	0801	1950	
LITTLE HOMEMAKER LIVING & DINING ROOM	0802	1950	15.00-20.00
LITTLE HOMEMAKER NURSERY & BEDROOM	0803	1950	15.00-20.00
LITTLE HOMEMAKER PATIO & PLAYGROUND	0804	1950	15.00-20.00
LITTLE HOSTESS BUFFET	7130	1969	15.00-20.00
LITTLE HOSTESS BUFFET W/ACCESSORIES	7140	1968	15.00-25.00
LITTLE RED SCHOOL HOUSE W/ACCESS.	3381-2	1956	
LITTLE WHEEL	J5020	1971	35.00-50.00
LITTLE WHEEL & CART	5028	1972	
LIVESTOCK, SET OF 10 PRIZE LIVESTOCK	0911MO	1963	
LIVESTOCK, SET OF PRIZE LIVESTOCK	0910MO	1959	3.00-5.00 each
LOCKER, AGENT WALL	1924MO	1972	3.00-5.00 each
LOCO	525	*	
LOCOMOTIVE	1348	1950	
LOCOMOTIVE	3970HK	1973	
LOCOMOTIVE, POLY, P011	2679-80	1959	
LONE RANGE CLICK PISTOL	35-36	1950s	
LONE RANGER FIGURES ASST.	0869	1954	
LONE RANGER OFFICIAL RANCH SET	3967-8-9	1957	
LONE RANGER RODEO	3696	1952	75.00-125.00
LONE RANGER TARGET GAME	G-61-62	1950	75.00-125.00

ITEM DESCRIPTION	ITEM NO.(S)	YEARS	PRICE VALUE GUIDE
LONE RANGER WESTERN SET FIGURES, 27-PIECE	0708	1957	25.00-50.00
LONG TOM SHELL SHOOTING CANNON	728	1963	
LONGHORN BIKE	5230	1973	
MAGNETIC CRANE DERRICK CAR	3560	*	
MAMMOTH DINASOURS ASST.	0889-90	1959	
MAMMOTH WESTERN WAGON SET	4997-8	1960	
MAN FROM U.N.C.L.E. ARCADE	G-256	1966	45.00-75.00
MARBLE GAME	G-1-2	1950	
MARBLE SKILL GAME	G-40-41	*	
MARINE BEACHHEAD LANDING SET	4731-2	1959	
MARINE BEACHHEAD LANDING SET	4734	1960	
MARINE BEACHHEAD SET	4736	1961	
MARINES ASST.	993	1955	
MARVEL THE MUSTANG	5004	1970	2.00-3.00 each
MARVEL THE MUSTANG	5006	1967-68-69-70-71-72	
MARVEL THE MUSTANG	5011	1973	
MARVEL THE MUSTANG (SEARS)	5005MO	1967	
MARXVILLE DINER	3769-70	1953	
MARXVILLE DINER W/ACCESS.	3771-2	1953	75.00-90.00
MARXWRITER W/LIGHT TOUCH	6829J	1973	75.00-125.00
MASTER BUILDER U.S. CAPITOL	4919-20	1962	25.00-35.00
MECH. BULLDOG TRACTOR & IMPLEMENT SET	4519-20	*	40.00-50.00
MECH. BULLDOG TRACTOR & IMPLEMENT SET	4560	*	
MECH. HOPPING FROG	82	*	
MECH. JALOPY	941-2	*	
MECH. LIGHTED & SILVER PONTIAC W/FRIC. MTR	2769F-70F	*	
MECH. LOCOMOTIVE TENDER	67-8	1949	
MECH. PECKING CHICKEN	83-84	*	
MECH. PLASTIC OIL TANKER	1174	1960s	
MECH. RACER	2776	1960	
MECH. RACER	887-8	*	
MECH. RACERS (SET OF 2)	2826	1961	
MECH. STATE FAIR STUNT PLANE W/PILOT	482	*	
MECH. STATION WAGON	622-3	*	
MECH. TRACTOR SET	922-4	*	
MECH. TRACTOR SET	926-8	*	
MECHANICAL CROW SHOOT ARCADE	G-146	1965	
MECHANICAL DISNEY WATCHES	6979J	1973	
MECHANICAL TRACTOR	6828J	1973	
MEDIEVAL CASTLE	5375MO	1970	
MEDIEVAL CASTLE FORTRESS SET	4709-10	1953	35.00-50.00
MEDIEVAL CASTLE SET W/MOAT	4734	1964	75.00-100.00
MEDIEVAL CASTLE SET W/MOAT & BASE	4704	1964	75.00-100/00
MEDIEVAL CASTLE, GIANT SIZE	5375	1971	75.00-100.00
MERCHANDISER GAMES OF SKILL, BAGATELLES	G-108M	1973	50.00-75.00
MICKEY MOUSE VELOCIPEDE	5270	1972	
MIKE HAZARD - I.S.A. FIGURE	2090	1966	
MILITARY ACADEMY	4713-4	1954	75.00-125.00
MILITARY ACADEMY W/SIX GENERALS	4715-6	1954	150.00-200.00
MILITARY ASSORTMENT	4602	1958	
MILITARY JEEP	4540	1973	
MILITARY JEEP W/TRAILER	888/246	*	
MILITARY SET	4187MO	1972	
MILKING COW SET	0408M0	1954	
MIN. FLATIRON	31	1950s	10.00-15.00
MIN. ROWBOAT	84-85	1950s	3.00-5.00

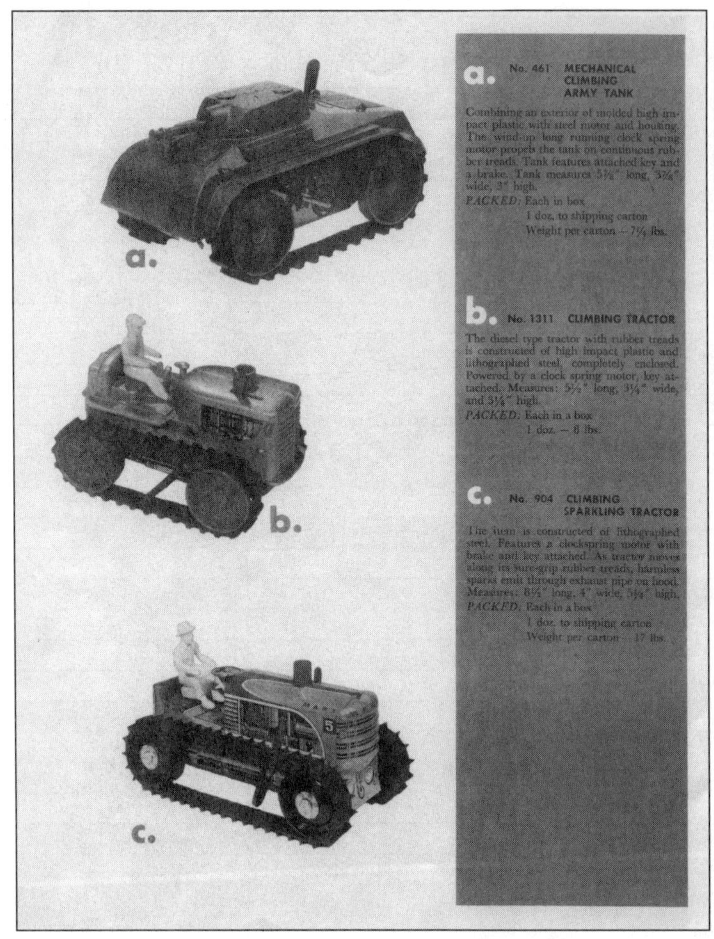

a. No. 461 MECHANICAL CLIMBING ARMY TANK

Combining an exterior of molded high impact plastic with steel motor and housing. The wind-up long running clock spring motor propels the tank on continuous rubber treads. Tank features attached key and a brake. Tank measures 5⅛" long, 3⅝" wide, 3" high.

PACKED: Each in box
1 doz. to shipping carton
Weight per carton – 7¼ lbs.

b. No. 1311 CLIMBING TRACTOR

The diesel type tractor with rubber treads is constructed of high impact plastic and lithographed steel, completely enclosed. Powered by a clock spring motor, key attached. Measures: 5½" long, 3¼" wide, and 3⅛" high.

PACKED: Each in a box
1 doz. – 8 lbs.

c. No. 904 CLIMBING SPARKLING TRACTOR

The item is constructed of lithographed steel. Features a clockspring motor with brake and key attached. As tractor moves along its sure-grip rubber treads, harmless sparks emit through exhaust pipe on hood. Measures: 8½" long, 4" wide, 5⅛" high.

PACKED: Each in a box
1 doz. to shipping carton
Weight per carton – 17 lbs.

Page from the *Marx Toys 1964 Promotional Catalog*.

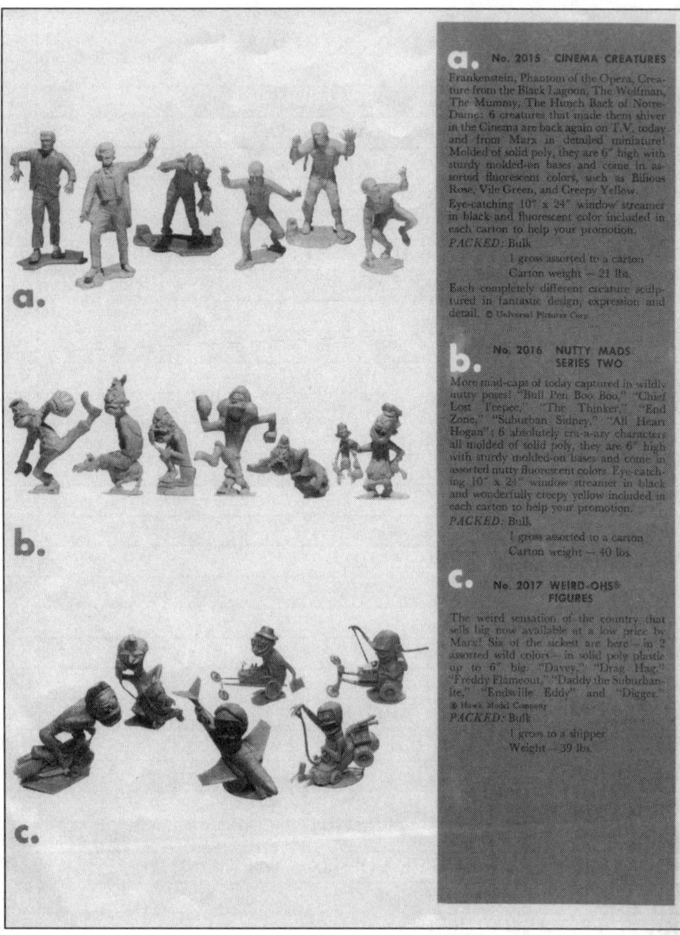

a. No. 2015 CINEMA CREATURES

Frankenstein, Phantom of the Opera, Creature from the Black Lagoon, The Wolfman, The Mummy, The Hunch Back of Notre-Dame: 6 creatures that made them shiver in the Cinema are back again on T.V. today and from Marx in detailed miniature! Molded of solid poly, they are 6" high with sturdy molded-on bases and come in assorted fluorescent colors, such as Bilious Rose, Vile Green, and Creepy Yellow.

Eye-catching 10" x 24" window streamer in black and fluorescent color included in each carton to help your promotion.

PACKED: Bulk
1 gross assorted to a carton
Carton weight – 21 lbs.

Each completely different creature sculptured in fantastic design, expression and detail. © Universal Pictures Corp.

b. No. 2016 NUTTY MADS SERIES TWO

More mad-caps of today captured in wildly nutty poses! "Bull Pen Boo Boo," "Chief Lost Teepee," "The Thinker," "End Zone," "Suburban Sidney," "All Heart Hogan": 6 absolutely cra-a-azy characters all molded of solid poly, they are 6" high with sturdy molded-on bases and come in assorted nutty fluorescent colors. Eye-catching 10" x 24" window streamer in black and wonderfully creepy yellow included in each carton to help your promotion.

PACKED: Bulk
1 gross assorted to a carton
Carton weight – 40 lbs.

c. No. 2017 WEIRD-OHS® FIGURES

The weird sensation of the country that sells big now available at a low price by Marx! Six of the sickest are here – in 2 assorted wild colors – in solid poly plastic up to 6" big: "Davey," "Drag Hag," "Freddy Flameout," "Daddy the Suburbanite," "Endsville Eddy" and "Digger." ® Hawk Model Company

PACKED: Bulk
1 gross to a shipper
Weight – 39 lbs.

Page from the *Marx Toys 1964 Promotional Catalog*.

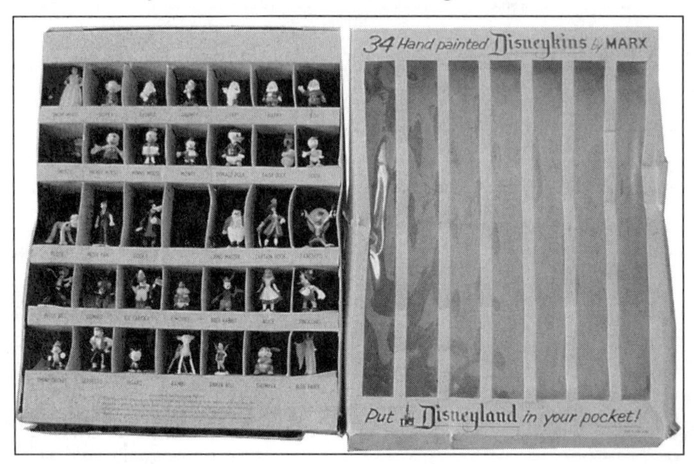

Marx Disneykins 34 hand-painted characters.

ITEM DESCRIPTION	ITEM NO.(S)	YEARS	PRICE VALUE GUIDE
MIN. SCORE BALL	G-48	*	3.00-5.00
MIN. SPIN SCORE	G-43	1964	
MINI-BIKE	3009	1973	
MINI-SCOOT SCOOTER	3063	1972-73	
MINI WHEEL	5014	1972-73	
MINI. COCA-COLA BOTTLES	0101	1950s	
MINI. COCA-COLA CASES	0100	1950s	1.00-2.00 each
MINI. FARM TRACTOR & IMPLEMENTS SET	0910	1950s	2.00-5.00 each

ITEM DESCRIPTION	ITEM NO.(S)	YEARS	PRICE VALUE GUIDE
MINI. TAKE-APART ASSORTMENT	0356	1956	
MINIATURE WAGON	319-20	1950s	
MOBILE HOWITZER CANNON W/SHELLS	76	1956	3.00-5.00
MOBILE HOWITZER W/CANNON	76	1965	
MODEL HELICOPTER KIT	M-141-2	1954	
MODEL KIT ASSORTMENT	M-244-6	1954	
MODEL KIT TRANSPORTATION SET	M-242	1954	
MOTORCYCLE	122	1950s	
MOTORCYCLE	2087	1967	
MOTORCYCLE	3043	1973	
MOTORCYCLE W/SIDE CAR	2089	1967	
MOUNTAIN GEAR	1925MO	1972	
MOVIE CAMERA (LITHO)	6-7	1950s	
MUSICAL TYPEWRITER	2872	1967	
MUSTANG "RENEGADE" HORSE	1701A	1967	25.00-35.00
MYSTERY KITTY KAT	358-9	*	15.00-30.00
MYSTERY PLUTO W/MOTOR	328-9	*	
NATIVITY STABLE	3325-6-8	1956	
NATIVITY STABLE SET	3315-16	1955	45.00-55.00
NAVY JEEP W/SEARCHLIGHT TRAILER	1077-8	1956	45.00-75.00
NAVY SHIPS & ARMY PLANES ASST.	0769	1950s	1.00-3.00 each
NEW CAR SALES & SERVICE CENTER W/LIGHTS	3466	1955	
NEW CAR SALES & SERVICE STATION (34655-SPIEGELS)	3465	1956	50.00-100.00
NEW WILD ANIMALS FIGURES SET FIGURES, 26-PIECE	0714	1957	50.00-100.00
NIKE ROCKET LAUNCHING SET	54/121	1958	1.00-3.00 each
NOAH'S ARK W/ANIMALS	2694	1955	
NORTH AMERICAN WILD ANIMALS	2761-2	1962	25.00-35.00
NORTH AMERICAN WILD LIFE SET	55/6	1956	2.00-5.00 each
NUCLEAR FIELD FUN	737-8	1963	2.00-5.00 each
NURSERY SET	2753-4	1960	
NURSERY SET	3369-70	1955	20.00-35.00
NUTTY MAD SHOOTING GALLERY	G-166	1964	25.00-50.00
NUTTY MADS	2022B	1973	
NUTTY MADS, FIRST SERIES	2014	1964	8.00-10.00 each
NUTTY MADS, SECOND SERIES	2016	1964	10.00-15.00 each
NUTTY MADS, THIRD SERIES	2021	1964	10.00-15.00 each
ODIN & HORSE	5442	1970	10.00-15.00 each
ODIN THE VIKING CHIEFTAIN	5440	1970	25.00-50.00
OLD FASHIONED LOCO. MODEL KIT	M-145-6	1954	20.00-35.00
OLD TIME FIRE WAGON KIT	M-153-4	1954	
OLD TIME STREETCAR KIT	M-155-6	1954	
PADDLE BOAT	0116	1950	
PAINT SET W/BRUSH	397	1950s	
PAINT SET W/BRUSH AND PRESIDENTS CATALOG	398	1954	
PAINT SET, BIRDS & FISH	2823-4	1950s	10.00-15.00
PAINT SET, DOG	0399-0400	1950s	
PAINT SET, LIQUID	395-6	*	
PAINT SET, PALLETE	386-5	1950s	
PAINT SET, PRESIDENTS	3046-7	1954	
PAINT SET, VINYL FIGURES	2848	1950s	
PANCHO HORSE	1061	1968	
PANCHO HORSE	1061A	1970-71	15.00-25.00
PANCHO PONY	1061 & BMO	1970	15.00-25.00
PARKING LOT	2700	1950s	15.00-25.00
PAUL REVERE RIDER ON HORSE	2791P-2P	1957	
PET SHOP SET	4209-10	1953	

ITEM DESCRIPTION	ITEM NO.(S)	YEARS	PRICE VALUE GUIDE
PETS, ASST.	0388	1950s	35.00-50.00
PICKET FENCE SET	0270	1950	3.00-5.00 each
PINTO W/CORRAL FENCE	2070MO	1970	10.00-15.00
PISTOL HOSS RANGE	0159	1966	15.00-25.00
PISTOL, CLICK	32-33	1950s/1960s	
PISTOL, CLICKER	048	1963	
PISTOL, CLICKER ASST.	367-8	1950s	
PISTOL, COLT	0160	1968/71	
PISTOL, COLT CLICK AUTO	53-4	*	
PISTOL, DANIEL BOONE DERRINGER	133	1964	
PISTOL, DANIEL BOONE FLINT	134	1964	
PISTOL, DANIEL BOONE FRONTIER	135	*	
PISTOL, DICK TRACEY CLICK	37-38	*	
PISTOL, DICK TRACY CLICK W/FIGURES	47-48	*	
PISTOL, DICK TRACY SIREN	64-5	1965	
PISTOL, LUGAR	175	1968	
PISTOL, LUNAR LANDING	242	1969	
PISTOL, LUNAR LANDING SECURITY	242/A/2	1969/72-73	
PISTOL, SHORTY MACHINE	240	1968	
PISTOL, SPARKLING POP	95	1949	
PISTOL, ZORRO DERRINGER	133Z	1966	
PISTOL, ZORRO DERRINGER	134Z	1966	
PL. MECH. LOCOMOTIVE	1367-8	*	
PLANE & TRACTOR SET	0778-9	1951	
PLANE, ARMY TRANSPORT	1219-20	1950	
PLANE, CLIPPER	F1522	1957	
PLANE, DC-6 TRANSPORT W/FIGURES	1649-50	*	
PLANE, FLYING BOX CARGO	1661-2	1954	
PLANE, JET	1231-2	1954	
PLANE, JET, ROCKET FIRING	2739-40	1961	
PLANE, MINI. T.A.P.	0251-2	1953	
PLANE, PAN AMERICAN "SUPER 7"	1519-20	*	
PLANE, PAN AMERICAN CLIPPER	1669	*	
PLANE, PAN AMERICAN CLIPPER	1678-9	*	
PLANE, PAN AMERICAN CLIPPER	1699	*	
PLANE, PAN AMERICAN CLIPPER W/RAMP	1689	*	
PLANE, PURSUIT	1400	*	
PLANE, SHELL SHOOTING	1459-660	*	
PLANE, TRANSPORT	1199-1200	1950s	
PLANE, TRANSPORT	1221-2	1950s	
PLANE, TWO-MOTOR CABIN	1499-1500	*	
PLANES & TRACTORS ASST.	0787-9	1951	
PLANES ASST.	0785-6	1951	3.00-5.00 each
PLANES, ASST. FUTURISTIC PLANES (4)	0328	1953	3.00-5.00 each
PLANES, JET, ASST.	1129-30	1953	
PLANET PATROL SPACE DROME	7040	1952	200.00-250.00
PLASTIC DEMO. COVER (LARGE)	3028/D	*	
PLASTIC DEMO. COVER (SMALL)	3027/D	*	
PLASTIC FENCE (LOG STYLE)	1136	1950s	2.00-4.00 each
PLASTIC LOCOMOTIVE W/CANDY	2767-8	2769	
PLASTIC PULL CAR ASST.	0156	1949	
PLASTIC PULL TRAIN	2766	*	
PLAY DESK, PRE-SCHOOL	3750	1955	
PLAY DESK, PRE-SCHOOL	3759-60	1953	
PLAY SET, (OFF. W.DISNEY) D.CROCKETT ALAMO (SEARS)	3544	1955	300.00-400.00
PLAY SET, (OFF. W.DISNEY) DAVY CROCKETT ALAMO	3534	1955	250.00-350.00

ITEM DESCRIPTION	ITEM NO.(S)	YEARS	PRICE VALUE GUIDE
PLAY SET, AIR FORCE	4807	1963	35.00-75.00
PLAY SET, ALAMO	3545-6	1960	150.00-250.00
PLAY SET, ALAMO (SEARS)	3543	1960	
PLAY SET, ALAMO W/METAL ALAMO	2707	1957	
PLAY SET, ALASKA	3707-8	1959	100.00-150.00
PLAY SET, ALASKA SET	2755-6	1960	
PLAY SET, ARMY BATTLEGROUND	4751	1960	75.00-125.00
PLAY SET, ARMY BATTLEGROUND	4752	1958	75.00-125.00
PLAY SET, ARMY BATTLEGROUND (SEARS)	4161	1962	
PLAY SET, ARMY COMBAT	4148	1963	
PLAY SET, BAR "M" RANCH SET (ROY ROGERS)	3995-6	1957	50.00-100.00
PLAY SET, BATTLE OF BLUE & GRAY	4644	1965	50.00-100.00
PLAY SET, BATTLE OF IWO JIMA (SEARS)	4154	1964	
PLAY SET, BATTLE OF IWO JIMA (U.S.&JAPANESE)	4147	1964	
PLAY SET, BATTLE OF THE BLUE & GRAY	4745-6	1959	300.00-400.00
PLAY SET, BATTLE OF THE BLUE & GRAY	4759-60	1958	
PLAY SET, BATTLE OF THE BLUE & GRAY	4761-2	1960	
PLAY SET, BATTLE OF THE BLUE & GRAY, SERIES 1000	2645-6	1960	100.00-200.00
PLAY SET, BATTLEGROUND	3747	1962	75.00-125.00
PLAY SET, BATTLEGROUND	3751	1962	
PLAY SET, BATTLEGROUND	4169MO	1965	75.00-100.00
PLAY SET, BATTLEGROUND	4747-8	1959	
PLAY SET, BATTLEGROUND	4753-4	1964-65/68-69/71-72-73	125.00-150.00
PLAY SET, BATTLEGROUND	4781	1964	75.00-125.00
PLAY SET, BATTLEGROUND (ALLIED)	4757 & MO	1964	125.00-150.00

-Level Parking Garage with uper speed down ramps.

Marx Alaska Play Set included igloos and dog sleds.

Battleground Play Set by Marx.

Official Ben-Hur Play Set.

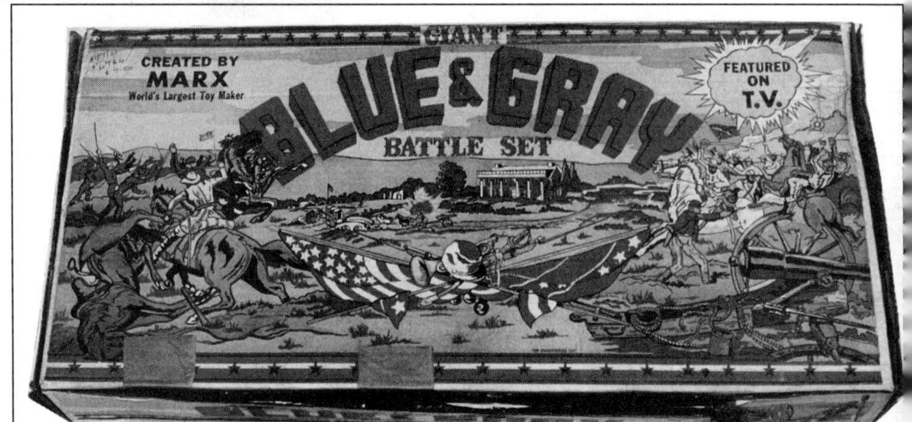

Marx Giant Blue & Gray battle set.

ITEM DESCRIPTION	ITEM NO.(S)	YEARS	PRICE VALUE GUIDE
PLAY SET, BATTLEGROUND (SEARS)	4150	1965	
PLAY SET, BATTLEGROUND (U.S. & GERMAN ARMIES)	4756 & D	1960s	
PLAY SET, BATTLEGROUND (WARDS)	4139	1965	
PLAY SET, BATTLEGROUND (WARDS)	4169	1965	75.00-100.00
PLAY SET, BATTLEGROUND CONVOY	3745-6	1962	150.00-250.00
PLAY SET, BATTLEGROUND, LARGE SIZE	4749-50	1958	275.00-350.00
PLAY SET, BEACHHEAD ASSAULT	0641	1963	75.00-125.00
PLAY SET, BEN HUR	2648	1960	425.00-475.00
PLAY SET, BEN HUR	4701-2	1959	575.00-650.00
PLAY SET, BIG RANCH	3999	1962	
PLAY SET, BLUE & GRAY	2747-8	1960s	
PLAY SET, BLUE & GRAY	4668	1962	
PLAY SET, BLUE & GRAY	4765 & D	1972	
PLAY SET, BLUE & GRAY BATTLEGROUND	4657-8	1962/64	400.00-450.00
PLAY SET, BLUE & GRAY CIVIL WAR SET	4744	1963	250.00-350.00
PLAY SET, CAPE CANAVERAL	4521-2	1960	75.00-100.00
PLAY SET, CAPE CANAVERAL	4535-6	1961	75.00-100.00
PLAY SET, CAPE CANAVERAL MISSILE CENTER	2685-6	1961	100.00-150.00
PLAY SET, CAPE CANAVERAL MISSILE CENTER SET	2656	1959	100.00-150.00
PLAY SET, CAPE KENNEDY PROJECT APOLLO SET	3528	1964	35.00-50.00
PLAY SET, CATTLE DRIVE	3983 & D	1972-73	35.00-50.00
PLAY SET, CIVIL WAR (WARDS)	4766	1962	
PLAY SET, COUNTY FAIR	4304	1959	
PLAY SET, CUSTER'S LAST STAND	4670	1963	175.00-250.00
PLAY SET, D-DAY (SEARS)	4141	1963	

ITEM DESCRIPTION	ITEM NO.(S)	YEARS	PRICE VALUE GUIDE
PLAY SET, D-DAY (SEARS)	4160	1963	
PLAY SET, DAKTARI	3717	1967	35.00-75.00
PLAY SET, DAKTARI (SEARS)	3718	1967	200.00-250.00
PLAY SET, DANIEL BOONE FRONTIER (NOT PROD.)	4671-2	1960s	N/A
PLAY SET, DANIEL BOONE FRONTIER SET	1393	1965	150.00-200.00
PLAY SET, DAVY CROCKETT ALAMO SET	3518	1955	
PLAY SET, DAVY CROCKETT ALAMO SET	3539-40	1955	
PLAY SET, DAVY CROCKETT AT ALAMO SET	3529-30	1955	300.00-400.00
PLAY SET, DAVY CROCKETT FRONTIER	3520	1955	
PLAY SET, DEMO, PREHISTORIC	3398D	1970s	
PLAY SET, DESERT PATROL (SEARS)	4177	1967	
PLAY SET, DESERT PATROL SET	4174	1967	200.00-250.00
PLAY SET, DICK TRACY	2694	1962	
PLAY SET, DISNEYLAND	5370	1961	
PLAY SET, FLINSTONE	4674	1961	225.00-250.00
PLAY SET, FLINTSTONE	1702	1960s	
PLAY SET, FLINTSTONE	2825	1961	
PLAY SET, FLINTSTONE	2669-70	1962	200.00-250.00
PLAY SET, FLINTSTONE	4532	1960s	
PLAY SET, FLINTSTONE HUNTING PARTY	2288	1961	
PLAY SET, FORT APACHE	3630	1952	
PLAY SET, FORT APACHE	3677-8	1958	75.00-100.00
PLAY SET, FORT APACHE	3680	1959	75.00-100.00
PLAY SET, FORT APACHE	3681	1965/67-68-69-70-71-72-73	50.00-75.00
PLAY SET, FORT APACHE	3681 D & S	1964	50.00-75.00
PLAY SET, FORT APACHE	3682	1959	75.00-100.00
PLAY SET, FORT APACHE (300+ PIECES)	3675	1957	
PLAY SET, FORT APACHE (300+ PIECES)	3692	1964	50.00-100.00
PLAY SET, FORT APACHE (GEN. MILLS)	5160MO	1962	
PLAY SET, FORT APACHE (METAL CASE)	4681 & MO	1967	
PLAY SET, FORT APACHE (SEARS)	3683	1968	50.00-75.00
PLAY SET, FORT APACHE (SEARS)	3698	1964	50.00-100.00
PLAY SET, FORT APACHE (SEARS) GIANT SET	3685	1966	350.00-400.00
PLAY SET, FORT APACHE (WARDS)	3684 & D	1964	50.00-100.00

The Flintstones Play Set with accessories.

I.G.Y. Arctic Satellite Base.

ITEM DESCRIPTION	ITEM NO.(S)	YEARS	PRICE VALUE GUIDE
PLAY SET, FORT DEARBORN	3688MO		
PLAY SET, FORT DEARBORN W/METAL FORT	2704-5	1957	125.00-150.00
PLAY SET, FORT MOHAWK	3751-2	1958	125.00-150.00
PLAY SET, FORT PITT	3741-2	1959	85.00-125.00
PLAY SET, GALLANT MEN ARMY	4632	1963	300.00-350.00
PLAY SET, GENERAL CUSTER'S LAST STAND	4779-80	1957	150.00-200.00
PLAY SET, GIANT BATTLEGROUND SET	47868	1963	
PLAY SET, GIANT BLUE & GRAY BATTLE SET	4763-4	1961	
PLAY SET, HAPPI-TIME CENTENIAL CIVIL WAR	4758	1961	
PLAY SET, HAPPI-TIME FORT APACHE	3690	1961	75.00-100.00
PLAY SET, HISTORY IN THE PACIFIC	4164 & D	1972-73	85.00-100.00
PLAY SET, I.G.Y. POLAR SATELLITE BASE	4800	1958	175.00-250.00
PLAY SET, IWO JIMA (SEARS)	4144	1964	50.00-75.00
PLAY SET, JELLYSTONE NATIONAL PARK	4363-4	1962	150.00-200.00
PLAY SET, JOHNNY TREMAIN	3401	1957	475.00-500.00
PLAY SET, JOHNNY WEST	2078	1966	
PLAY SET, JOHNNY WEST	2078MO	1967	
PLAY SET, JUNGLE JIM	3705-6	1957	250.00-300.00
PLAY SET, LARGE ARMY BATTLEFIELD SET	R-4756	1958	
PLAY SET, LARGE, DAKTARI (SEARS)	3720	1967	250.00-350.00
PLAY SET, LITTLE BIG HORN	4679MO	1972	325.00-400.00
PLAY SET, MAIN STREET	2644	1950s	65.00-80.00
PLAY SET, MEDIEVAL	0630	1964	
PLAY SET, MEDIEVAL CASTLE	4699-4700	1959	75.00-100.00
PLAY SET, MEDIEVAL CASTLE	4708	1959	175.00-200.00
PLAY SET, MEDIEVAL CASTLE	4727-8F	1963	
PLAY SET, MEDIEVAL CASTLE	4725-6	1959	
PLAY SET, MILITARY	4198MO	1972	
PLAY SET, MINIATURE FORT APACHE (90 PC.)	HK-7526	1965	50.00-75.00
PLAY SET, MINIATURE KNIGHTS & CASTLE (132 PC.)	HK-7563	1965	50.00-75.00
PLAY SET, MOON LANDING	4656	1970	
PLAY SET, MOONBASE SET	4646	1967	100.00-150.00
PLAY SET, MOONBASE SET	4652	1962	
PLAY SET, OFF. ROBIN HOOD CASTLE SET	4721-2	1956	350.00-450.00
PLAY SET, OFF. SLEEPING BEAUTY CASTLE SET	4703-4	1959	
PLAY SET, OFF. WAGON TRAIN SET	4777	1958	
PLAY SET, OFFICIAL "UNTOUCHABLES"	4675-6	1961	550.00-650.00
PLAY SET, OFFICIAL BEN HUR	4695-6	1960	400.00-500.00
PLAY SET, OFFICIAL FLINSTONE	4671-2	1961	100.00-150.00
PLAY SET, OFFICIAL GALLANT MEN ARMY	4633-4	1963	125.00-175.00
PLAY SET, OFFICIAL WAGON TRAIN	4805	*	
PLAY SET, OFFICIAL WAGON TRAIN	4888	1959	
PLAY SET, OFFICIAL WAGON TRAIN, SERIES 5000	4788	1959	200.00-250.00
PLAY SET, OLD WESTERN TOWN SET	4229-30	1952	125.00-150.00
PLAY SET, OPERATION MOON BASE SET	4653-4	1962	55.00-75.00
PLAY SET, PREHISTORIC	2650	1961	100.00-125.00
PLAY SET, PREHISTORIC	3389-90	1957	200.00-250.00
PLAY SET, PREHISTORIC	3391-2	1958	
PLAY SET, PREHISTORIC	3393-4	1959	
PLAY SET, PREHISTORIC	3398S	1969	75.00-100.00
PLAY SET, PREHISTORIC	0645	1963	
PLAY SET, PREHISTORIC TIMES	3375-6	1963	
PLAY SET, PREHISTORIC TIMES	3388	1958	75.00-100.00
PLAY SET, PREHISTORIC TIMES	3397-8	1961/70-71-72-73	75.00-100.00
PLAY SET, PRINCE VALIANT CASTLE SET	4705-6	1954	250.00-350.00
PLAY SET, PRINCE VALIANT CASTLE SET	4711-12	1954	

umpmaster Paratrooper Set.

Navarone vertical Play Set with five levels.

he Battle of Little Big Horn
lay Set.

Medieval Castle Fort complete
with accessories.

Prince Valiant Castle Fort with accessories.

"The Rifleman" Ranch box.

Robin Hood Castle set with accessories.

Roy Rogers Rodeo Ranch.

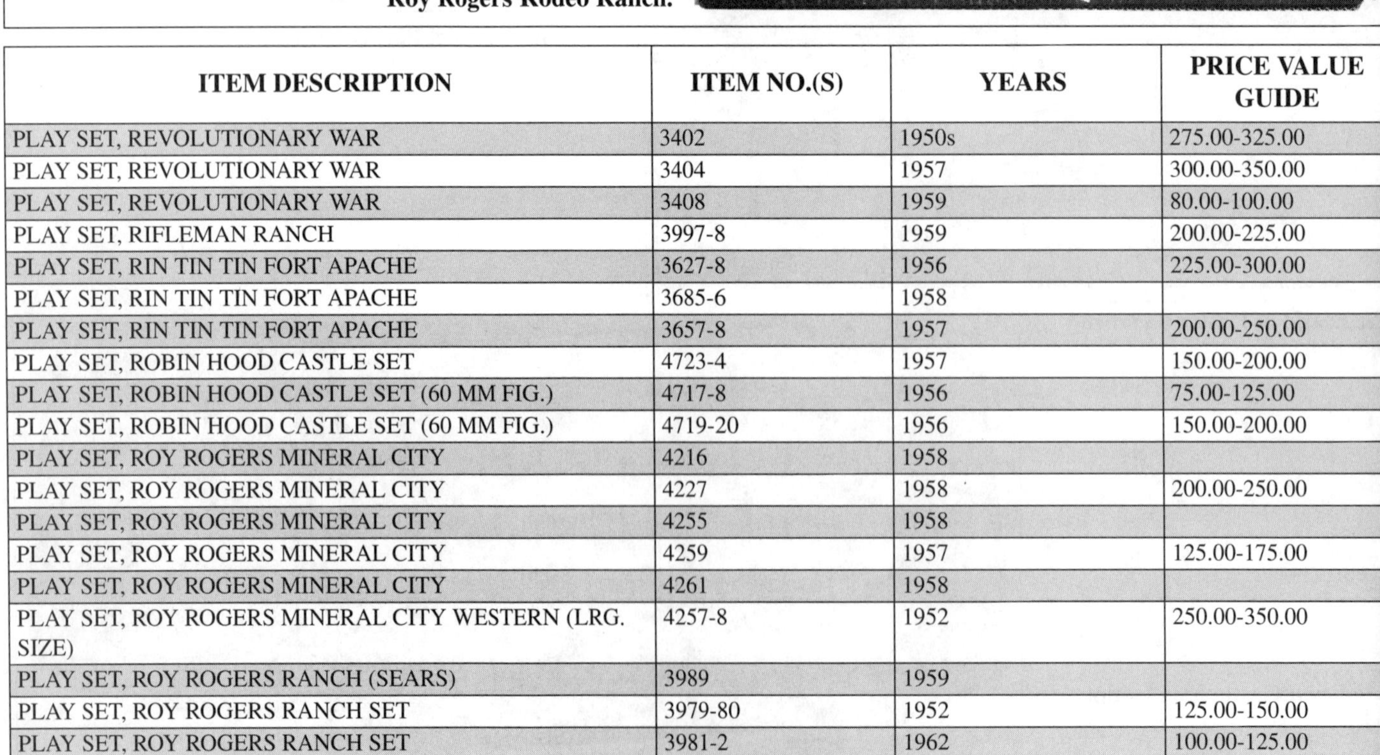

ITEM DESCRIPTION	ITEM NO.(S)	YEARS	PRICE VALUE GUIDE
PLAY SET, REVOLUTIONARY WAR	3402	1950s	275.00-325.00
PLAY SET, REVOLUTIONARY WAR	3404	1957	300.00-350.00
PLAY SET, REVOLUTIONARY WAR	3408	1959	80.00-100.00
PLAY SET, RIFLEMAN RANCH	3997-8	1959	200.00-225.00
PLAY SET, RIN TIN TIN FORT APACHE	3627-8	1956	225.00-300.00
PLAY SET, RIN TIN TIN FORT APACHE	3685-6	1958	
PLAY SET, RIN TIN TIN FORT APACHE	3657-8	1957	200.00-250.00
PLAY SET, ROBIN HOOD CASTLE SET	4723-4	1957	150.00-200.00
PLAY SET, ROBIN HOOD CASTLE SET (60 MM FIG.)	4717-8	1956	75.00-125.00
PLAY SET, ROBIN HOOD CASTLE SET (60 MM FIG.)	4719-20	1956	150.00-200.00
PLAY SET, ROY ROGERS MINERAL CITY	4216	1958	
PLAY SET, ROY ROGERS MINERAL CITY	4227	1958	200.00-250.00
PLAY SET, ROY ROGERS MINERAL CITY	4255	1958	
PLAY SET, ROY ROGERS MINERAL CITY	4259	1957	125.00-175.00
PLAY SET, ROY ROGERS MINERAL CITY	4261	1958	
PLAY SET, ROY ROGERS MINERAL CITY WESTERN (LRG. SIZE)	4257-8	1952	250.00-350.00
PLAY SET, ROY ROGERS RANCH (SEARS)	3989	1959	
PLAY SET, ROY ROGERS RANCH SET	3979-80	1952	125.00-150.00
PLAY SET, ROY ROGERS RANCH SET	3981-2	1962	100.00-125.00

ITEM DESCRIPTION	ITEM NO.(S)	YEARS	PRICE VALUE GUIDE
PLAY SET, ROY ROGERS RODEO	3689-90	1952	50.00-100.00
PLAY SET, ROY ROGERS RODEO RANCH	3987-8	1957	125.00-175.00
PLAY SET, ROY ROGERS RODEO RANCH	3992	1955	50.00-100.00
PLAY SET, S.A.C. BASE	4794	1964	65.00-100.00
PLAY SET, S.A.C. BASE SET	4804	1963	
PLAY SET, SHOPPING PLAZA	3755-6	1962	90.00-125.00
PLAY SET, SILVER CITY FRONTIER TOWN	4219-20	1955	100.00-150.00
PLAY SET, SILVER CITY WESTERN TOWN	4268	1956	
PLAY SET, SILVER CITY WESTERN TOWN (WARDS)	4256	1954	
PLAY SET, SUPER CAR CITY	3492 & D	1968-69-70-71-72-73	50.00-100.00
PLAY SET, SUPER CIRCUS	4302	1954	
PLAY SET, SUPER CIRCUS	4306	1954	
PLAY SET, SUPER CIRCUS	4319-20	1952	200.00-300.00
PLAY SET, TREASURE COVE PIRATE SET	4597-8	1962	
PLAY SET, UNTOUCHABLES	2723-4	1961	
PLAY SET, WAGON TRAIN, SERIES 1000	4785-6	1960	300.00-400.00
PLAY SET, WELLS FARGO WESTERN TOWN	4263-4	1959	200.00-300.00
PLAY SET, WELLS FARGO WESTERN TWN W/D. ROBERTSON	4262	1959	
PLAY SET, WESTERN FRONTIER SET	3964	1950	
PLAY SET, WESTERN MINING TOWN	4265-6	1960	200.00-300.00
PLAY SET, WESTERN TOWN	4260	1957	
PLAY SET, WESTERN TOWN	2652	1959	
PLAY SET, WESTERN TOWN	4249-50	1950s	
PLAY SET, WW II EUROPEAN THEATER	4142	1965	
PLAY SET, WWII BATTLEGROUND	4173	1966	
PLAY SET, WWII EUROPEAN THEATER	4143	1966	
PLAY SET, WWII EUROPEAN THEATER (SEARS)	4182	1965	
PLAY SET, ZORRO	3758	1965	275.00-300.00
PLAY SET, ZORRO (OFF. W.DISNEY)	3753-4	1958	300.00-350.00
PLAY STOVE	K-15-6-7	1950s	25.00-50.00
PLAY STOVE	K-29-30-34	1950s	25.00-50.00
PLAY TIRE	6315	1970	
PLAY TIRE	6315B	1973	
PLAY TRAY, "ROMPER ROOM"	3747-8	1956	
PLAYGROUND EQUIPMENT SET	0275	1950	8.00-10.00
POLICE STATION W/ACCESS., PRE-FAB	3721-2	1954	50.00-75.00

Super Market complete with accessories.

Zorro Play Set with figures, building and other accessories

ITEM DESCRIPTION	ITEM NO.(S)	YEARS	PRICE VALUE GUIDE
POLICE STATION, PRE-FAB	3719-20	1954	
POLY JEEP	1561-2	1958	
POLY STAKE WAGON	3107-8	1960	
POOCH	1346	1950	
PORTABLE B/O POWER UNIT	3900	1961	
POWER BOAT SQUADRON	1570	1968	
POWER SQUADRON ASSORTMENT	1560	1968	
PRAIRIE CHUCK WAGON	1371-2	1960	
PREHISTORIC ANIMALS	0892-C	1961	3.00-8.00 each
PREHISTORIC ANIMALS (19 PIECE) SET	1703	1960s	2.00-5.00 each
PREHISTORIC ANIMALS, LARGE ASST.	0885-6	1956	5.00-10.00 each
PREHISTORIC FIGURES BAGGED	1691	1960s	2.00-5.00 each
PREHISTORIC MONSTERS & MAMMALS	0897	1961	5.00-10.00 each
PREHISTORIC MONSTERS & MAMMALS ASST.	0891-2	1961	3.00-8.00 each
PREHISTORIC MONSTERS, LARGE ASST.	0887-8	1957	5.00-10.00 each
PREHISTORIC SET (16 PIECES)	54/118	1958	3.00-5.00 each
PREHISTORIC SET (35 PIECES)	54/18	1957	1.00-2.00 each
PRESIDENTIAL BOOKLETS	54/1	1955	5.00-6.00 each
PRESIDENTIAL FIGURES	3031-37	1950s	3.00-8.00 each
PRESIDENTS BOOKS	1954/1	1954	5.00-8.00
PRESIDENTS PAINT FOLDER	54/4	1955	5.00-8.00
PRIDE OF THE WEST DEMONSTRATOR	1870/D	1967	
PRIDE OF THE WEST DEMONSTRATOR	1870/GD	1967	
PRIDE OF THE WEST DEMONSTRATOR	1870/GD-1	1967	
PRINCE VALIANT & HORSES	3149MO	1954	
PRINTING PRESS	344	*	
PRIVET HEDGE SET	0260	1950	10.00-20.00
PRIZE LIVESTOCK (SET OF 10)	2763-4	*	3.00-5.00 each
PRO FOOTBALL SET	1690	1967	
PROJECT APOLLO CAPE KENNEDY SET	4518	1967	
PROJECT APOLLO CAPE KENNEDY SET	4523	1966	50.00-75.00
PROJECT APOLLO SET	4515	1962	
PROJECT MERCURY CAPE CANAVERAL SET	3526	1962	
PROJECT MERCURY CAPE CANAVERAL SET	4523-4	1959	40.00-65.00
PROJECT MERCURY MISSILE BASE SET	4525-6	1958	
PROJECT MERCURY MISSILE BASE SET	4527-8	1959	
PROJECT MERCURY RECOVERY SET	2745-6	1961	
PULL AMBULANCE	1429-30	*	
PULL COUPE	1417-18	*	
PULL FIRE ENGINE	0134	*	
PULL JEEP	0131	*	
PULL JEEP	0154	*	
PULL JEEP	0254	1949	
PULL JEEP	1403-4	*	
PULL LOCOMOTIVE	0135	*	
PULL PICKUP TRUCK	0153	*	
PULL RACER	0132	*	
PULL RACER	0151	*	
PULL ROADSTER	0152	*	
PULL TAXI	0136	*	
PULL TAXI	1401-2	*	
PULL VAN	0137	*	
PULL WRECKER	0133	*	
PUSH & RIDE DOG	3081	1973	
PUT-TOGETHER COWBOYS	T-153-4	1954	
PUT-TOGETHER ENGLISH SOLDIERS	T-151-2	1953	

Marx Kitchen Utensils accessories contained everything from meat products to a muffin pan.

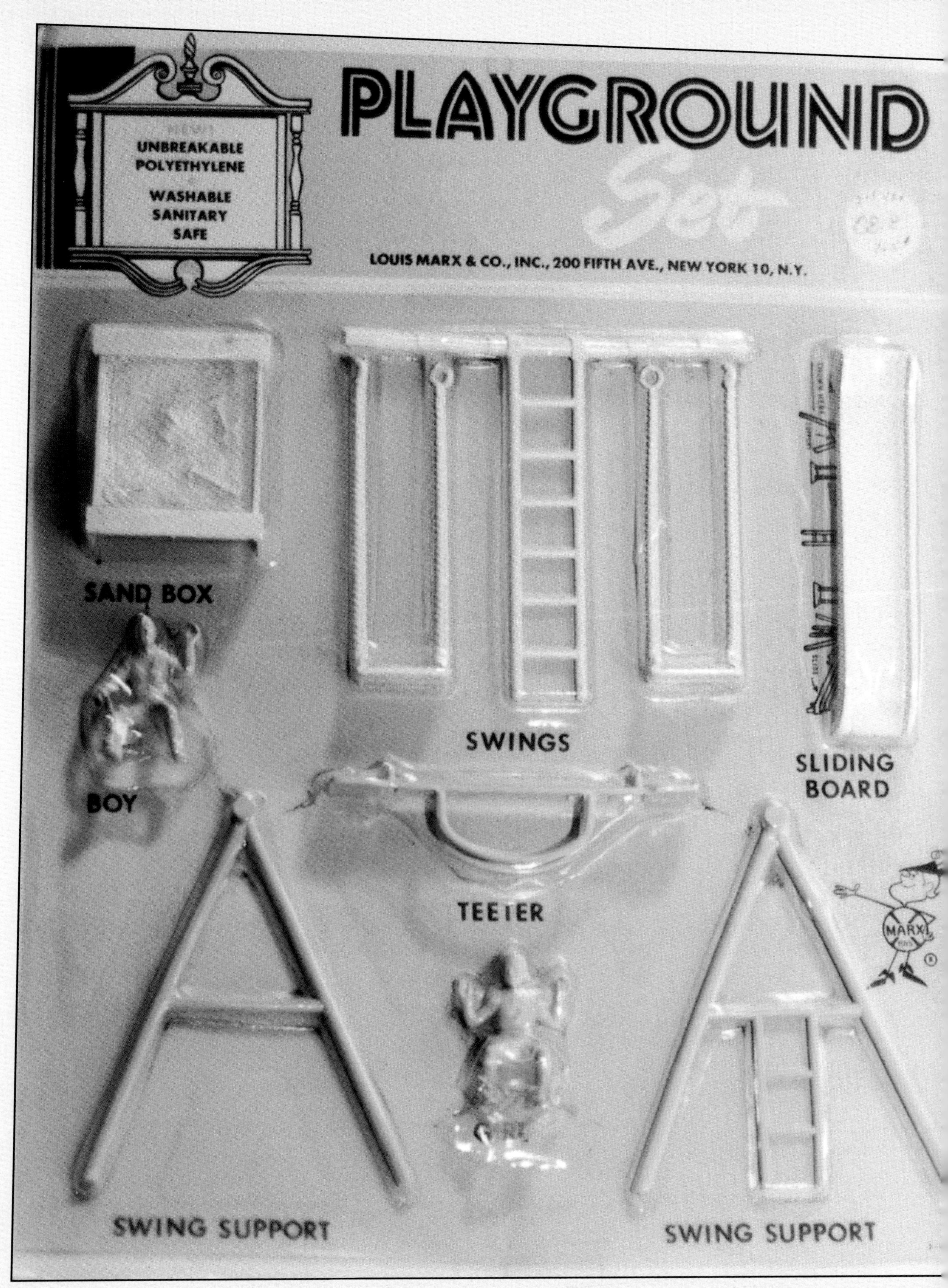

The polyethylene Playground Set came with a sandbox and a slide.

The Two-Story Colonial Doll House was completely furnished.

The Babyland Nursery included a nurse, babies, cribs, blankets and other accessories.

This Doll House accessory set had a swimming pool, playground equipment, a fence, lamp post, gate, and over 20 figures.

This Doll House Family was complete right down to the family dog.

The box for a Marx Metal Dollhouse that came with furniture.

The popular Daktari play set came with natives, animals, huts, trees, ferns, and more.

Marx Super Circus set with box.

The Yogi Bear Jellystone National Park play set.

Wards Service Center containing gasoline pump with water feature.

The "Modern" Service Station came with cars, station attendants, gas pumps, a grease rack, and other accessories.

Midtown Service Station offered 24-hour service.

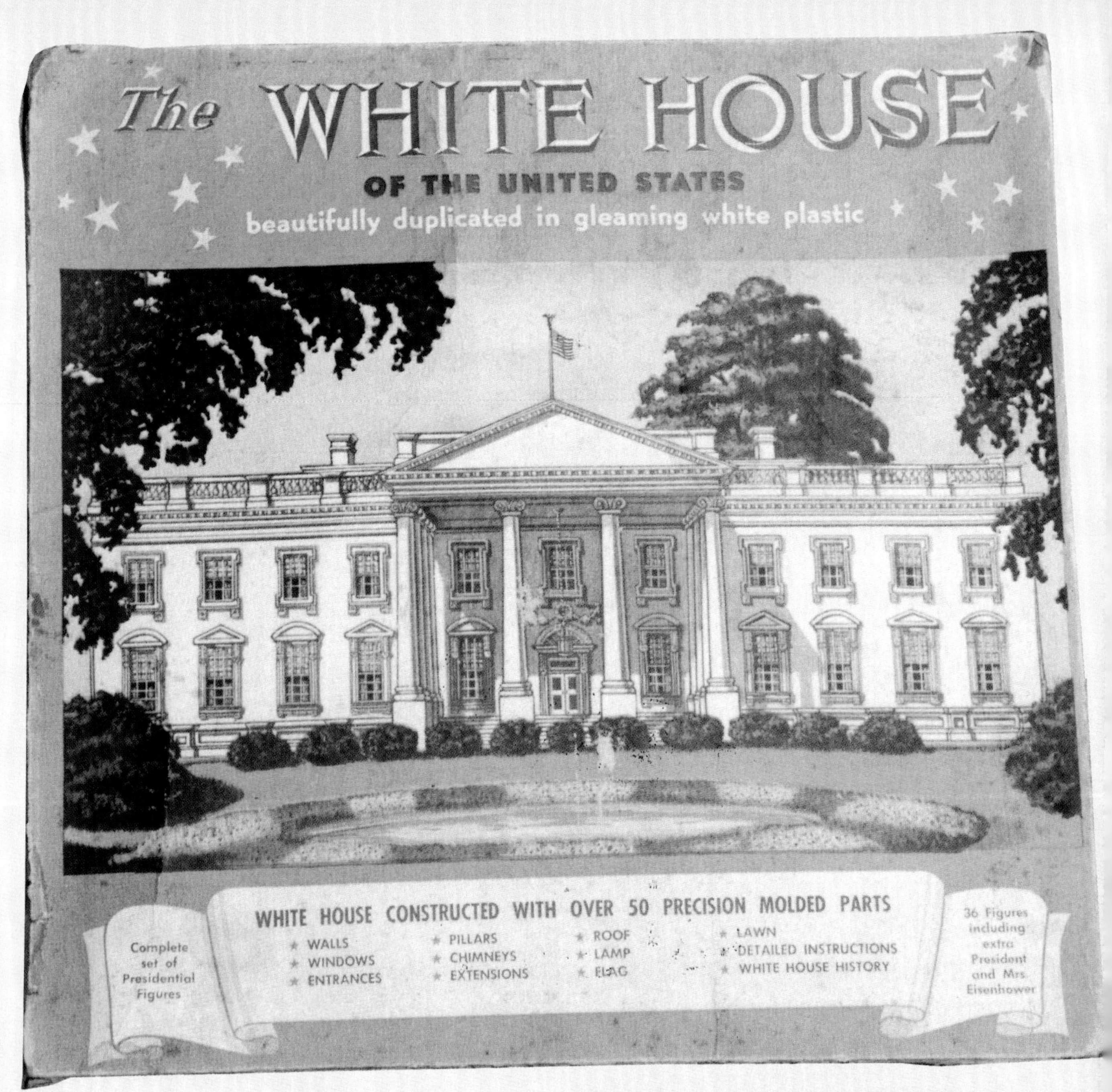

The White House play set, "beautifully duplicated in gleaming white plastic."

One of several Blue & Gray play sets.

ITEM DESCRIPTION	ITEM NO.(S)	YEARS	PRICE VALUE GUIDE
QUACKSIE DUCK	63B	1969/73	
RACER	876-7	*	
RACER W/HORN	878-9	*	
RACER W/HORN & MOTOR	889	*	
RACER, MECH. W/BATTERY HORN	1287-8	1950s	
RACK FOR GUNS DEAL (GRANT)	540D/1	1969	
RADIO BANK	727	*	
RADIO CAR	48	*	
RAILROAD FIGURE SET (30 PIECES)	54/19	1957	3.00-5.00 each
RAILROAD FIGURES (30 PIECES)	54/119	1958	3.00-5.00 each
RAILROAD FOOT BRIDGE	1340	*	
RAILROAD STATION	3879-80	1952	50.00-100.00
RAILROAD STATION	4409-10	1954	50.00-100.00
RAILROAD STATION SET	3881-2	1952	
RAILROAD STATION W/ACCESS.	4411-12	1952	50.00-100.00
RAILROAD STATION W/LIGHTS	4416	1952	50.00-125.00
RAILROAD STATION W/VOICE BOX	4417-18	1956	50.00-125.00
RAILROAD TRESTLE BRIDGE	1320	*	
RAILROAD TRESTLE BRIDGE W/REVOLVING BEACON	1324	*	
RAILROAD, SUBURBAN PLATFORM	3877-8	1955	
RAKE, MINIATURE	375	1950s	5.00-8.00
RANCH	5275MO	1970	
RANCH SET, HAPPI-TIME ROY ROGERS RODEO	3990	1953	50.00-100.00
RANCH SET, ROY ROGERS DOUBLE BAR RODEO	3985-6	1954	80.00-125.00
RANCH SET, WESTERN	3954	1960s	50.00-75.00
RANCH SET, WESTERN	3959-60	1950	50.00-75.00
RANCH SET, WESTERN	3962-3	1950	50.00-75.00
RANCH SET, WILD WEST	3955-6	1950	75.00-100.00
RANCH, "CIRCLE X"	5275	1968	
RANGE RIDER ON HORSE	2795-6	1957	5.00-10.00
RED CLOUD INDIAN	1703	1967	25.00-35.00
EFRIGERATOR	342	1960s	25.00-50.00
EFRIGERATOR W/CONTROL	K-41-2	1950s	25.00-50.00
EFRIGERATOR, H.G.	K-99	1950s	25.00-50.00
EFRIGERATOR, TRU-COLD	K-85	1950s	25.00-50.00
ENEGADE SAM COBRA	2072	1970	25.00-50.00
EVOLUTIONARY WAR SET	2662	1950s	
EX MARS FIGURES ASST.	0904	1953	5.00-8.00 each
EX MARS PLANET PATROL	7014	1953	
EX MARS SPACE DROME	7015-6	1954	
EX MARS SPACE PORT	7004	1955	
EX MARS SPACE PORT	7024	1953	
HINO	58/4	1957	5.00-10.00
IDE ON RACER	3069	1972	
IDE'EM "OLD FASHIONED" LOCOMOTIVE	3111-12	1957	
IDE'EM "THE CHIEF" LOCOMOTIVE	3016R	1969	
IDE'EM "THE CHIEF" LOCOMOTIVE	3016	1972	
IDE'EM AIR FORCE W/POM POM	3289-90	1959	
IDE'EM ASST.	3039	1967	
IDE'EM CAR (NEW ENGLAND TRADING)	3033NE	1967	
IDE'EM DAIRY VAN TRUCK	3287-8	1958	
IDE'EM DINOSAUR "BRONTO"	3045	1970	
DE'EM DONALD DUCK	3060	1972-73	
DE'EM DUCK	3037 & MO	1968-69-70	
DE'EM FIRE CHIEF CAR	3036	1968	
DE'EM FIRE TRUCK	3030	1965	

Revolutionary War set with blockhouse, stockade fence, etc.

LOUIS MARX & CO., INC.
200 FIFTH AVE. NEW YORK

MARX TOYS

GLENDALE DIV.
F.O.B. Factory — Glendale, W. Va.

a. No. 1751 ROCKER DUMP TRUCK

Heavy duty two-wheel diesel type hauler. Spacious rocker dumping type body attached with swivel mounting to the power unit. Body is raised by means of crank behind driver's seat. Finished in attractive baked enamel colors with decals on rocker dump support arms. Meas. 17½" long, 5¾" wide, 4½" high.
PACKED: Each in box
½ doz. to shipping carton
Weight per carton — 24¾ lbs.

b. No. 1756 HIGH LIFT LOADER W/SCOOP

Measures: 15½" long overall, 6⅜" wide, 5" high. Made of heavy gauge steel. Finished in bright baked enamel colors. Rear wheels steerable from steering wheel. Heavy duty scoop bucket at front. Lever raises bucket and locks in position until released by trip lever for dumping.
PACKED: Each in box
¼ doz. to shipping carton
Weight per carton — 12 lbs.

c. No. 1760 ROAD GRADER

The all steel constructed item is finished in baked enamel. The item features the following: a cab enclosure over drivers' compartment, a road scraper which may be lifted and set in angles and a motor block under hood with the exhaust stack mounted on top of hood. Measures 17" long, 5¼" wide, 5¾" high.
PACKED: ¼ doz. to shipping carton
Weight per carton — 14 lbs.

d. No. 1782 DIESEL POWER SHOVEL

Measures: 18" long overall, 6¼" wide, 13¼" high. Shovel equipped with automatic scooping operation and automatic bucket release action. This newly designed, single crank controls automatic loading, raising and lowering of the boom, and unloading the shovel.
PACKED: Each in a box
¼ doz. to shipping carton
Weight per carton — 15¼ lbs.

Page from the *Marx Toys 1964 Promotional Catalog*.

ITEM DESCRIPTION	ITEM NO.(S)	YEARS	PRICE VALUE GUIDE
RIDE'EM FIRE TRUCK	3319-20	1956	
RIDE'EM FIRE TRUCK (KRESGE)	3318	1958	
RIDE'EM FIRE TRUCK W/FLASHER LIGHT	3337	1960	
RIDE'EM FIRE TRUCK W/FLASHER LIGHT & SIREN	3338	1960	
RIDE'EM FIRE TRUCK W/LIGHTS	3321-2	1956	
RIDE'EM FIRE TRUCK W/SEARCHLIGHT & SIREN	3321S-2S	1957	
RIDE'EM FIRE TRUCK W/SIREN	3299-3000	*	
RIDE'EM FIRE TRUCK W/SIREN	3331-32	1959	
RIDE'EM FIRE TRUCK W/SIREN	3335-36	1959	
RIDE'EM HORSE	3018	1972-73	
RIDE'EM INDY RACER	3074	1971-72-73	
RIDE'EM LOCO & GONDOLA	3129-30	1954	
RIDE'EM LOCOMOTIVE	3016 & HR	1969-70-71-72-73	
RIDE'EM LOCOMOTIVE	3025 & HR & MO	1970	
RIDE'EM LOCOMOTIVE	3026R	1968/70/73	
RIDE'EM LOCOMOTIVE	3099-3100	1970s	
RIDE'EM LOCOMOTIVE	3109-10	1953	
RIDE'EM LOCOMOTIVE W/WHISTLE & BELL	3026 & A	1965/71-72	
RIDE'EM PLANE	3092	1973	
RIDE'EM POLICE CAR	3035	1968-69	
RIDE'EM PONY	3028	1965	
RIDE'EM PONY	3028	1968	
RIDE'EM ROCKET SHIP W/LAUNCHER	3329-30	1958	
RIDE'EM SCHOOL BUS	3093	1973	
RIDE'EM STAKE TRUCK	3032	1967	
RIDE'EM STAKE TRUCK	3084-5	1970s	
RIDE'EM TANK	3076	1968	

ITEM DESCRIPTION	ITEM NO.(S)	YEARS	PRICE VALUE GUIDE
RIDE'EM TURTLE	3040	1968-69	
RIDE'EM WRECKER TRUCK	3125-6	1957	
RIDE'EM WRECKER TRUCK	3165-6	1957	
RIDE'EM WRECKER TRUCK W/HORN	3168	1958	
RIDE'EM, THE WORM	3017	1972-73	
RIDERS & HORSES ASST.	2799	1958	2.00-3.00 each
RIFLE, ARMY W/STRAP	220	*	
RIFLE, ARMY, W/"O" STRAP	219	*	
RIFLE, B&G "SHARPS" BULLET SHOOTING CAP	226/1	1963	
RIFLE, BIG SHOT	292/1	1969	
RIFLE, BIG SHOT	547/1	1972	
RIFLE, BIG SHOT	548/B	1972-73	
RIFLE, CLICKER	130	1963	
RIFLE, DANIEL BOONE FLINT LOCK	196	1964	
RIFLE, GI COMBAT	232/1	1964	
RIFLE, GI COMBAT, M-1 GARAND BULLET SHOOTING	231/1	1969/72	
RIFLE, JOHNNY WEST "BIG SHOT"	293/1	1968-69-70-71-72	
RIFLE, JOHNNY WEST RANCH	275	1968-69-70/72	
RIFLE, JUNIOR TRAINING	219	*	
RIFLE, LANDING	2268	1971	
RIFLE, LANDING	2268B	1972-73	
RIFLE, MOON LANDING	2268	1969	
RIFLE, MOON LANDING	2268	1970	
RIFLE, MOON LANDING AUTOMATIC	2253,B,B/2,/1	1969-70-71	
RIFLE, TRAINING	229/30	1950	
RIFLE, WESTERN SADDLE	238	1963	
RING TOSS	944	1971-72-73	
RIVER QUEEN	2816	1950s	
ROAD GRADER	1760	1964/65/68/69	
ROAD GRADER	1760	1970	
ROAD GRADER	1760	1972-73	35.00-50.00
ROAD GRADER W/SHOVEL	1701/3091	1960s	35.00-55.00
ROADSTER - SEDAN - RACER	555-6	*	
ROBIN HOOD SET	55/14	1956	
ROBIN HOOD SET	55/3	1956	
ROCK-ALONG HORSE	3089	1972	
ROCK-ALONG HORSE	3089	1973	
ROCKER, HUSKI BUILT	5191	1973	
ROCKER, MUSICIAL, HUSKI BUILT	5193	1973	
ROCKET LAUNCHER	1526-7	1959	
ROCKET LAUNCHER SET	5185	1959	
ROCKET SET, 3-STAGE	443-4	1959	
ROLLER SKATES	205-6	1960s	
ROLLER SKATES	303	*	
ROLLER SKATES W/DUST CARS	106	1950s	
ROLLOVER PLUTO	92-8	*	
ROOSTER & CART	087	1950s	
ROY ROGERS & FARM FIGURES	0814	1953	5.00-15.00 each
ROY ROGERS & FRONTIER FIGURES W/ACCESSORIES	0770	1956	5.00-15.00 each
ROY ROGERS & INDIAN RIDERS W/HORSES	0788	1956	5.00-15.00 each
ROY ROGERS COWBOY SET FIGURES, 27-PIECE	0707	1957	5.00-15.00 each
ROY ROGERS HAULER & VAN TRAILER	767-8	1954	
ROY ROGERS HAULER & VAN TRAILER W/FIGURES & JEEP	769	1956	
ROY ROGERS RIDER & HORSE	2695-6	1956	
ROY ROGERS W/ACCESSORIES	0740	1956	

ITEM DESCRIPTION	ITEM NO.(S)	YEARS	PRICE VALUE GUIDE
RUNNING RABBIT & CAR	095	*	
RUSTY RIDER ON HORSE	2793-4	1957	
SAFARI	G-67	1964	
SAFARI BAGATELLE	G-68	1964	
SAIL BOAT	137-8	1954	
SAILORS IN BAG SET	3197-8	1956	5.00-10.00 each
SAM COBRA	2072	1972-73	20.00-45.00
SAM COBRA & THUNDERBOLT SET	2074MO	1972	35.00-50.00
SARGENT BAKER	1712A	1967	20.00-35.00
SARGENT JACK MOFFITT	1711B	1967	20.00-35.00
SARGENT SAM TROY	1711A	1967	20.00-35.00
SARGENT STARR	1712B	1967	20.00-35.00
SATELLITE LAUNCHING STATION	2664	1958	
SCHOOL HOUSE PRE-FAB	3820	1952	25.00-50.00
SCHOOL HOUSE W/ACCESS. PRE-FAB	3821-2	1952	25.00-60.00
SCOOTER KIT	3150MO	*	
SCOPE, COMBAT 4-WAY	1038C	1964	
SEA & SNO BOB	6340	1970-71-72-73	
SEARS STORE (SHOPPING CENTER)	5490	1961	
SECRET AGENT SET, INTERNATIONAL	2463	1968	
SEDAN, MECH. PL.	1173	1960s	

Page from the *Marx Toys 1975 Promotional Catalog*.

LOUIS MARX & CO., INC.
200 FIFTH AVE. NEW YORK

MARX TOYS

ERIE DIVISION
F.O.B. Factory – Erie, Pa.

No. 2050
MILITARY ORDERS:
FROM MARX TO "STONY"
—THE BATTLING SOLDIER

You will report to retail counters in 1964 and carry with you the following equipment:

SMALL ARMS:
Rifle-M1 w/sling
Rifle-B.A.R. w/sling
Gun-machine, hand
Carbine-w/sling
Pistol-.45 w/holster
Grenades-hand, 3
Gun-machine, 50 cal w/tripod

COMMUNICATIONS GEAR:
Walkie-Talkie w/straps
Binoculars w/case and straps
Bugle

PERSONAL ISSUE:
Hat-G.I. fatigue
Helmet-G.I. w/netting
Mess Kit w/knife, fork and spoon
Canteen w/cap
Rations-2 cans-K
Belt-w/canteen, cap and bayonet sheath

EQUIPMENT-FIELD:
Pack-field w/straps
Tools-entrenching w/blade, handle and cover
Bayonet
Knife-paratrooper w/sheath and strap.

STONY FEATURES:
- Over 11" tall.
- All equipment supplied made to true scale.
- Of rugged poly with vinyl head and painted decorations.
- Jointed shoulders, elbows and wrists.
- Turning head.

PACKED: Complete with all equipment appearing on this page. Each in a telescope litho lid box, 1 dz. to a shipper.
Weight — 8 lbs.

3

Page from the *Marx Toys 1964 Promotional Catalog*.

Model School House with accessories.

Marx Colonial Service Station.

ITEM DESCRIPTION	ITEM NO.(S)	YEARS	PRICE VALUE GUIDE
SERVICE AREA, TURNPIKE	3497	1961	50.00-125.00
SERVICE CENTER, AUTOMOTIVE	3482	1964	45.00-75.00
SERVICE STATION	3420	1960	35.00-50.00
SERVICE STATION	3430	1959	35.00-50.00
SERVICE STATION	3442	1961	35.00-50.00
SERVICE STATION	3596	1963	45.00-75.00
SERVICE STATION & SERVICE TRUCK W/FLASHING LIGHT	3476	1957	50.00-100.00
SERVICE STATION PLAYSET (BLISTER)	2751-2	1960	
SERVICE STATION TAKE-APART SET	3893	1953	45.00-75.00
SERVICE STATION W/ACCESS.	3457-8	1958/64-65	35.00-50.00
SERVICE STATION W/ACCESS.	3459-60	1953	35.00-65.00
SERVICE STATION W/ACCESS.	3462	1953	35.00-65.00
SERVICE STATION W/ACCESS.	3467-8	1956	35.00-65.00
SERVICE STATION W/ACCESS.	3469-70	1956	35.00-65.00
SERVICE STATION W/ACCESS.	3471-2	1956/67	35.00-65.00
SERVICE STATION W/ACCESS.	3473-4	1957/64-65	35.00-65.00
SERVICE STATION W/ACCESS.	3474	1967	35.00-65.00

ITEM DESCRIPTION	ITEM NO.(S)	YEARS	PRICE VALUE GUIDE
SERVICE STATION W/ACCESS.	3475	1958/69-70	35.00-65.00
SERVICE STATION W/ACCESS.	3477-8	1958	35.00-65.00
SERVICE STATION W/ACCESS.	3569	1963	45.00-75.00
SERVICE STATION W/ACCESS. (MONT.WARD)	3483 & D	1958	50.00-100.00
SERVICE STATION W/ACCESS. (MONTGOMERY WARD)	3461	1962	45.00-70.00
SERVICE STATION W/AUTO TRANSPORT & ACCESS.	3462/0740	1954	45.00-75.00
SERVICE STATION W/ELECTRIC ELEVATOR	3485-6	1957	50.00-100.00
SERVICE STATION W/ELEVATOR	3495	1964/66/68-69-70	50.00-75.00
SERVICE STATION W/HELIPORT	3487	1959	50.00-100.00
SERVICE STATION W/PARKING GARAGE	3485-6	1961	50.00-100.00
SERVICE STATION W/PARKING GARAGE	3489-90	1959	50.00-100.00
SERVICE STATION W/TALKING UNIT	3508	1966	50.00-100.00
SERVICE STATION W/TALKING UNIT	3516	1966	50.00-100.00
SERVICE STATION W/TALKING UNIT (SEARS)	3511/12	1965	50.00-100.00
SERVICE STATION, 3-LEVEL	3506	1965/68/70	50.00-100.00
SERVICE STATION, 3-LEVEL W/CARS & ACCESS.	3513	1971	50.00-90.00
SERVICE STATION, 4-LEVEL	3501-2	1962/64	50.00-125.00
SERVICE STATION, 4-LEVEL (SEARS)	3509	1963	50.00-100.00
SERVICE STATION, ALLSTATE	3451-2	1958	35.00-65.00
SERVICE STATION, ALLSTATE	3455	1957	35.00-65.00
SERVICE STATION, ALLSTATE	3493-4	1959	45.00-75.00
SERVICE STATION, ALLSTATE 4-LEVEL	3499	1962	50.00-100.00
SERVICE STATION, ALLSTATE W/ ELECT. ELEVATOR	3498	1961	50.00-100.00
SERVICE STATION, ALLSTATE W/ACCESS.	3443	1961	50.00-75.00
SERVICE STATION, ALLSTATE W/ELEC.ELEVATORF	3491-2 & D	1957	50.00-100.00
SERVICE STATION, ALLSTATE, W/FRICTION CARS	3481-2	1957	50.00-100.00
SERVICE STATION, CAR CITY	3493	1968	45.00-75.00
SERVICE STATION, CARRY CASE, WARD'S "BIG MIKE"	3410	1967	45.00-75.00
SERVICE STATION, CITIES	3453-4	1955	35.00-65.00
SERVICE STATION, COLONIAL SERVICE W/ACCESS.	3449-50	1952	50.00-75.00
SERVICE STATION, FILLING STATION	17	1960s	50.00-75.00
SERVICE STATION, HAPPI-TIME W/ACCESS.	3464	1953	45.00-75.00
SERVICE STATION, MIDTOWN, W/CARS	3500 & D	1971-72-73	45.00-75.00
SERVICE STATION, PARKING W/ ELECT. ELEVATOR	3495-6	1960/65	50.00-100.00
SERVICE STATION, PENNY'S	3485	1967	50.00-100.00
SERVICE STATION, PRE-FAB	3889-92	1952	45.00-75.00
SERVICE STATION, SEARS	3507	1966	45.00-75.00
SERVICE STATION, SEARS	3487	1966	45.00-75.00
SERVICE STATION, SEARS	3504	1963	45.00-75.00
SERVICE STATION, SEARS	3505	1965	45.00-75.00
SERVICE STATION, SEARS ALLSTATE	3484	1960	45.00-75.00
SERVICE STATION, SUPER	2449-50	1950s	50.00-100.00
SERVICE STATION, SUPER CAR CITY W/CARS & ACC.	3494	1971	45.00-75.00
SERVICE STATION, SUPER W/CARS & ACCESS.	3483	1971/73	45.00-75.00
SERVICE STATION, TURNPIKE	3459-60	1961	35.00-65.00
SERVICE STATION, TURNPIKE	3479-80	1955	45.00-75.00

ITEM DESCRIPTION	ITEM NO.(S)	YEARS	PRICE VALUE GUIDE
SERVICE STATION, WARD'S	3503	1967	45.00-75.00
SERVICE STATION, WARD'S RIVERSIDE	3489	1968	35.00-65.00
SERVICE STATION, WESTGATE	3485	1968-69-70	50.00-100.00
SERVICE STATION, WESTGATE W/CARS & ACCESS.	3491	1971-73	45.00-75.00
SERVICE STATION. SPEC.M.WARD W/PARKING GAR.	3488	1959	50.00-100.00
SET OF AIRPLANE MODEL KITS	M-200	*	
SET OF TWO SIDE CHAIRS	4106	1956	5.00-8.00
SEWING MACHINE	325	*	
SEWING TABLE	7152	1973	
SHADOW BOX	11	1955	
SHELL SHOOTING MACHINE GUN	75	*	
SHERIFF	2085	1970	
SHERIFF GARRETT	2085	1973	35.00-50.00
SHERIFF GARRETT & THUNDERBOLT	2094MO	1973	50.00-75.00
SHIP, HESS VOYAGER	2900	1966	
SHIPS, NAVY, ASST.	0756-7	1951	
SHOOTING GALLERY	G-28-30	1948	
SHOVEL	265	*	3.00-5.00
SHOVEL, H.G. MINI.	245	1952	3.00-5.00
SHOWROOM, NEW CAR SALES	156	1950s	45.00-75.00
SHUFFLE BOARD SET "STEP LIVELY"	928	1972-73	
SIGNATURE SINK	K-83	1950s	25.00-50.00
SIGNATURE STOVE	K-81	1950s	25.00-50.00
SILLY SAMMY RIDER DUCK	5055	1973	
SILVER KNIGHT & HORSE	5392MO	1970	35.00-70.00
SINK W/UTENSILS & RUNNING WATER	K-39-40	1950s	25.00-50.00
SIR GORDEN THE GOLD KNIGHT W/GOLD ACCESSORIES	5366	1968-69	25.00-70.00
SIR GORDON THE GOLD KNIGHT W/ACCESS.	5366	1970-71	
SIR STUART THE SILVER KNIGHT W/ACCESS.	5364	1970-71	
SIR STUART THE SILVER KNIGHT W/SILVER ACCESSO-RIES	5364	1968-69	25.00-70.00
SIX ASST. GAMES OF SKILL	G-108	1964	
SKEE BALL GAME	G-277/78	1963	
SKILL BALL GAME	G-23-25	1948	
SKILL BALL GAME	G-258	1964	
SKYSCRAPER W/ELEVATOR	5449-50	1957	75.00-100.00
SKYSCRAPER W/ELEVATOR & LIGHT (WARDS)	5450M	1957	75.00-100.00
LEEPING BEAUTY	2805-6	1959	
SLIDE-A-ROO	5300	1970-71	
MALL DISNEY PAIL & SHOVEL	0449-0450	1950	
MALL TELEPHONE	2-4	1960s	5.00-10.00
MALL WASHING MACHINE	89	1950s	5.00-10.00
NO TOBOGGAN	6360	1970-71-72-73	
NO TOBOGGAN	6360MO	1970	
NOWMOBILE, GIANT	3099	1972-73	
SOLDIER COMBAT SET	3101-02	*	

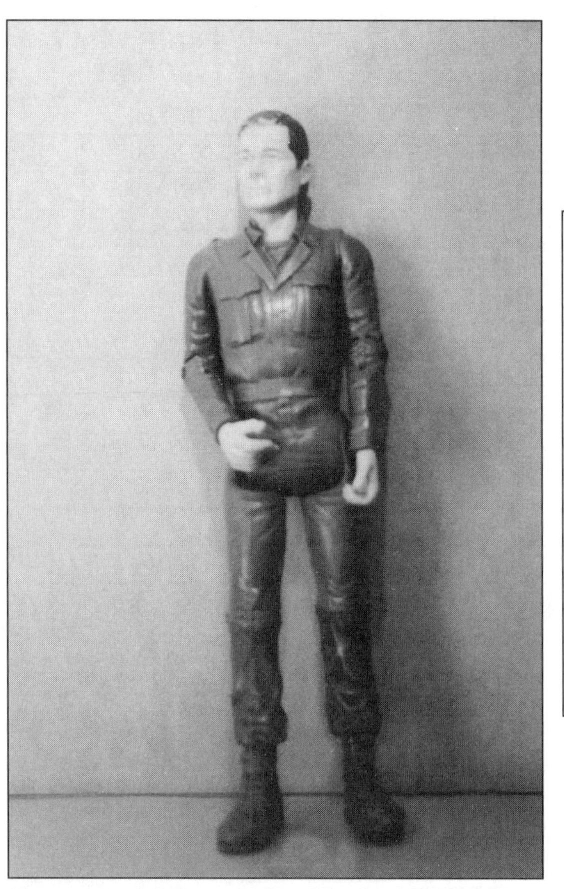

Stony the Soldier - 1960s. (Gaylord Whipkey Collection. Photo by M.L. Smith)

New Car Sales and Service Center.

Talking Radio Station with accessories.

ITEM DESCRIPTION	ITEM NO.(S)	YEARS	PRICE VALUE GUIDE
SOLDIER SET	3005-6-8	*	
SOLDIER SET (10 PC.)	3105-6	*	
SOLDIER SET (31 PIECES)	54/11	1957	1.00-3.00 each
SOLDIER SET (38 PIECES)	54/12	1957	1.00-3.00 each
SOLDIER SET (68 PIECES)	54/120	1958	1.00-3.00 each
SOLDIERS (102 PIECES)	1712	1960s	1.00-3.00 each
SOLDIERS IN BAG SET	3194/96	1956	1.00-3.00 each
SOLDIERS, ASST. PLASTIC	0580	*	1.00-3.00 each
SOLDIERS, COMBAT SET, 100-PIECE	0585/86	1963	
SOLDIERS, JAPANESE SET, 100-PIECE	0587	1963	
SONS OF LIBERTY	4170	1972	
SPACE CAPSULE & ASTRONAUT FIGS.	2765-6	1962	
SPACE ITEMS ASSORTMENT	2727	1960s	
SPACE PATROL ACADEMY	7019-20	1952	125.00-150.00
SPACE ROCKET TARGET SET	2703-4	1959	
SPACE VEHICLE W/ASTRONAUTS	1734	1968-69	
SPADE SHOVEL, MINIATURE	373	1950s	3.00-5.00
SPEC. TRUCK RAIL TERMINAL	5421-2	1954	45.00-75.00
SPORT BAGATELLE	G-184-E	1972-73	
SPORTS CAR DEMONSTRATOR	2500/D	*	
SPORTS WHEEL	5077	1973	
SQUEESIE'EM BIRD	75B	1972-73	
STAGE COACH SET W/COWBOYS & INDIANS	3814 & D	1972-73	15.00-25.00
STAGECOACH	1373-4	1960	10.00-15.00
STAKE WAGON KIT	3200MO	1973	
STANDING RABBIT & CART	093	*	
STARLITE VANITY	7118	1968	
STATE FAIR BAGATELLE	G-183-4	1964	
STATE FAIR BAGETELLE	G-184MO	1967/69-70/73	
STATUE OF LIBERTY	2901-2	1955	
STATUE OF LIBERTY	2911-12	1955	15.00-25.00
STEAM SHOVEL	798	1952	35.00-50.00
STEEL HELMET	529-30	*	
STEP LADDER, PLASTIC	0827	1950s	
STONY "FIELD EQUIPMENT"	2047	1965	
STONY "STONEWALL" SMITH	2050	1964	
STONY ACCESSORIES	2043&MO	1965	
STONY COMBAT GEAR ASSORTMENT	2044	1965	
STONY COMBAT TEAM	2059	1965	
STONY ON BIVOUAC (RECONNAISSANCE SET)	2055	1965	
STONY ON MANEUVERS	2058	1965	
STONY ON MANEUVERS (PARATROOPER)	2056	1965	
STONY SMITH COMBAT SET	4185	1967	
STONY SMITH FIELD SET	2057	1965	
STONY THE PARATROOPER	2054	1965	50.00-75.00
STONY THE SKY COMMANDO	2052	1965	50.00-75.00

ITEM DESCRIPTION	ITEM NO.(S)	YEARS	PRICE VALUE GUIDE
STORM CLOUD PINTO	2071	1973	20.00-25.00
STORM CLOUD PINTO HORSE	2071	1973	
STOVE W/UTENSILS	K-37-8	1950s	25.00-50.00
STOVE, H.G.	K-35	1955	25.00-50.00
SUITCASE BANK	718	*	
SURPRISE PACKAGE (BOYS)	5702	1953	
SURPRISE PACKAGE (GIRLS)	5704	1953	
T.A.P. ASSORTMENTS	0253-5-6-7	*	
TABLE LAMPS, SET OF 3	0488MO	1962	5.00-10.00
TAKE-APART HELICOPTER	2557-8	1954	
TAKE-APART WRECKER & HOT ROD	2709-10]	1961	
TANDEM LITTLE WHEEL	5022	1972	
TANK BATTLE (SEARS)	4172	1964	
TANK BATTLE (SEARS)	4176	1964	
TANK BATTLE (SEARS)	4180	1964	
TANK BATTLE (SEARS)	4184	1964	
TANK, ARMY	0623-4	*	
TANK, DESERT PATROL	1556	1967	
TANK, ERIE	1554	1964	
TANK, SMALL ARMY	128	1950s	20.00-45.00
TANK, SOUND-OF-POWER	3072	1968	
TANK, SUPER SPARKLING	1976	1964/69/70	
TAPPAN PLAY STOVE	K-96-7	1957	25.00-50.00
TAPPEN STOVE W/UTENSILS	K-98	1950s	25.00-50.00
TARGET ARCADE	G-128	1964	
TARGET GAME	G-26-27	1948	
TARGET GAME	G-59-60	1950	
TARGET SHOOTING GALLERY W/SHOTGUN	G-261	1967	
TAXI CAB, MECH. PL.	1171	1960s	
TAXI CAB, PLASTIC YELLOW	1316	*	
TAXI W/MYSTERY MOTOR	620	*	
TAXI, PL. SKYVIEW	1393-4	*	
TAXI, SKYVIEW	1395-6	*	
THE CHIEF SKATE	503	*	
THE SLUGGER	2225	1967	
THREE GANG PLOW	242	*	
THUNDERBOLT	2061&AMO,BMO	1965/68	25.00-45.00
THUNDERBOLT & THUNDERCOLT	2032	1966	35.00-50.00
THUNDERBOLT ASSORTED HORSES	2061	1970-71-72-73	25.00-35.00
THUNDERBOLT HORSE, ASSORTED	1061	1972-73	
THUNDERCOLT (BROWN W/BLACK TRIM)	2031B	1966	20.00-35.00
THUNDERCOLT (PALOMINO W/WHITE TRIM)	2031A	1966	20.00-25.00
THUNDERCOLT HORSE (ASST. COLORS)	2031	1968	20.00-25.00
TIGER	57/2	1957	5.00-10.00
TIN LIZZIE	3010	1972	
TINY BIKE	3083MO	1971-72	

ITEM DESCRIPTION	ITEM NO.(S)	YEARS	PRICE VALUE GUIDE
TOM & JERRY RADIO	6627HK	1973	10.00-20.00
TOM & JERRY WATER GUNS	6611HK	1973	
TOM CORBETT SPACE ACADEMY	7009-10	1952	200.00-250.00
TOM CORBETT SPACE ACADEMY	7012	1953	200.00-250.00
TOOL SET (9 PIECES)	378	1958	5.00-10.00
TOY ASSORTMENT, ALDEN	1970	1964	
TOY GUN ASSORTMENT	179	1970	
TOYS, ASSORTMENT POLYETHYLENE	800	*	
TOYS, ASST. MINI. TAKE-APART	0357	1954	
TOYS, CONSTRUCTION ASST.	1126P	1958	
TOYS, FRICTION DISNEY	19	1946	15.00-25.00
TRACTOR & IMPLEMENT SET	2741-2	1959	
TRACTOR ASSEMBLY SET	1714	*	
TRACTOR MOWER	3041	1970	
TRACTOR MOWER	3041	1972-73	
TRACTOR, BULLDOZER	1647-8	*	
TRACTOR, FARM CULTIVATOR	1627-8	*	
TRACTOR, H.G. FARM	1709-10	*	
TRACTOR, MINI FARM	1317-8	*	
TRACTOR, PLASTIC BULLDOZER	608-9	*	
TRADING POST TOYS	9/9MO	1955	
TRAILER, HAULER & GRAIN	2430	1959	
TRAILER, HAULER & TANDEM	2442	1959	
TRAILER, HAULER & VAN	2422	1960	
TRAILER, HAULER & VAN	2432	1959	
TRAILER, HAULER & VAN ALLSTATE	2432AS	1960	
TRAILER, HUALER & TANDEM (ALLSTATE)	2442AS	1960	
TRAILER, POWERHOUSE HYD. GRAIN	2551-2	1959	
TRAILER, TWO-WHEEL UTILITY	246	*	
TRAILER, WESTERN CATTLE VAN	2428	1959	
TRAIN	511-12	*	
TRAIN SET, 3-UNIT PULL	535-36	1948	
TRAIN SET, 3-UNIT PULL W/GUN/CANDY (WALGREEN)	536-S	1948	
TRAIN SET, MINI. PULL	1523-4	*	
TRAIN W/BELL	546	*	
TRAIN, MILITARY TRUCK	1427	1950s	
TRAIN, SCENIC EXPRESS	1932	1966	
TRANSPORT, PLASTIC	0739-40	1951	
TREASURE COVE	4608	*	
TRESTLE BRIDGE W/LIGHT	1380	1950	
TRESTLE BRIDGE W/REVOLVING BEACON	1384	*	
TRIKE, MINI.	3009	1972-73	
TRUCK ARMY COMBAT UNIT	5170	1965	15.00-30.00
TRUCK ASSORTMENT	1161-2	1952	
TRUCK ASSORTMENT	2389-90	*	
TRUCK ASSORTMENT	650	1957	

ITEM DESCRIPTION	ITEM NO.(S)	YEARS	PRICE VALUE GUIDE
TRUCK ASSORTMENT	667	1952	
TRUCK ASSORTMENT	797	*	
TRUCK ASSORTMENT	996	1956	
TRUCK ASST.	0177	1950	
TRUCK ASST.	0246K	1950	
TRUCK ASST.	627	1952	
TRUCK SET, 3 PC.	5090	1962	
TRUCK SET, ALLSTATE	2458-60	1959	
TRUCK SET, ARMED FORCES	4600	1958	
TRUCK SET, KRESGE	5100	1961	
TRUCK TERMINAL	5401-2	1962	
TRUCK TERMINAL	5412	1955	
TRUCK, "ACME" HAULER & VAN TRAILER	3632A	1961	
TRUCK, "ALPHA BETA" HAULER & VAN TRAILER	3632AB	*	
TRUCK, "BIG BOSS CARRIER" W/RAMP & 4 CARS	5250	1965	
TRUCK, "BIG JOB" DUMP	5214	1965	25.00-45.00
TRUCK, "BILLUPS" HAULER & VAN TRAILER	3632B	1957	
TRUCK, "B'LONY" BUBBLE GUM	1191-2	1950s	
TRUCK, "LONG TOME" SHELL SHOOTING CANNON	4469-70	*	
TRUCK, "SHOP-RITE" HAULER & VAN TRAILER	3640SR	1966	
TRUCK, "SHOP-RITE" SUPERMARKET HAULER & VAN	3632SR	*	
TRUCK, "WHITES" HAULER & VAN TRAILER	3631W-32W	1955	
TRUCK, 4-WAY LOAD AND DUMP	685	*	
TRUCK, 4-WAY LOAD AND DUMP	690	1959	
TRUCK, 4-WAY LOAD AND DUMP	692-3	1954	
TRUCK, 4-WAY LOAD AND DUMP W/SHOVEL	685-S	*	
TRUCK, A&P HAULER & VAN TRAILER	3632AP	1961	
TRUCK, A&P VAN TRAILER	1022AP	1962	
TRUCK, AERIAL EXTENSION, FIRE, HOOK & LADDER	3215-6	1956	
TRUCK, AERIAL FIRE, HOOK & LADDER	3213-4	1956	
TRUCK, AIR FORCE	2417	1959	25.00-45.00
TRUCK, AIR FORCE EMERGENCY SEARCHLIGHT	4484AF	1957	
TRUCK, AIR FORCE TRANSPORT	3617-18AF	1957	
TRUCK, ALLIED COMBAT SET (MOBILE S.L. TRK SET)	3689-90	1957	
TRUCK, ALLSTATE AIR FORCE	2417AS	1960	
TRUCK, ALLSTATE DUMP	2408AS	1960	
TRUCK, ALLSTATE HYD. DUMP	2413AS	1960	
TRUCK, ALLSTATE HYD. DUMP	2414AS	1960	
TRUCK, AMPHIBIOUS MARINE	3669-70	1958	
TRUCK, ARM W/CANNON	3621-2	1958	
TRUCK, ARMED FORCES SEARCHLIGHT	4473AF-74F	1957-58	
TRUCK, ARMY	2418	*	
TRUCK, ARMY	497	*	
TRUCK, ARMY ENGINEERS W/WINCH & BOOM	3667-8	1958	
TRUCK, ARMY HEAVY DUTY TRANSPORT	3627-8	1952	
TRUCK, ARMY MOBILE UNIT	3655-6	1956	45.00-75.00

LOUIS MARX & CO., INC.
200 FIFTH AVE. NEW YORK

MARX TOYS

GLENDALE DIV.
F.O.B. Factory — Glendale, W. Va.

a. No. 829 COCA COLA BEVERAGE TRUCK

Truck is equipped with shelves in body and all steel construction. Yellow finish with all the necessary embellishments and trademarks. Six Coca Cola cases with 24 miniature empty bottles furnished with a metal hand truck for carting the cases. Truck equipped with free rolling wheels. Measures: 12⅝" long, 4¾" wide and 5½" high.
PACKED: Each in box
1 doz. to shipping carton
Weight per carton — 29¾ lbs.

b. No. 978 HEAVY GAUGE DUMP TRUCK

The item is constructed of steel, includes a lithographed cab with fender grille and headlight details. Spacious 11" long, 7¼" wide dump body. The Truck is mounted on 4 polyethylene tires. Measures: 17¾" long, 5¼" high, 7¼" wide.
PACKED: ½ doz. to carton
Weight per carton — 11 lbs.

c. No. 1010 FARM STAKE TRUCK

The lithographed steel truck features the following: Cab-over-engine design, Stake body measuring 12¼" long, 6" wide, and 2¾" deep, and free-rolling poly wheels with tin plate hub discs. Measures: 17¾" long, 6¼" wide and 5½" high.
PACKED: ½ doz. to carton
Weight — 19 lbs.

d. No. 868 JEEP WITH CANVAS TARP AND DRIVER

An all heavy gauge steel 11½" jeep which features an opening hood, collapsing windshield and removable canvas camouflage tarpaulin roof. Driver in characteristic pose of polyethylene. Comes with heavy plastic wheels and tin plate hub caps. A "must" item for every junior General's military force.
PACKED: Each in an illustrated carton
½ doz. to a shipper
Weight — 15 lbs.

Page from the *Marx Toys 1964 Promotional Catalog*.

ITEM DESCRIPTION	ITEM NO.(S)	YEARS	PRICE VALUE GUIDE
TRUCK, ARMY SEARCHLIGHT W/806 CANNON	4498	*	
TRUCK, ARMY TRANSPORT	1165-6	1962	
TRUCK, ARMY TRANSPORT	1169	1972-73	
TRUCK, ARMY TRANSPORT	3615	1957	
TRUCK, ARMY TRANSPORT (SEARS)	681-A	1955	
TRUCK, ARMY TRANSPORT CONVOY	3624	1956	
TRUCK, ARMY TRANSPORT W/6 SOLDIERS	1175-6	1963	
TRUCK, ARMY TRANSPORT W/SOLDIERS	3617-8	1955	
TRUCK, ARMY TRANSPORT W/SOLDIERS	3630	*	
TRUCK, ARMY W/3 GERMAN SOLDIERS	1170D	1964	
TRUCK, ARMY W/3 JAPANESE SOLDIERS	1170B	1964	
TRUCK, ARMY W/3 RUSSIAN SOLDIERS	1170C	1964	
TRUCK, ARMY W/3 U.S. MARINES	1170A	1964-65	
TRUCK, ARMY W/CANNON	937-8	1950s	45.00-50.00
TRUCK, ARMY W/CANNON (1900 HAS 5 SOLDIERS)	1899-1900	1957	45.00-50.00
TRUCK, ARMY W/SEARCHLIGHT TRAILER	3653-4	1956	35.00-50.00
TRUCK, ARMY, B/M W/MOTOR NOISE	70	1965	
TRUCK, ARMY, W/CANNON	2452	1959	45.00-50.00
TRUCK, AUTOMATED DUMP	1264	1950s	
TRUCK, B/M CRANE (LI'L WRECKER)	69	1965	
TRUCK, B/M FARM	73	1965	
TRUCK, BAKERY	2566	*	
TRUCK, BAKERY W/BELL	660	*	
TRUCK, BARREL	530-4	*	
TRUCK, BARTONS	2276B	1949	
TRUCK, BARTONS	2286B	1952	
TRUCK, C.O.E. 4-WAY LOAD AND DUMP	695	1954	
TRUCK, C.O.E. CLOSED VAN HAULER & TRAILER	3631-2	1955	
TRUCK, C.O.E. DUMP	683-4	1954	
TRUCK, C.O.E. DUMP	694	1954	
TRUCK, C.O.E. DUMP W/BANK	684-B	*	
TRUCK, C.O.E. GROCERY	711	1954	
TRUCK, C.O.E. HAULER & VAN TRAILER	3641-2	1954	
TRUCK, C.O.E. STAKE	661	1954	
TRUCK, C.O.E. STAKE	681	1954	
TRUCK, C.O.E. W/RIVAL CANS	681-C	*	
TRUCK, CANNON	466	*	
TRUCK, CARPENTERS	662	1949	
TRUCK, CATTLE VAN TRAILER W/VOICE	763-4	1955	
TRUCK, CEMET MIXER	2420	1959	
TRUCK, CEMET MIXER ALLSTATE	2420AS	1960	
TRUCK, CHARMS CANDY	2591	1949	
TRUCK, CIRCUS	2584	*	
TRUCK, CIRCUS	6652HK	1973	
TRUCK, CITIES SERVICE WRECKER W/FLASHER	2602	1958	
TRUCK, COCA-C0LA	1427-8	1950	

ITEM DESCRIPTION	ITEM NO.(S)	YEARS	PRICE VALUE GUIDE
TRUCK, COCA-COLA	1009-10	1957	
TRUCK, COCA-COLA	1087-8	1950s	
TRUCK, COCA-COLA	1089-90	1956	
TRUCK, COCA-COLA	1128	1967	
TRUCK, COCA-COLA	829-30	1955	
TRUCK, COCA-COLA	990-1	1950s	
TRUCK, COCA-COLA PLASTIC	2377-8	*	
TRUCK, COCA-COLA STAKE	1005	1957	
TRUCK, COCA-COLA W/6 CASES	2367	*	
TRUCK, COMBAT UNIT	5166	1963	
TRUCK, COMBAT UNIT	5176A	1964	
TRUCK, COMBAT UNIT W/PLASTIC TANK	5180	1964-65	
TRUCK, CONTRACTORS	534-N	*	
TRUCK, CRANE W/CLAM BUCKET	3734	1956	
TRUCK, CUNNINGHAM	2286C	1951	
TRUCK, CUNNINGHAM	2296C	1952	
TRUCK, CUNNINGHAM DUMP	661-C	1954	
TRUCK, CUNNINGHAM VAN	2276C	1949	
TRUCK, CURTISS CANDY	2391-2	1950s	
TRUCK, CURTISS CANDY	2494	*	
TRUCK, CURTISS CANDY	2975	*	
TRUCK, CURTISS PULL PICKUP	1162C	1950s	
TRUCK, DELIVER MILK	831-32	*	
TRUCK, DELIVERY	1171-2	1960s	
TRUCK, DELIVERY	2552	1952	
TRUCK, DELIVERY	820-21	*	
TRUCK, DELIVERY	830-31	1964	
TRUCK, DUMP	1080	1959	
TRUCK, DUMP	1081-2	1957	
TRUCK, DUMP	1163-4	1962	
TRUCK, DUMP	2024	1960s	
TRUCK, DUMP	204	1950s	
TRUCK, DUMP	524	1952	
TRUCK, DUMP	554	1956	
TRUCK, DUMP	624	1950	
TRUCK, DUMP	654	1956	
TRUCK, DUMP	674	*	
TRUCK, DUMP	961-2	*	
TRUCK, DUMP	977-8	1959	
TRUCK, DUMP	978S	1963	35.00-50.00
TRUCK, DUMP RACK	2408	1959	
TRUCK, DUMP W/SHOVEL	625	1952	
TRUCK, DUMP, W/BLOCKS	544	1955	
TRUCK, DUMP, W/GUM	2985-6	*	
TRUCK, DUMP, W/GUN	2795	*	
TRUCK, EL. MOTORIZED HAULER & VAN	2824	*	

ITEM DESCRIPTION	ITEM NO.(S)	YEARS	PRICE VALUE GUIDE
TRUCK, EMERGENCY SEARCHLIGHT	4483-4	1955	
TRUCK, EMERGENCY WRECKER W/FLASHER	2603-4	1956	
TRUCK, EMERGENCY/PUMPER FIRE	2641-2	1959	
TRUCK, FANNY FARMER	2286FF	1954	
TRUCK, FARM STAKE	1010	1970	
TRUCK, FIRE	628	1950s	50.00-100.00
TRUCK, FIRE	673	1948	
TRUCK, FIRE, HOOK & LADDER	3208	1959	
TRUCK, FIRE, HOOK & LADDER	3211	1959	
TRUCK, FIRE, HOOK & LADDER W/ACTION LADDERS	3217-8	1957	
TRUCK, FIRESTONE PICKUP	896	*	
TRUCK, FIRST NATIONAL HAULER & VAN	3632FN	1960	
TRUCK, FIRST NAT'L STORES VAN TRAILER	1022FN	1962	
TRUCK, FLATBED TRAILER	618-9	*	
TRUCK, FRICTION DUMP	1894	1954	20.00-35.00
TRUCK, FRICTION STAKE	1881	1954	20.00-35.00
TRUCK, GARDENERS	663	1949	
TRUCK, GRAND WAY HAULER & VAN	3632GW	1961	
TRUCK, GRAVEL DUMP	344	1952	
TRUCK, GRAVEL DUMP	495	*	
TRUCK, GROCERY	673	1948	
TRUCK, GUIDED MISSILE	4487-8	1958	
TRUCK, GUIDED MISSILE LAUNCHER	4490	1958	
TRUCK, H.G. DUMP	1085-6	1957	
TRUCK, H.G. DUMP	1083-4	1955	
TRUCK, H.G. DUMP (KRESGE)	2518	*	
TRUCK, H.G. HAULER & VAN TRAILER	3601-2	1959	
TRUCK, H.G. STAKE	670-1	1953	
TRUCK, HANDYMAN W/TOOLS	897-8	1956	
TRUCK, HAULER & 2 TRAILERS W/SHED BOX	835	*	
TRUCK, HAULER & C. TRAILER	833-4	1953	
TRUCK, HAULER & CATTLE VAN TRAILER	3635-6	1955	
TRUCK, HAULER & CATTLE VAN TRAILER	3637-8	1957	
TRUCK, HAULER & CLOSED TRAILER	847-8	1954	
TRUCK, HAULER & CLOSED VAN TRAILER	851-2	*	
TRUCK, HAULER & CLOSED VAN TRAILER	881-2	1957	
TRUCK, HAULER & LIVESTOCK TRAILER	839-40	1953	
TRUCK, HAULER & LIVESTOCK TRL W/ANIMALS	849-50	1954	
TRUCK, HAULER & LIVESTOCK TRL W/COW VOICE	854	*	
TRUCK, HAULER & LOW SIDE TRAILER	3619-20	1955	
TRUCK, HAULER & OPEN TRAILER	831-2	1953	
TRUCK, HAULER & OPEN TRAILER	845-6	1954	
TRUCK, HAULER & STAKE TRAILER	3647-8	1954	
TRUCK, HAULER & STAKE TRAILER	3657-8	1951	
TRUCK, HAULER & STK TRL W/14 FARM ANIMALS	842-P	*	
TRUCK, HAULER & TRAILER ASSORTMENT	657-9	1950	

ITEM DESCRIPTION	ITEM NO.(S)	YEARS	PRICE VALUE GUIDE
TRUCK, HAULER & TRAILER SET	3682	1955	
TRUCK, HAULER & VAN TRAILER	0635-6	1949	
TRUCK, HAULER & VAN TRAILER	0651-2	1952	
TRUCK, HAULER & VAN TRAILER	3634	1957	
TRUCK, HAULER & VAN TRAILER	759-60	1955	
TRUCK, HAULER & VAN, WALGREEN STORES	3232WS	*	
TRUCK, HAULER&CLOSED TRL (SPEC. OKLA. TIRE)	848	*	
TRUCK, HAULER&LIVESTOCK TRL W/VOICE&ANIMALS	854MO	*	
TRUCK, HAULERS & TRAILERS ASST.	0639	1949	
TRUCK, HEAVY DUTY DUMPER	2528	1970	
TRUCK, HEAVY DUTY TRANSPORT	3625-6	1952	
TRUCK, HERSHEYS CANDY	2972	*	
TRUCK, HESS	8000	1972	
TRUCK, HESS CHEMICALS	3000C	1967	
TRUCK, HESS TANK	3000	1967	
TRUCK, HI-LIFT SCISSOR COAL DUMP	724	*	
TRUCK, HI-LIFT SCISSOR SAND & GRAVEL DUMP	723	*	
TRUCK, HI-WAY VAN	785-6	*	
TRUCK, HIGHWAY WRECKER W/FLASHER	2601	1957	
TRUCK, HOME HARDWARE TRAILER	8693	1971	
TRUCK, HOOK & LADDER	3219-20	1958	
TRUCK, HORSE TRAILER	4539	1966	
TRUCK, HOWARD JOHNSON	2286HJ	1952	
TRUCK, HYD. DUMP	1167-8	1962	
TRUCK, HYD. DUMP	2947-8	*	
TRUCK, HYDRAULIC DUMP	1001-2	1959	
TRUCK, HYDRAULIC DUMP	1003-4	1963	
TRUCK, HYDRAULIC DUMP	1006	1964	
TRUCK, HYDRAULIC DUMP	1023-4	1957	
TRUCK, HYDRAULIC DUMP	1027-8	1950s	
TRUCK, HYDRAULIC DUMP	2547-8	1959	
TRUCK, HYDRUALIC DUMP	1035-6	1950s	
TRUCK, HYDRUALIC DUMP	2414	1959	
TRUCK, ICE	498	*	
TRUCK, ICE	675	1960	
TRUCK, INTERNATIONAL TASK FORCE	1173	1967	
TRUCK, JEEP PICKUP	871-2	*	
TRUCK, JEEP PICKUP, WRECKER	873-4	*	
TRUCK, KANSAS CITY DELIVERY	M-149-50	1954	
TRUCK, KENTUCKY DERBY HORSE VAN	770	1957	
TRUCK, LADDER DUMP	634	1955	
TRUCK, LARGE HAULER & VAN TRAILER	3651	1953	
TRUCK, LARGE HAULER & VAN TRAILER	3652	1950	
TRUCK, LARGE HAULER & VAN TRAILER	3661-2	1955	
TRUCK, LARGE POLY DUMP	1150-P	1960s	
TRUCK, LARGE STEEL COAL	963-4	1957	

ITEM DESCRIPTION	ITEM NO.(S)	YEARS	PRICE VALUE GUIDE
TRUCK, LITHO COAL	694	*	
TRUCK, LITHO COAL DUMP	264	*	
TRUCK, LITHO DELIVERY	672	*	
TRUCK, LITHO DELIVERY	782	*	
TRUCK, LITHO DUMP	494	*	
TRUCK, LITHO TRAILER & COUPE	850	*	
TRUCK, LIVESTOCK HUALER TRAILER	852MO	*	
TRUCK, LOAD & DUMP	2362	1952	
TRUCK, LOAD & DUMP	847-P	*	
TRUCK, LOAD & DUMP (894-1949)	894-5	1953	
TRUCK, LOAD & DUMP W/SCOPE	850-P	1959	
TRUCK, LOAD & LIFT	1033-4	1957	
TRUCK, LOAD AND DUMP W/LIGHTS	696	1957	
TRUCK, LOBLAW'S HAULER & VAN	3632L	1962	
TRUCK, LOFT VAN	2276L	1949	
TRUCK, LOG TRAILER W/LOGS	845-6	1951	
TRUCK, LRG. AUTO TRANSPORT W/FRICTION CARS	3663-4	1957	
TRUCK, LRG. AUTO TRANSPORT W/FRICTION CARS	3665-6	1958	
TRUCK, LUMAR DUMP	1017-18	1953	
TRUCK, LUMAR VAN	1011-12	1954	
TRUCK, LUMAR VAN	1012-14	1950s	
TRUCK, LUMBER HAULER & TRAILER	3645-6	1956	
TRUCK, MACHINERY MOVING	1015-16	1951	
TRUCK, MAGNETIC CRANE	975-6	1954	50.00-75.00
TRUCK, MARINE CORPS	682	1958	
TRUCK, MARSHALL	2286M	1951	
TRUCK, MARSHALL	2296M	1952	
TRUCK, MARSHALL DUMP	661-M	1954	
TRUCK, MEAT	2568	*	
TRUCK, MECH. DELIVERY	930-31	*	
TRUCK, MECH. DELIVERY STAKE	2381	1950s	
TRUCK, MECH. DUMP	1466	*	
TRUCK, MECH. FIRE	1148	1950s	
TRUCK, MECH. FIRE PUMPER	1445-6	*	
TRUCK, MECH. FIRE TRAILER	755-6	*	
TRUCK, MECH. HAULER & TRAILER	742	*	
TRUCK, MECH. HOOK & LADDER	1443-4	*	
TRUCK, MECH. HYD. DUMP	1013-14	1956	
TRUCK, MECH. HYD. DUMP	1017-18	1950s	
TRUCK, MECH. HYDRAULIC DUMP	1003-4	1958	
TRUCK, MECH. LOG HAULING TRAILER	753-4	*	
TRUCK, MECH. OVERHEAD DUMP	1474	*	
TRUCK, MECH. PANEL DUMP	1471	*	
TRUCK, MECH. PICKUP	1475	*	
TRUCK, MECH. PICKUP	442	*	
TRUCK, MECH. PICKUP DELIVERY	2380	1950s	

ITEM DESCRIPTION	ITEM NO.(S)	YEARS	PRICE VALUE GUIDE
TRUCK, MECH. PL. DUMP	2374	*	
TRUCK, MECH. PL. OVERHEAD DUMP	2375	*	
TRUCK, MECH. PL. STATE	2371	1950s	
TRUCK, MECH. PL. VAN	1172	1960s	
TRUCK, MECH. PL. WRECKER	2373	*	
TRUCK, MECH. PLASTIC PANEL	1176	1960s	
TRUCK, MECH. STAKE	1464	*	
TRUCK, MECH. STAKE TRAILER	737-8	*	
TRUCK, MECH. TANK TRAILER	733-4	*	
TRUCK, MECH. TRAILER ASSORTMENT	757	*	
TRUCK, MECH. VAN	1473	*	
TRUCK, MECH. VAN TRAILER	735-6	*	
TRUCK, MECH. WRECKER	1448	*	
TRUCK, MECH. WRECKER	1472	*	
TRUCK, MILITARY HAULER W/STK TLR & SOLDIERS	831-P	1958	
TRUCK, MILITARY HAULER W/STK TRL & 16 SOLDIERS	841-P	1958	
TRUCK, MILITARY MOBILE ARMORED COMBAT SET	3687-8	1957	
TRUCK, MILITARY TRANSPORT W/CANNON	1897-8	1955	
TRUCK, MILK	674	*	
TRUCK, MILK, W/SLIDING DOOR	1528	*	
TRUCK, MINI. DUMP	134	1957	
TRUCK, MINI. STAKE	131	1950s	
TRUCK, MOBILE CRANE	2721-2	1956	
TRUCK, MOBILE CRANE CONSTRUCTION	2733-4	1957/65	
TRUCK, NEWBERRY VAN	792-J	1961	
TRUCK, NEWBERRY'S HAULER & VAN	3632JJ	1961	
TRUCK, NORTH AMERICAN HAULER & VAN	752-NA	*	
TRUCK, NOVELTY ASSORTMENT	677-8	*	
TRUCK, NOVELTY ASSORTMENT	696-7-8	*	
TRUCK, NOVELTY ASSORTMENT	715-7	1954	
TRUCK, ONE MAN DELIVERY (MILKMAN)	527-8	*	
TRUCK, OVERSIZE DUMP	345	*	
TRUCK, OVERSIZE MECH. DUMP	445	1948	
TRUCK, PAINTERS	664	1949	
TRUCK, PANEL DELIVERY	1426	1950s	
TRUCK, PATHE NEWS W/6-7 CAMERA ON TOP	51-2	*	
TRUCK, PEPSI-COLA	2467	1950s	35.00-50.00
TRUCK, PEPSI COLA	1105-6	1950	
TRUCK, PET SHOP W/DOGS	2563-4	1951	45.00-65.00
TRUCK, PICKUP	1262	1950s	
TRUCK, PICKUP	1421-22	1950s	
TRUCK, PICKUP	342	*	
TRUCK, PICKUP	672	*	
TRUCK, PICKUP	892-3	*	
TRUCK, PICKUP (ARMY ALSO)	0174	*	
TRUCK, PICKUP DUMP	341-3	*	

ITEM DESCRIPTION	ITEM NO.(S)	YEARS	PRICE VALUE GUIDE
TRUCK, PICKUP W/CONTENTS	899-900	1957	
TRUCK, PICKUP W/LIGHTS	1071-2	1960s	
TRUCK, PICKUP W/LIGHTS	1091-2	1960s	
TRUCK, PICKUP W/TRAILER	875-6	1958	
TRUCK, PL. DUMP TRUCK W/TOOTSIE ROLLS	2671-2	*	
TRUCK, PL. DUMP, LIFE-SAVERS	2490-1	*	
TRUCK, PL. LOAD BUILDERS DUMP	2372	1950s	
TRUCK, PL. OVERHEAD DUMP	2475	*	
TRUCK, PL. PULL PICKUP	1162	1950s	
TRUCK, PL. PULL PICKUP	1163-4	1960s	
TRUCK, PL. PULL VAN	2376	*	
TRUCK, PL. VAN TRUCK W/TOOTSIE FRUITEES	2675-6	*	
TRUCK, PL. VAN W/BEDROOM	2521-2	*	
TRUCK, PL. VAN W/DINING ROOM	2529-30	*	
TRUCK, PL. VAN W/KITCHEN	2523-4	*	
TRUCK, PL. VAN W/LIVING ROOM	2519-20	*	
TRUCK, PL. VAN W/TOOTSIE CHEWEES	2673-4	*	
TRUCK, PL. VAN W/TOOTSIE MIDGIES	2678	*	
TRUCK, PLATFORM (ARMY ALSO)	0172	*	
TRUCK, PLUMBER REPAIR PICKUP	1093-4	1960s	
TRUCK, POLY HAULER & VAN TRAILER	851P-2P	*	
TRUCK, POM POM CANNON	4471-2	*	
TRUCK, POWERHOUSE AIR FORCE	2537-8	1959	
TRUCK, POWERHOUSE CEMENT MIXER	2549-50	1960	
TRUCK, POWERHOUSE DUMP	2527-8	1959/68-69/71-72-73	
TRUCK, POWERHOUSE DUMP W/PWR STEERING	2927-8	1962/65	
TRUCK, POWERHOUSE HYD. DUMP	2987-8	1964-65	
TRUCK, POWERHOUSE HYD. DUMP W/PWR STEERING	2588	1961/69-70/73	
TRUCK, POWERHOUSE HYD. DUMP W/PWR. STEERING	2588	1968	
TRUCK, POWERHOUSE SCISSORS HYD. DUMP	2567-8	1959/65	
TRUCK, POWERHOUSE SCISSORS HYD. DUMP	2967-8	1964	
TRUCK, POWERHOUSE STAKE RACK	2525-6	1959	
TRUCK, POWERHOUSE VAN	2929-30	1962	
TRUCK, POWERHOUSE WRECKER	2535-6	1959/68-69/72-73	
TRUCK, POWERHOUSE WRECKER	2935-6	1962/65	
TRUCK, PULL HAULER & OPEN VAN	633-4-6	1949	
TRUCK, PULL HAULER AND FIRE TRAILER	655-6	1949	
TRUCK, PULL HAULER AND LITHO VAN	651-2	1949	
TRUCK, PULL HAULER AND LOG TRAILER	653-4	1949	
TRUCK, PUMPER FIRE	4000	1969	
TRUCK, PUSH LEVER TOW	1440	1950s	
TRUCK, RAILWAY EXPRESS W/LEVER ACT. TAILGATE	1021-2	1957	
TRUCK, RAILWAY EXPRESS W/LEVER ACT. TAILGATE	1032	1958	
TRUCK, REED DRUG	671-R	1952	
TRUCK, REED DUMP	2024R	1960s	
TRUCK, REVOLVING SEARCHLIGHT	2426	1959	

ITEM DESCRIPTION	ITEM NO.(S)	YEARS	PRICE VALUE GUIDE
TRUCK, REVOLVING SEARCHLIGHT ALLSTATE	2426AS	1960	
TRUCK, RIDE'EM MARX EXPRESS	3032	1968	
TRUCK, ROCKER DUMP	1751	1964	
TRUCK, ROCKET LAUNCHER	2565-6	*	
TRUCK, ROCKET LAUNCHER	4467-8	1958	
TRUCK, SAND & GRAVEL DUMP	534	1953	
TRUCK, SANITATION	678-9	*	
TRUCK, SCISSORS ACTION DUMP	857	*	
TRUCK, SCISSORS DUMP	2424	1959	
TRUCK, SEARCHLIGHT	2545-6	1959	
TRUCK, SEARCHLIGHT	4474	1955	
TRUCK, SEARCHLIGHT	4594-5	1954	
TRUCK, SEARCHLIGHT TRAILER	4463	1957	
TRUCK, SEARCHLIGHT W/REVOLVING LIGHT	4493-4	1958	
TRUCK, SEARS HAULER & VAN TRAILER	3566	1958	
TRUCK, SIGNAL	2479	1951	
TRUCK, SINCLAIR HAULER & TANK TRAILER	837-8	1954	
TRUCK, SIREN FIRE	8990-9000	*	
TRUCK, SOLDIERS	484	*	
TRUCK, SPEC. BOWMAN MILK	836	*	
TRUCK, SPEC. HOOK&LADDER FIRE FOR CANADA	6770	1958	
TRUCK, SPEC. TEXACO PUMPER FIRE	2643	*	
TRUCK, SPECIAL DUMP W/09 LEVER	1001	1967	
TRUCK, STAKE	1001-2	1954	
TRUCK, STAKE	1006-7	1958	
TRUCK, STAKE	1008	1957	
TRUCK, STAKE	1159-60	1962	
TRUCK, STAKE	531	*	
TRUCK, STAKE	551	1955	
TRUCK, STAKE	561	1956	
TRUCK, STAKE	651	1956	
TRUCK, STAKE	675	1955	
TRUCK, STAKE	675-6	1955	
TRUCK, STAKE (LARGE STEEL)	891	*	
TRUCK, STAKE (SEARS)	676-S	*	
TRUCK, STAKE RACK	2406	1959	
TRUCK, STAKE TRAILER	855-6	*	
TRUCK, STAKE TRAILER W/CONTENTS	857-8	*	
TRUCK, STAKE W/BLOCKS	541	*	
TRUCK, STAKE W/LIGHTS	1091-2	1960s	
TRUCK, STAKE W/LIGHTS	F1071-2	*	
TRUCK, STAKE W/RUBBER TOYS	671-S	1948	
TRUCK, STAKE W/STEERS	1006S	1950s	
TRUCK, STAKE, "LAZY DAYS FARM"	1010	1959/65/71-72-73	
TRUCK, STAKE, W/BANK	661-B	*	
TRUCK, STAKE, W/GUN	2790	*	

ITEM DESCRIPTION	ITEM NO.(S)	YEARS	PRICE VALUE GUIDE
TRUCK, SWIFTS VAN	2376S	1950s	
TRUCK, TANDEM HAULER & CATTLE TRUCK SET	3673-4	1957	
TRUCK, TANDEM HAULER & VAN TRAILER SET	3671-2	1957	
TRUCK, TANDEM HAULER & VAN TRAILER SET	947-8	*	
TRUCK, TELEPHONE	1043	1950s	
TRUCK, TELEPHONE W/ACCESS.	1041-2	1950s	
TRUCK, TELEPHONE, PL.	2479	*	
TRUCK, TELEPHONE, PLASTIC	2379	*	
TRUCK, TOY TOWN EXPRESS VAN	779-80	1954	75.00-100.00
TRUCK, TOY TOWN VAN	775-6	1953	
TRUCK, TRAILER TRAIN	1437-8	1950s	
TRUCK, TRAILER, TRANS. SET	997-8	*	
TRUCK, U.S. MAIL HAULER & VAN TRAILER	3631M-2M	*	
TRUCK, U.S. MAIL VAN	781-2	1956	
TRUCK, U.S. MAIL VAN	791-92	1957	
TRUCK, U.S. MAIL VAN (SEARS)	792-S	1957	
TRUCK, U.S.M.C. AMPHIBIOUS	3670	1964	
TRUCK, UNITED PARCEL POST	2559-60	1951	
TRUCK, UNITED VAN LINES	642	*	
TRUCK, UNITED VAN LINES	742	*	
TRUCK, UTILITY SERVICE	2941-2	*	
TRUCK, UTILITY TELEPHONE	935-6	1958	
TRUCK, VACATION	499	*	
TRUCK, VAN	2276	1949	
TRUCK, VAN	2466	*	
TRUCK, WALGREEN HAULER & VAN ICE CREAM TRK.	852W	*	
TRUCK, WALGREEN SALERNO	779-W	1956	
TRUCK, WESTERN AUTO HAULER & STAKE TRAILER	3639	1967	
TRUCK, WHISTLING FIRE W/BELL	62	1964	
TRUCK, WILLY'S PICKUP	1077-8	1960s	
TRUCK, WINCH	677	*	
TRUCK, WINCH W/STEAM SHOVEL	898-99	1953	
TRUCK, WOOLWORTH'S HAULER & VAN	3632FWW	1962	
TRUCK, WOOLWORTHS VAN TRAILER	1022FWW	1962	
TRUCK, WRECKER	496	*	
TRUCK, WRECKER	2536	1970	
TRUCK, WRECKER	2416	1959	50.00-75.00
TRUCK, WRECKER SET	1025-6	1957	
TRUCK, WRECKER TOWING	625-6	1955	
TRUCK, WRECKER, ALLSTATE	2416AS	1960	
TRUCK, WRECKER, CITIES SERVICES	2536CS	*	
TRUCK, WRECKER, MINI. T.A.P.	0243-4	1953	
TRUCK,W RECKER	1423-4	1950s	
TRUCK,WRECKER	1173-4	1962	
TRUCK,WRECKER	636	*	
TRUCKS ASST.	1507	1950s	

U.S. Armed Forces training center box.

ITEM DESCRIPTION	ITEM NO.(S)	YEARS	PRICE VALUE GUIDE
TRUCKS, ASST. (8)	0358-9	1953	
TRUCKS, FLEET OF CANDY	2999	*	
TRUCKS, MECH. ASST.	441-3	1949	
TRUCKS, MIGHTY MARX	6782J	1973	
TRUCKS, MILITARY, ASST.	0687	1951	
TRUCKS, SCOOT MARX	6813J	1973	
TUGBOAT	6320	1970-71-72	
TUGBOAT	66B	1969/73	
TWIN RUNNER ICE SKATES	752-3	*	
TWINKIE DOLL W/MOLDED CLOTHING	1670	1966	
TWINKIE DOLLS (PARIS, HONG KONG, NEW YORK)	1662A,B,&C	1967	
TWO-CAR GARAGE W/T.A.P. CARS	4825-6	1954	
TYPEWRITER DESK	7102	1966	
TYPEWRITER W/DRAWER	5423J	1973	25.00-35.00
U.N.C.L.E. BAGATELLE	G-194	1966	
U.S. ARTILLERY SET (SEARS)	874	1964	
U.S. CAPITOL BUILDING	4901-2	1950s	35.00-50.00
U.S. CAPITOL BUILDING	4909-10	1954	35.00-50.00
U.S. CAPITOL BUILDING	4912	1954	35.00-50.00
U.S. CAPITOL BUILDING W/PRESIDENTS	4915-6	1963	50.00-75.00
U.S. MILITARY POST W/METAL PORTS	2706	1957	
UNDER & OVER	G-47	1964	
UNITED STATES LINER KIT	M-161-2	1954	
UPPER/LOWER CASE TYPEWRITER	6893J	1973	25.00-35.00
USED CAR LOT	2600	1950s	
USED CAR LOT	2650	1950s	
VACUUM CLEANER	82	*	
VACUUM CLEANER	794	1970	

ITEM DESCRIPTION	ITEM NO.(S)	YEARS	PRICE VALUE GUIDE
VACUUM CLEANER	794B	1973	
VACUUM CLEANER W/NOISE	184	1960s	
VALOR HORSE W/SILVER ARMOR	5361	1968-71	20.00-35.00
VAN, ALLSTATE AIRLIFT HYD.	2411AS	1960	
VAN, DELIVERY	2412	1959	
VANITY	7110	1970	
VANITY & HAIR DRYER SET	7121	1968	
VANITY REFILL (COSMETICS)	7114RF	1965	
VANITY SET	7159	1973	
VANITY TABLE W/LIGHTS & HASSOCK	7154	1967/72	
VANITY W/HASSOCK	7172MO	1973	
VANITY W/NEW HASSOCK	7168	1971-72-73	
VANITY W/O LIGHTS, LITTLE HOSTESS	7112 & MO	1969-70	
VEGETABLE GARDEN W/IRRIGATION SYSTEM	3901	1963	25.00-45.00
VEHICLE SET, ARMY	0667	*	
VEHICLE, ARMY, ASST.	0637	*	
VEHICLE, PLASTIC ASSORTMENT	0146	1949	
VEHICLES, ASST. MILITARY	0259-60	*	
VEHICLES, CONSTRUCTION ASST.	1127	1954	
VEHICLES, MECH. PLASTIC ASST.	1177-8	1960s	
VEHICLES, PL. ASST.	1449	*	
VIKING & HORSE	5434MO	1970	35.00-45.00
VIKING HORSE	5381	1970-71	20.00-30.00
VILLAGE BUILDING DISPLAY, 5 PC.	3897/D	1950s	
VILLAGE BUILDINGS, ASST. PRE-FAB	3894-5-6	1954	25.00-35.00
VILLAGE, TOY TOWN, ASST. W/DEMO	3899	1953	
VOODOO JET SCALE MODEL KIT	M-103-4	1953	
WAGON, STREAMLINE	119-20	1948	
WAGON, SUPERSPORT RALLY	3073	1972-73	
WAGON, TEA	128	1950s	
WASHING MACHINE	K-53-4	1954	25.00-50.00
WEATHER GAME	G-70	1964	
WEAVING SET (BLUE CHIP)	4188	1971	
WELLS FARGO STAGE COACH KIT	M-151-2	1953	
WELSH PONY (BAY)	1061A	1967	15.00-25.00
WELSH PONY (PALOMINO)	1061B	1967	15.00-25.00
WESTERN COWBOYS & HORSES	55/9	1956	2.00-3.00 each
WESTERN HORSE & SADDLE	3176MO	1952	10.00-15.00
WESTERN STAGECOACH SET (LG. COWBOYS & INDIANS)	1395	1965	45.00-65.00
WESTERN TOWN W/VACUUM SHEET	4260	1965	
WHEELBARROW	121-22	1950s	
WHEELBARROW, MINI.	150-51	1948	3.00-8.00
WHISTLING MALLET, "GIANT SOCK IT"	310	1969-70/73	
WHITE HOUSE	3901-2	1954	35.00-50.00
WHITE HOUSE W/33 PRESIDENTS & IKE & MAMIE	3918-20	1954	50.00-100.00
WHITE HOUSE W/8 PRESIDENTS & IKE & MAMIE	3912	1954	45.00-75.00

ITEM DESCRIPTION	ITEM NO.(S)	YEARS	PRICE VALUE GUIDE
WHITE HOUSE W/9 PRESIDENTS (WARDS)	3911	1954	45.00-75.00
WHITE HOUSE W/PRESIDENT	3921MO	1972	45.00-50.00
WHITE HOUSE W/PRESIDENTS	3909-10	1954	50.00-75.00
WIDE TRACKER	3095	1973	
WILD ANIMAL SET	3179-80	1955	3.00-5.00 each
WILD ANIMAL SET	54/16-17	1957	3.00-5.00 each
WILD LIFE SET (31 PIECES)	54/6	1957	2.00-5.00 each
WILD RIDER	5888	1971-72	
WILD RIDER DISPLAY	588D	1971	
WILLY JEEP (867 W/METAL WHEELS, 868 W/R. WHEELS)	867-8	1964	
WILLYS JEEP W/TRAILER	887-8	1957	
WINGSHOT BAGATELLE	G-68	1970/73	
WISE PLUTO	40-41	*	
WORKERS, CONSTRUCTION, ASST.	0784	1950s	2.00-3.00 each
WORLD GLOBE	107-8	1951	
WYATT EARP DODGE CITY	4226	1958	
WYATT EARP DODGE CITY	4228	1957	
ZA-ZOOM FRICTION RACER	780	1964	
ZA-ZOOM LAWN MOWER	790	1964-65/69	
ZA-ZOOM LAWNMOWER	790B	1973	
ZA-ZOOM VACUUM CLEANER	794	1965/69-70	
ZEB ZACHARY CALVARY FIGURE	1862	1968/70	25.00-45.00
ZOOM MOBILE (37-1/2"L,15"H, 14"W)	4830	1965	
ZORRO RIDER & HORSE	2801-2	1958	15.00-25.00

U. S. Presidents, gold/bronze finish, 1960s. (T. Spencer collection, photo by M. L. Smith)

Plastic Mold Assignment Numbers for Figures and Accessories

In the course of my research on the Marx Toy Company's Glen Dale plant, I came across many fascinating facts. One, in particular, that stood out from the other items of record was a listing for plastic figures and accessories produced for service stations, dollhouses and the numerous play sets. Gaylord Whipkey said that each year blocks of approximately 100 numbers would be established for assignment to new plastic mold items. This block of numbers might vary a little, he noted, but 100 numbers was generally the rule. **The PL-Number (mold number) did not appear on the item(s) itself or packaging. The only number appearing on the packaging was the assigned Item Number for any Marx Toy Company item.**

Gaylord stated that many PL-Numbers listed for the 1950s were likely those molds used in the Famous Marx Miniature Sculptured Figures or used for the numerous play sets and/or dollhouses. Gaylord also stated that the Model Department even created "early" molds of some political candidates before they were actually elected to office. If or when the candidate did win, his mold was already established, and it could promptly be put into production.

The following listings are not a complete Marx Toy Company listing of all molds ever made, but they do shed new light on the complex line of plastic molds that were used to produce countless Marx Toy Company figures and accessories. Although only a partial listing of molds, it does provide a better idea of when some items were manufactured.

Marx Toy Company artists and modelers were quite talented and creative, and they used many different approaches when they were creating a new toy mold. They often used photographs, drawings, or other information supplied by government agencies and movie production companies as a guide. This material provided the basis for creating authentic looking figure and accessory molds.

Keep in mind that the following listings are not totally complete, and that there are possibly some gaps because information was taken from only a relatively few sheets of still-retrievable papers. They are grouped here by early, mid, or late-years of production (1950s/early 1960s).

NOTE: Keep in mind that these PL-Numbers are NOT assigned item numbers. Only assigned item numbers were printed on the final packaging of Marx Toy Company products. The PL- numbers are only assigned *mold* numbers.

People, Figures & Accessories

Early 1950s

PL-#	Item
81	Dollhouse People
170	Family People - Standing
192	Sitting People
193	Railroad Figures
194	Service Station Figures
195	Farm People
200	Fire Chief
322	Frontiersmen
323	Mounties
330	Huntsmen
359	Rodeo Figures
366	Band Figures
367	Circus Figures
378	Railroad Figures & Farm Figures
379	Church & Service Station People
379-1	Service Station People
379-2	House People
379-3	Church Figures
409	Circus People

Mid-1950s

PL-#	Item
415	Sailors
416	Roy Rogers Figure
416A	Standing Roy Rogers
421	Ranch Children
428	Dollhouse Children
442	Cavalry Figures
445	Railroad Figures (thins)
479	Space Cadet Figures
480	Super Circus Figures
490	Space Patrol Figures (12 different designs)
493	Fantasy Figures
494	School House Figures
495	Super Market Figures
497	Lone Ranger Figures
503	Disney Peter Pan Figures
504	Tight Rope Circus Figures
505	Space Cadet Figures
508	Comic Figures

PL-#	Item
509	Comic Figures
534	Construction Camp Figures
535	Large Space Figures-4" Tall
541	Police Station Figures
542	Fire Station Figures
586	Air Corps Figures
592	Pirate Figures
596	Sports Figures
601	West Point Cadets
602	Chauffeur
603	Prince Valiant Figures
607	Firemen
612	Eisenhower Figure
616	Military Academy Figures
622	Lincoln & Washington Figures
622A	Lincoln, Washington, Ike, Kennedy
623	Presidential Figures

PL-#	Item
624	Presidential Figures
632	Presidential Figures
633	Ike
634	Mamie Eisenhower
635	Jack & Wrench
637	Generals
638	General Vandegrift
639	Ike (w/hands up)
648	Leaders of U. S. Forces
649	Leaders of U. S. Forces
650	Miniature Ike
651	Winston Churchill
655	Miniature Presidential Figures
655A	Jackie Kennedy
656	British Royal Family
659	Adlai Stevenson
660	Harry S. Truman
661	President Roosevelt

Mid- Late-1950s

PL-#	Item
726A	Davy Crockett
728	Official Davy Crockett
729	Miniature Davy Crockett
735	Mexicans and Davy Crockett
737	Nurse & Babies
738	American Beauty
739	Pope Pius XII
740	Robin Hood Figures
740A	Robin Hood Merrymen
740B	Official Robin Hood Figures
741	Roy Rogers and Davy Crockett-4"

PL-#	Item
742	Arabian Figures
743	French Foreign Legion Figures
744	Roy Rogers & Davy Crockett Accessories
744A	Roy Rogers Accessories
744B	Davy Crockett Accessories
745	Alamo Frontiersmen
746	Prehistoric Cavemen
748	Viking Figures
752	Anthony Eden
753	Boy Scouts
756	Louis Marx Figure
766	Jackie Gleason

Late 1950s

PL-#	Item
800	Bride and Groom
807	African Hunters
808	African Natives
808A	African Natives (shut off Tamba)
5	Robin Hood Figures-2-1/4"
16	Robin Hood Accessories
17	Robin Hood Merrymen
51	Firemen Figures
51A	Firemen Figures-3-1/4"

PL-#	Item
851B	Firemen Figures
852	Telephone Workers
863	Construction Workers-3-1/2"
866	Colonial Rider (Johnny Tremain)
867	Rusty Figure
868	Rusty and Colonial Rider Accessories
879	Roy Rogers Figures
880	Civilian Figures
880A	Civilian Figures

PL-#	Item
885	Pat Brady-Dale Evans-Bullet
892	Johnny Tremain Figures
896	Truck Drivers
897	Wyatt Earp
898	Farm People
900	Revolutionary War Riders
901	Dollhouse People (obsolete)
901A	Dollhouse People (new)
902	Generals Grant & Lee, President Lincoln
902A	Davis, Lincoln, Grant & Lee
904	Buffalo Bill (canceled)
912	Arctic Eskimo
913	Arctic Explorer Set
922	Lone Ranger & Tonto-2-1/4"
928	Sailors-2-1/4"
929	Combat Marines
936	Zorro Figures
949	Marine -6"
949A	Marines-6"
968	Zorro Riding Figure w/cape
969	Zorro Character
970	Mexicans
971	Wagon Train Drivers
973	Nixon
974	Major Adams & Flint McCullough
976	Civil War Figures
982	Cape Canaveral Figures

PL-#	Item
983	Prince & Princess
991	Wagon Driver & Whip
1000	Figures for 1910 Ford
1013	Sleeping Beauty Figures-2-1/4" (canceled)
1014	Alaska Frontier Figures
1014A	Alaska Figures
1014B	Alaska Figures
1015	Riflemen Figures
1037	Roman Figures
1038	Ben Hur Figures
1059	Airport Figures
1059A	Airport Figures (no Jet Pilot, Radioman, Fireman)
1059B	Airport Figures (no Jet Pilot, man w/CO-2)
1059C	Airport Figures
1059D	Airport Figures
1073	Gunsmoke Figures
1074	Johnny Ringo
1079	Senator Kennedy
1080	Magic Marxie (Marx Company Logo Character)
1081	Skin Diver & accessories
1089	Jeff Davis
1093	Civil War Figures
1096	Elliot Ness & Al Capone
1097	Untouchables Characters

Early 1960s

PL-#	Item
1103	Jointed Dollhouse Figures
1120	Astronauts
1128	Flinstone Figures
1130	Store Figures-1-1/2"
1131	Still-Untouchables
1136	Professor Ludwig Van Drake
1139	Flinstone Figures-3-1/2" (1 Barney & 1 tree)
1151	Pirates-(Cavities only)

PL-#	Item
1152	Jacqueline Kennedy
1184	The Gallant Men
1196	Japanese Figures-5-1/2"
1196-1	Japanese Figures-5-1/2"
1222	Cavalry Figures-5-1/2"
1223	Viking Figures-5-1/2"
1224	Knight Figure-5-1/2"
1225	Frontiersmen Figure-5-1/2"

Early-Mid-1960s

PL-#	Item
1226	Daniel Boone Arms
1227	Daniel Boone Body
1230	Frontiersmen Figures-2-1/4"

PL-#	Item
1240	Erie Stony Fig. Mold #19939-2 Body
1241	Erie Stony Fig. Mold #19940-8 Arms
1242	Erie Stony Fig. Mold #19937, Head & Hands

PL-#	Item
246	Knights-2-1/4"
247	Viking Figures-2-1/4"
248	French Figures
249	British Figures
250	Russian Figures
255	Articulated Stony Smith
266-2J	Jesse James Body, Arms & Legs
271-72	All American Player
290	Vice President Humphrey-2-7/8"
291	Vice President Humphrey-2-7/8"
292	35 Cast President Figures for Hong Kong-2-1/2"
293	5 Case Cav./Presidential Statutes for Hong Kong
303	Daniel Boone Rifle Set Canteen Cap
307	International Secret Agent-11-1/2"-accessories
307-1	International Secret Agent Acc's Dup. Mold
308	Secret Agent Vinyl Accessories
309	Mike Hazard's Body, Arms & Legs
309-1	Mike Hazard - Dup. Mold
311	Secret Agent Head, Hands, and False Faces
327	Eisenhower Figures-2-3/4"
328	Pope Paul VI Figure for Hong Kong
331	Zorro Guard
332	Secret Agent Figure-6"
333	Goldwater Figure-2-5/8"
334	President Johnson Figure-2-5/8"
335	President Johnson Figure-1-1/2"
336	U.N.C.L.E. Figures
337	Jesse James Body, Legs
338	Cast Cav. 2-1/2" President Johnson
1339	Cast Cav. 2-1/2" President Roosevelt w/cap (F.D.)
1340	Cast Cav. 2-1/2" President Eisenhower
1341	Cast Cav. 2-1/2" President George Washington
1351	Girl Spy-11"
1352	Girl Spy Accessories
1362	Man from U.N.C.L.E.
1368B	General Custer Head
1369	Lady Finger White Vinyl Acc. Mold
1370	Ann Danger-11" -Girl Spy Clothing
1375	Cast Cav. John Adams for Hong Kong
1376	Cast Cav. Thomas Jefferson for Hong Kong
1377	Cast Cav. James Monroe for Hong Kong
1378	Cav. James Madison for Hong Kong
1379	Cav. John Q. Adams for Hong Kong
1380	Cav. William Harrison for Hong Kong
1381	Cav. John Tyler for Hong Kong
1385C	Service Station Attendant
1401	Girl Spy-11"-Head & Hands
1412A	General Custer Torso
1419	Football Players-2-3/8"
1429	Romney Figure-2-3/4"
1433	Super Heroes Figures-6"
1437	Robert Kennedy Figure for Hong Kong
1438	Rockefeller Figure-2-1/4"-for Hong Kong
1439	Governor Reagan-2-1/4"
1448	Percy Figure-2-3/4"
1455	7-1/2" Astronaut Body, Arms & Legs
1471	Dollhouse People (Model #2775)
1480	Senator Eugene McCarthy for Hong Kong
1500	Astronauts-6"
1503	Apollo Figures-2-3/8"

Cowboys, Indians & Accessories

Early- Mid-1950s

PL-#	Item
29	Cowboys
24A	Cowboys Figure (to be used in PL-324 shoe)
28	Riding Cowboys
29	Standing Cowboys
89	Cowboys (14 x 2 Rifle)
98	Thin Cowboys
16	Roy Rogers
416A	Standing Roy Rogers
463	Cowboy Figures
597	Cowboy Bodies & Arms
598	Cowboy Legs
599	Cowboy Heads
600	Cowboy Vests & Hats
668	Cowboys

PL-#	Item	PL-#	Item
672	Cowboys & Indians	744A	Roy Rogers accessories
718	Cowboys	776	Cowboy Rider for 775 Horse Cowboy accessories
744	Roy Rogers - Davy Crockett accessories	791	Cowboys - 3-1/2"

Mid- Late-1950s

PL-#	Item	PL-#	Item
833	Cowboys	891	Cowboy & Indian accessories
879	Roy Rogers Figures	891B	Cowboy accessories

Mid-1960s

PL-#	Item	PL-#	Item
1219	Cowboys - 5-1/2"	1345	7-1/2" Cowboy accessories
1323	11-1/2" Cowgirl Head & Hands	1348	James West Body
1323A	New Jane West Head	1356	James West Poly accessories
1324	11-1/2" Cowgirl accessories	1367	James West Head
1325	11-1/2" Cowgirl Body, Arms & Legs & accessories	1368A	James West Head
1342	7-1/2" Cowboy Bad Guy Body, Arms & Legs	1403	Johnny West Jr., Body & Arms
1343	7-1/2" Cowboy Good Guy Body, Arms & Legs	1404	Johnny West, Jr., Head & Hands
1344	7-1/2" Cowboy Good Guy Head & Hands	1405	Johnny West, Jr., accessories
		1406	Johnny West Cowgirl Body, Arms & Legs
		1407	9-1/2" Cowgirl Vinyl accessories
		1408	9-1/2" Cowgirl Head & Hands

Dollhouse Furniture & Accessories

1949

PL-#	Item	PL-#	Item
68	Living Room Furniture	75	Bedroom Furniture
72	Dining Room Furniture	76	Nursery Furniture
73	Kitchen Furniture	77	Patio Furniture
74	Bathroom Furniture	77A	Chairs
		93	Playground Furniture

Early 1950s

PL-#	Item	PL-#	Item
105	Patio Furniture	132A	Bathroom Furniture
106	Kitchen Furniture	133	Lamps
107	Nursery Furniture	135	Den Furniture
107A	Nursery Furniture	139	Kitchen Appliances
116	Wash Stand	140	Living Room & Dining Room Accessories
124	Dining Room Furniture	196	Utility Room Furniture
125	Bedroom Furniture	335	Utility Room Furniture
126	Living Room Furniture-Large	354	Household accessories
127	Ranch House Furniture	374	Lawn Furniture
132	Bathroom Furniture	376	Miniature Freight House accessories

PL-#	Item	PL-#	Item
386	Old West Furniture (inside)	518B	Settee & Chaise Lounge
387	Old West Furniture (inside)	518C	Breakfast Bar Only
388	Western Town Furniture (outside)	519	Kitchen & Bathroom Furniture
449	Sink accessories	536	Ranch Type House Furniture
450	Refrigerator accessories	568	Breakfast Bar & Cupola
516	Mid- Late-1950s Wooden Furniture	577	Dishwasher
517	Upholstered Furniture	701	Nursery Set
518	Patio & Breakfast Bar	788	Utility Room & Patio Furniture
518A	Patio Furniture Only	789	Den Furniture
		790	Living Room & Dining Room Furniture

Late 1950s

PL-#	Item	PL-#	Item
303	Table	806	Bunk Bed
304	Chair	818	Vanity
305	Bed	845	Bedroom & Nursery Furniture
305A	11" Bed	916	Roomette Cupboard

Animals

1949

PL-#	Item
30	Pets

Early 1950s

PL-#	Item	PL-#	Item
03	Dogs	274	Noah's Ark Animals
62	Domestic Animals	275	Hopping Frog
63	Domestic Animals	276	Pecking Chick
64	Domestic Animals	344	Wild Animals
64A	Domestic Animals	344A	Wild Animals
65	Domestic Animals (Fowl)	344B	Wild Animals
66	Elephants	360	Rodeo Animals (Thin)
67	Wild Animals	361	Monkeys
68	Wild Animals	408	Circus Animals (Thin)
69	Wild Animals	408A	Circus Animals
76	Domestic Animals	444	Horses
73	Noah's Ark Animals	460	Rodeo Animals

Mid-1950s

PL-#	Item	PL-#	Item
23	Farm Animals - 11 designs	537	Dog & Cat Puzzle for Peg Table
23A	Farm Animals	671	Horses
23B	Farm Animals	688	Livestock Animals
93	Dogs	692	Indian Horses

Mid-Late-1950s

PL-#	Item
731	Horse-5"
746	Cavemen
749	Prehistoric Animals (large size) (1-Kronosaurus, 1-Brontonaurus, 1-Tyrannosaurus)
750	Prehistoric Animals (medium size) (1-Stegosaurus, 1-Hadrosaurus, 1-Allosaurus, 1-Trachodon, 1-Ankylosaurus, 1-Pteranudon)
755	Prehistoric Animals (small size) (1-Cynognathus, 2-Dimetrodon, 1-Tricratops, 2-Plateoaurus, 1-Spenacodon)
770	North American Wild Animals
770A	Deer
771	North American Wild Animals
771A	Wild Animals
771B	Wild Animals
825	Wild Animals
826	Wild Animals
827	Wild Animals
830	Western Horse
831	Long Horn Steer
853	Large Running Horse
865	Horses
878	Farm Animals
911	Arctic Animals (seals, bears)
911A	Sled Dogs
977	Prehistoric Animals (1-Brontosaurus, 1-Tyrannusaurus, 1-Allosaurus, 1-Stegosaurus, 1-Trachadon, 1-Tricetops, 1-Dimetrodon, 1-Ankylosaurus)
978	Large Farm Animals

Late 1950s

1001	Prize Livestock
1083	Prehistoric Animals (1-Smilodon, 1-Woolly Mammoth, 1-Megatherium, 1-Styracosaurus, 1-Iguanodon, 1-Para-saurolophus, 1-Moschops, 1-Struthiomimus)
1099	Pack Horses & accessories

Early 1960s

PL-#	Item
1153	Fallen Horse & Rider
1169	Yogi Bear accessories
1251	Ridem Horse Head & Sound Box
1252	Ridem Horse Wheels & Bushings
272	Horse accessories
1272-2	Large Horse accessories
1273	Large Horse Body
1273-2	Large Horse Body - Dup. Mold
1273-3	Large Horse Body - 3rd Mold
1312-2	Flame Horse
1416	12-1/2" Welch Pony Body
1417	12-1/2" Welch Pony accessories
1423	Buffalo
1430	#5006 Galloping Horse Head, Cover & Plug
1430-2	#5006 Horse - Dup. Mold
1431	#5006 Horse Saddle
1432	#5006 Horse accessories
1440	Jungle Book Monkeys (3) 1 Cav. each
1466	Burro Head
1467	Burro Ears

Mid-1960s

PL-#	Item
1501	#5381 Articulated Horse Body
1502	#5381 Articulated Horse Head & accessories

Service Station Accessories

Early 1950s

PL-#	Item
30	Cadillac Sedan
123	Cars (5 cent size)

PL-#	Item
150 & A	Early 1950s Service Station accessories
151	" Grease & Wash Rack
159	" B/O Gas Pump
194	" Service Station Figures
282	Cars
283	288 T.A.P. Jaguar Car
289	Corvette
316	Cars (5 cent size)
379	" Service Station People
379-1	" Service Station People
381	" Service Station accessories

Mid-1950s

PL-#	Item
438	T.A.P. Ford Card
459	T.A.P. Hot Rod
467	T.A.P. Wrecker
553	Cars
635	Jack & Wrench
702	Station accessories

Late 1950s

PL-#	Item
992	Station accessories
1066	Cars
1068	Sports Cars
1088	Station accessories
1115	Gas Pump w/Water Feature
1164	Station accessories
1166	Elevator
1167	Railing Posts

Early 1960s

PL-#	Item
1111	Car w/Water Feature
1180	Tank Truck w/accessories
1181	Falcon Car w/Water Feature
1182	Cars
1182A	Pickups

Foreign Service Station Cars & Accessories

1960s

PL-#	Item
JW-4262	Friction Car
JW-4282	Friction Car
JW-4665	Friction Car
JW-5161	Friction Wrecker
J-2503	Friction Cars

Soldiers

Early 1950s

PL-#	Item
318	Soldiers
319	Soldiers
320	Soldiers
349	Flat Soldier Figures
357	Thin Soldiers (16 designs)
358	Sitting Soldiers
358A	Sitting Soldiers
383	Combat Soldiers
384	Medical Soldiers
385	Crouching Soldiers
392	Thin Soldiers
393	Thin Soldiers (Duplicate of 357)
399	Thin Soldiers

Mid-1950s

PL-#	Item
555	English Soldier Parts
556	English Soldier Parts
557	English Soldier Parts
587	Union Soldiers
588	Confederate Soldiers
589	Revolutionary Soldiers
590	World War I Soldiers
604	Marching Soldiers
605	Barracks Soldiers
637	Generals
669	Combat Soldiers
670	West Point Marching Soldiers
674	Mexican War Soldiers

Mid-1950s

PL-#	Item
675	Spanish American War Soldiers

Late 1950s

PL-#	Item
711	U.N. Soldiers
772	Roman Soldiers
785	Revolutionary War Soldiers
848	Confederate Soldiers
849	Union & Confederate Riders
926	Combat Soldiers
926A	Combat Soldiers
927	Marching Soldiers-2-1/4"
932	Sitting Military Figures
938	Assault Raft Soldiers
952	Large Sitting Military Figure

Early 1960s

PL-#	Item
1185	German Soldiers-2-1/4"
1193	Paratroops Figures
1194	German Soldiers
1195	American Soldiers-2-1/4"
1195-1	Combat Soldiers-2-1/4"
1199	Japanese Soldiers-2-1/4"
1201	Russian Soldiers-5-1/2"
1211	Sitting German Soldiers
1239	Cartoon Soldiers-5-1/2"
1269	Articulated Soldiers Legs & Arms
1270	Articulated Soldiers Body Parts
1271	Articulated Soldier Head & Hands
385	7-1/2" Articulated Soldier Body, Arms & Legs (Starr)
1385A	Sgt. Baker Body w/Field Jacket
1385B	Sgt. Jack Moffitt & Sgt. Sam Troy
1386	7-1/2" Soldiers Poly accessories

Mid-1960s

PL-#	Item
1412A	General Custer Torso
1413A	General Custer Hat

First Series—Nutty Mad—#2706, Item #2014

"Nutty Mads"/"Blame Its" Figures
1960s

PL-#	Item
1198- 6 Cavities	The Boxer, The Car Driver, The Skin Diver, The Captain with Boat, The Weight Lifter, and The Hot Rod Driver
1198-1	Duplicate #1
1198-2	Duplicate #2

Nutty Mads Manny the Reckless Mariner, Donald the Demon, Roddy the Hot Rod, U.S. Male, Rocky the Champ, and Bull Pen Louie.

Nutty Mads Manny the Reckless Mariner.

Second Series—Nutty Mad—#2706, Item #2016

1960s

PL-#	Item
1202-6	Cavities Baseball Player, Cop & Robber Football Player, Thinker, Sick Indian, and Man on Tricycle
1202-1-6	Cavities End Zone, All Heart Hogan, Chief Lost Teepee, Suburban Sidney, Bull Pen Bo Boo, and The Thinker
1202-2-6	Cavities

Nutty Mads Suburban Sidney.

Nutty Mads Waldo the Weightlifter, All Heart Hogan, The Thinker, Rocky the Champ.

Third Series—Nutty Mad—#2026, Item #2021

960s

PL-#	Item
221-6	Cavities Fireman, Teacher, Woman Bowler, Postman, Mother, and Doctor

Nutty Mads Mudder.

Nutty Mads Gutterball Annie.

Nutty Mads Smokey Sam.

Weird-Ohs Figures—#2706-2

*1960s_*

PL-#	Item
1207-6	Cavities Drag Hag, Daddy, Digger, Freddie Flameout, Davey, and Endsville Eddie
1207-1	Duplicate

Weird-Ohs Davey figure.

Weird-Ohs Digger.

Blame-It Figures—#7828X

*1960s_*

PL-#	Item
1216-6	Cavities I Didn't Do It, I Didn't Break It, I Didn't Push Him, I Didn't Eat Him, I Didn't Get Dirty, and I Didn't Paint It

Cartoon Figures

1960s

PL-#	Item
1239-6	Cavities American Soldier—Sergeant Sweet German Soldier—Eric Von Strudel Cuban—Manual Maracca English—Col. Allistair McDuff Russian—Igor the Mild Japanese Lieutenant—Sake Sake

Appendix A

A Look Inside the Glen Dale Marx Plant

he following photographs provide a rarely seen inside look at toy-making operations at the Glen Dale plant. These photos were originally published in the December, 1970 Christmas issue of the Weirton Steel Company's Employees Bulletin, *and are used herein with ermission. Weirton Steel, then a division of National Steel Corporation, was a major supplier of raw materials for the Marx Toy Comany plant in Glen Dale. The photographs displayed here are presented here through the courtesy of Weirton Steel.*

anta gives his okay to a shipment of black plate steel that has ist arrived at the Marx plant in Glen Dale.

Santa, along with Daniel Terrill, plant superintendent, and Mike Yeager, foreman of the plant's steel department, examines a piece of Weirite black plate steel in a receiving area. Weitron provided much of the steel sheeting used to manufacture Marx's renowned lithographed toys.

The toy truck assembly line at Glen Dale. The plant employed about 1,100 workers in 1970, and manufactured toys for shipment throughout the United States and for export to Europe and Africa.

In the lithography process, a piece of black plate steel could emerge from the press as a doll house, barn, fort, service station, or any number of other fun-filled toys.

Santa helps assembly line worker Helen Cuchta affix wheels to a toy semi-trailer.

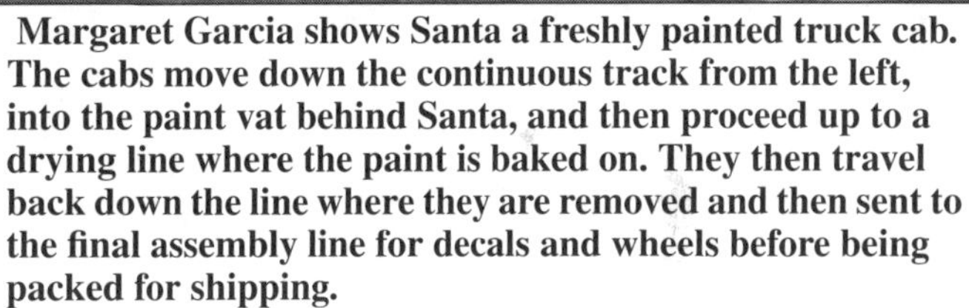

Margaret Garcia shows Santa a freshly painted truck cab. The cabs move down the continuous track from the left, into the paint vat behind Santa, and then proceed up to a drying line where the paint is baked on. They then travel back down the line where they are removed and then sent to the final assembly line for decals and wheels before being packed for shipping.

Iarx employees Katherine Purcharick, foreman, and Daniel Bud" Terrill, plant superintendent, receive congratulations from anta as a pallet of toy trucks is readied for loading on Santa's eigh.

A scene from the doll house packing line. The Glen Dale plant produced more than 150,000 steel dollhouses annually.

Santa visits one of the many storage areas for finished toys at the Glen Dale plant.

Appendix B

Marx Toys Timeline

896	Louis Marx is born.
912	Louis Marx starts working for toy manufacturer, Ferdinand Strauss.
916	Louis Marx starts managing Strauss' toy company.
917	About 1917-1918, Louis Marx served in the U.S. Army.
919	Louis Marx starts his own business to sell toys as a sales representative.
921	Louis Marx begins manufacturing with discontinued, used tooling acquired from Strauss.
arly 1930s	Louis Marx acquires three toy companies in the United States.
933	Louis Marx purchases old Fokker Aircraft Corp. plant in Glen Dale, West Virginia. This company site initially produced all-metal trucks and non-mechanical toys.
ate 1930s	Glen Dale plant expands to include lithographing.
930s-1950s	Plant sites include Glen Dale, West Virginia (approx. 1931); Erie, Pennsylvania (approx. 1933); Girard, Pennsylvania (approx. 1934); England (Swansea, 1939); Japan (approx. 1946); Mexico (approx. 1952); Hong Kong, B.C.C. (approx. 1952); Germany; and Canada.
930s-1950s	Four unions are active at the Glen Dale plant, including a. Steelworkers Machinist C.I.O. b. Toy Makers Retail, Wholesale & Department Store International (R.W.D.S.U.) Local 149 c. Office Workers Clerical Union d. Lithograph Photography Union
948-1949	Glen Dale plant is expanded to include plastics production. Metal dollhouses and plastic accessories are introduced into toy production lines.
950s-1960s	Play sets, service stations, and dollhouse lines increase in popularity. Worldwide plants are producing over 5,000 toys of all types for the marketplace.
972	Louis Marx sells his company to the Quaker Oats Company for approximately 52 million dollars.
975	Quaker Oats sells U.S. and Hong Kong operations to Dunbee-Combex-Marx, of England, for an estmated 15 million.
979	Dunbee-Combex-Marx decides to close all plant operations (Erie plant is closed first).
980	Dunbee-Combex-Marx Company enters bankruptcy proceedings.
982	Louis Marx dies close to time of bankruptcy proceedings American Plastic Equipment, Inc., of Florida, buys company assets in bankruptcy proceedings.
990	Marx Toys, Inc. is formed in Florida to manufacture collectible toys.
992	Marx Trains is formed in Illinois to produce Marx electric trains.
995	Marx Toy Corporation is formed, with a plant site in Sebring, Ohio, producing toys made from original Marx Toys molds.
999	Marx Toy LLC is formed in Saddlebrook, New Jersey, to manufacture toys for the mass market.

Index